Psychop
Personality Disord

Bridget Dolan, PhD, CPsychol, is Research Fellow and Honorary Lecturer at Henderson Hospital, Sutton, Surrey SM2 5LT, and at the Section of Forensic Psychiatry, St George's Hospital Medical School, London SW17 0RE

Jeremy Coid, MRCPsych, MPhil, DipCriminol, is Senior Lecturer in Forensic Psychiatry, Department of Psychological Medicine, St Bartholomew's Hospital, London EC1A 7BE

BRIDGET DOLAN
JEREMY COID

Psychopathic and Antisocial Personality Disorders

Treatment and Research Issues

GASKELL

Reprinted 1995

Gaskell is an imprint of the Royal College of Psychiatrists,
17 Belgrave Square, London SW1X 8PG

British Library Cataloguing-in-Publication Data

Dolan, Bridget
Psychopathic and Antisocial Personality
Disorders: Treatment and Research Issues
I. Title II. Coid, Jeremy
616.85

ISBN 0902241-66-4

Distributed in North America
by American Psychiatric Press, Inc.
ISBN 088048 630 9

Printed by Bell & Bain Ltd, Glasgow

Dedicated to
Ray and Denis Dolan
and
Bina and Felix Coid

Contents

Foreword. *John Reed* ix
Acknowledgements xi

1 Introduction 1

Previous statements about treatment outcome · Use of the term 'psychopathy' · Criteria for inclusion in this report · The aims of the present review · Sources of material · Format of the review

2 Contemporary diagnostic approaches 10

The legal category 'psychopathic disorder' · ICD–10: dyssocial personality disorder · DSM–III–R: antisocial personality disorder · Hare's Psychopathy Check-List · Blackburn's typology derived from MMPI profiles · Psychodynamic classification · Recommendations on the use of diagnostic systems · Assessing the severity of personality disorder

3 Natural history 33

Prospective studies of deviant children and adolescents · Studies of the development of delinquency · The natural history of untreated psychopathic disorder · Maturity and 'burn-out' in the psychopath · Psychopathic disorder and mortality rates · The natural history of offending behaviour and recidivism · Conclusion

4 Pharmacological treatment 63

Studies discussed · Neuroleptic medication · Antidepressants · Monoamine oxidase inhibitors · Benzodiazepines · Anticonvulsants · Psychostimulants · Lithium · Towards a rational strategy for pharmacological treatment · Conclusions

5 Physical treatment 121

Electro-shock therapy · Cold wet sheet packs · Psychosurgery · Summary

6 Psychotherapeutic approaches 126

Out-patient psychotherapy · In-patient psychotherapy · Summary

7 Cognitive and behavioural approaches 136

Behavioural programmes · Cognitive–behavioural approaches · Cognitive therapy · Summary

8 Therapeutic Community approaches 146

Health Service Therapeutic Communities · Therapeutic Community units in British prisons · Therapeutic Communities in non-British prisons · Maximum-security hospital Therapeutic Communities · Hierarchical Therapeutic Community model · Summary

9 Hospital admission and 'milieu' therapy 181

In-patient treatment in non-secure hospitals · Hospital careers of legal psychopaths · In-patient treatment in medium-secure units · In-patient treatment in British Special Hospitals · In-patient 'milieu treatment' in non-British maximum-security units · Summary

10 Community supervision 206

Evaluating community surveillance of psychopaths · Problems of community supervision · Case management for psychopaths · Conclusions

11 Methodological issues 220

Definition and measurement of psychopathic disorder · Random allocation of subjects · Descriptions of treatment · Measures of outcome · Length of follow-up · The power of statistical findings

12 Summary of findings and recommendations for future research 261

Summary of reviewed research · Conclusions and recommendations · Naturalistic studies: an interim paradigm

Appendix Towards a standardised assessment of psychopathic disorder 277

References 294

Index 1 Subject index 318

Index 2 Treatment outcome studies 322

Foreword

JOHN REED

Psychopathic disorder is one of the four categories of mental disorder recognised by the Mental Health Act 1983, where it is defined as:

> "a persistent disorder or disability of mind (whether or not including significant impairment of intelligence) which results in abnormally aggressive or seriously irresponsible conduct."

People with personality disorders of this type often pose a very significant challenge to society, and make heavy demands on a range of services both in the criminal justice system and in health and social care. People with such difficult personalities are not solely an issue for the forensic psychiatry service. All mental health care services will have contact with this difficult and demanding group. The challenges they pose are compounded by the absence of consensus on the defining characteristics and aetiology of psychopathic disorder, and by differing opinions about effective management and treatment. There are many complex issues that have to be resolved before we can be confident that we are making soundly based, rational decisions about the provision of appropriate services for people with psychopathic disorder and about who should be dealt with in the penal system and who by health and social care agencies.

In September 1992 the Department of Health and the Home Office set up a joint working group to consider these and related problems. It became clear early in the group's work that there was considerable uncertainty about the effectiveness of treatments for psychopathic disorder and that the literature had not been fully reviewed in the recent past. The working group commissioned Dr Bridget Dolan and Dr Jeremy Coid to carry out such a review and their comprehensive findings were a great help to the group in producing its own report.

Dr Dolan and Dr Coid's review shows all too clearly how poorly advanced our understanding is of the treatment and management of psychopathic disorder and how difficult research in this field can be. No doubt this partly reflects the lack of agreement about the definition and aetiology of psychopathic disorder. Even so, allowing for the inadequacy of the basic information, their review provides many useful pointers both to approaches which deserve to be explored further and to pitfalls to avoid when researching this difficult area. I hope that its publication will stimulate further research and that this will succeed in overcoming the many and varied methodological problems that Dr Dolan and Dr Coid show has flawed so much of the research up to now. Publication is particularly timely given the heightened awareness of the needs of mentally disordered offenders generally and the high priority given by Ministers to services meeting these needs. Mental illness is one the five "key areas" targeted for heath gain in the White Paper *The Health of the Nation* (Cm 1986), and in the 1994/95 priorities and planning guidance for the National Health Service, services for mentally disordered offenders, including people with psychopathic disorder, are a "first order priority". In order to get some estimate of the need for services, the Department of Health has recently completed a national needs assessment exercise, the findings of which will greatly assist future service planning.

In welcoming the publication of this important review, I would like to record again the thanks that the working group expressed to Dr Dolan and Dr Coid for their invaluable contribution.

Dr John Reed, CB, FRCP, FRCPsych
Special Adviser in Forensic Psychiatry to the Department of Health,
Chair of the Psychopathic Disorder Working Group

November 1993

Acknowledgements

We are indebted to several people who went to a lot of trouble to help us in producing this book. Louise Murch, Psychology Assistant at St George's Hospital Medical School, was of immeasurable help and remained totally uncomplaining of incessant requests for library searches, photocopying and cups of coffee. Dr Kingsley Norton, Consultant Psychotherapist at Henderson Hospital, gave his free time to read drafts of the document and, as always, was both speedy and constructive in his criticism and encouragement. Dr Chris Evans, Senior Lecturer in Psychodynamic Psychotherapy at St George's Hospital Medical School, has reviewed earlier drafts of the report, realigned the improbabilities, and contributed greatly to the discussion of methodological issues and summary sections. Mrs Bina Coid, Institute of Psychiatry, helped with re-analysis of data, and, finally, Professor Ron Blackburn, Ashworth Hospital, Liverpool, made helpful comments on our original report for the 'Reed' committee.

We were also helped by several other colleagues who provided us with published and unpublished information for the review. These include: Dr Eric Cullen, Mr John Shine, and Ms Margaret Newton of the Psychology Department, HMP Grendon Underwood; Dr Thomas-Peter, Director of Psychological Services at the Reaside Clinic; Dr Derek Perkins and Ms Carol Sellars, Broadmoor Hospital; Dr John Hodge, Rampton Hospital; Professor Dr N. W. de Smit, Psychiatric Adviser to the Dutch Ministry of Justice; Dr Frans Derks of the Van der Hoeven Kliniek, Holland; Dr J. H. Blankstein, Director of the Prompekliniek, Holland; and Dr Wolfgang Berner, Justizanstallt Mittersteig, Vienna, Austria.

It is trite but true to say that the book could not have been completed without the support of these people, and we want to say 'thank you' to you all for your help.

1 Introduction

This book has its origins in a review commissioned for the joint Department of Health/Home Office *Review of Health and Social Services for Mentally Disordered Offenders and Others Requiring Similar Services,* headed by Dr John Reed (Department of Health & Home Office, 1992). The interim report of the Research Advisory Group to this committee recommended that in the development of a strategic plan for dealing with mentally disordered offenders, the highest priority for action should be given to research into the treatment and treatability of psychopathic disorders (Department of Health & Home Office, 1992, p.31). Subsequently the working group on psychopathic disorder was established, with one of its main terms of reference being

> "to consider, in the light of present knowledge, what methods of management or treatment are most likely to be most effective in reducing violent or offending behaviour in those individuals with psychopathic disorder."

A shorter version of the text presented here was delivered to that working group in December 1992.

Placing this work in its contemporary context, it may at first seem surprising that considerable effort should go into the evaluation of treatment for a diagnostic entity that now is no longer included in psychiatric glossaries, particularly at a time when the legal category 'psychopathic disorder' is rarely invoked for compulsory admissions in the UK other than to Special Hospitals. The concept of psychopathy is contentious and has generated an extensive literature, embodying many different views (Blackburn, 1983). Almost 20 years ago, Butler (1975) discussed the legal concept of psychopathy and found it logically flawed, stating that the class of persons to whom psychopathic disorder relates is not a single category identified by any medical, biological or psychological criteria. Gunn & Robinson (1976) suggested that there are only five agreed facts about the term 'psychopathic disorder':

(a) the diagnosis is unreliable
(b) authors disagree about its definition
(c) it is used in the vernacular as a term of derogation
(d) it has legal use in England and Wales
(e) doctors use it to indicate that a patient is incurable or untreatable.

However, to date, the terms 'psychopath', 'psychopathy', and 'psychopathic disorder' have not disappeared from everyday usage or informal clinical use. The concerns expressed over the past two decades have not resulted in the removal of the term 'psychopathic disorder' from British legal statutes. Psychopathic disorder is a concept that has outlived its obituarists, and 'psychopaths' continue to be recognised as a group even though the group *is* ill defined and the label *is* unsatisfactory. Indeed, the diagnostic concept of the psychopathic personality has undergone a recent revival within both DSM–III 'antisocial personality disorder' (American Psychiatric Association, 1980) and the ICD–10 classification of 'dyssocial personality disorder' (World Health Organization, 1992).

Cleckley (1952) suggested that the behaviour of

> "psychopaths is so inappropriate, self-damaging and inadequately motivated that [they] should be regarded as psychotic, despite their powers of abstract reasoning."

It has been argued by others that psychopathic personality could be considered as a 'disease' in that it exerts a malign influence and puts the sufferer at a biological disadvantage (Gunn, 1992). However, there is an uncomfortable suspicion that an illness model is inappropriate for the concept of psychopathy, and that the solution to its description lies in other models. Chiswick *et al* (1984) showed that many psychiatrists were unwilling to accept psychopathically disordered offenders for treatment, in part because of a doubt about the psychiatric validity of the concept. Although the conceptual coherence and ethical implications of the terminology are important, the debate is too extensive to cover adequately here and is not within the remit of this review (for further discussion see, *inter alia*, Blair (1975*a,b*), Butler (1975),

Grounds (1987), Tennent *et al* (1990), and Chiswick (1992). What is of major relevance to this review is the fact that until the nature of the defect state/states in psychopathy are clarified, 'treatment', in traditional illness terms, is necessarily problematic.

Pessimism regarding possible change in psychopaths has led to the opinion that rehabilitation is impossible by any method. Bluglass, as recently as 1988, has stated that we are singularly unsuccessful in devising methods of treatment or management in medical or sociological fields, while in the USA this view is reflected in the reintroduction of the death penalty in many states and the move away from mandatory sentences which ensured a prisoner's release regardless of his/her current mental state (Rubin, 1979).

In Britain, many professionals still remain profoundly pessimistic about the success of treatment of psychopaths. They are alarmed at the potential of psychopaths to disrupt, or, at times, to behave dangerously in hospital. More recently, concerns have been expressed that clinicians may be held responsible for these patients when they offend or behave in a manner dangerous to the public (Coid & Cordess, 1992).

Despite these real concerns, it remains clear that much manifest psychological disturbance is shown by psychopathic patients; that they frequently present at various health care agencies; and that they exhibit behaviour that will inevitably cause others to intervene in their lives. Thus, despite their unpopularity with many clinicians, they will inevitably present themselves in settings and situations where professional involvement from health carers is not only unavoidable but warranted.

Previous statements about treatment outcome

It is impossible to review the research literature on treatment of psychopathy without being impressed by two major features: firstly, that research investigations of treatment outcome of psychopathy are few and of poor quality; secondly, and more worryingly, that despite several decades of reviewers commenting to that effect, no obvious improvement has come about to date.

The following are some statements that have been made.

> "No satisfactory means of dealing with them [psychopaths] was presented by any psychiatric authority, and meanwhile their status in the eyes of the law made it impossible to treat them at all." (Cleckley, 1941)

> "Until research can be undertaken the problem of treatment and management of these patients is likely to continue to be far more costly and far more difficult than is at present generally understood" (Stafford-Clark *et al*, 1951)

> "All forms of treatment of psychopaths are as yet inadequately, or not at all, assessed, and, furthermore, it would seem that a variety of methods are being applied without adequate assessment of the individuals to be treated" (Scott, 1963)

> "There is, of course, no evidence to demonstrate or to indicate that psychiatry has yet found a therapy that cures or profoundly changes the psychopath" (Cleckley, 1964)

> "at this point no one knows what the best approach is, and many programmes are still in their initial and experimental stages" (Carney, 1976)

> "in answering the question of whether personality disorder can be treated by psychological methods, the answer must be 'possibly' since more investigation and long-term follow-ups are needed before an affirmative answer can be given" (Blackburn, 1983)

> "One cannot review the literature on treatment of personality disorder without being impressed with how little we know about these conditions" (Frosch, 1983)

> "The state of the treatment literature on antisocial personality disorder is inadequate" (Quality Assurance Project, 1991)

This book could add another negative dismissal to this list, as much of the evidence of effectiveness reviewed here is conflicting or disappointing. However, the reader should not be put off by this conclusion at such an early stage of our report. In particular, the reader should repeatedly question what might have been found if the researchers had taken a more rigorous approach to diagnostic assessment before embarking on treatment, had described the treatment given more accurately, and had adopted appropriate measures of change. Many treatment methods remain *unproven* in their effectiveness: the negative findings are no more conclusive than positive reports. Nevertheless, a number of promising leads have been identified, which, if properly followed up in the future, may demonstrate better results, at least in certain subgroups of patients, or along separate dimensions of psychopathology within an individual subject.

Use of the term 'psychopathy'

Despite the inadequacy of the terms, alluded to above, 'psychopath', 'psychopathy' and 'psychopathic' will be used throughout this book.

These terms could be used specifically as in the Mental Health Act 1983, which describes psychopathic disorder as:

> "A persistent disorder or disability of mind (whether or not including significant impairment of intelligence) which results in abnormally aggressive or seriously irresponsible conduct."

However, the Mental Health Act definition refers to patients presenting with a wide range of poorly delineated psychopathology who may exhibit antisocial and other dysfunctional behaviour. The model of psychopathy employed in this review will imply some internal structured determinants of behaviour and, as such, is not a purely behavioural model. The broad generic concept selected thus encompasses a range of psychological and behavioural disturbances. This has the advantage of being broadly compatible with the current Mental Health Act legal category but has the obvious disadvantage of lacking diagnostic precision. Thus, this review does not refer to a unitary concept.

Certain syndromes of personality traits and behaviour – for example, those described by Hare (1991) in the Psychopathy Check-List (PCL), or antisocial personality disorder in DSM–III–R (American Psychiatric Association, 1987) – do appear reliable and have established some validity as core diagnostic entities to describe the psychopath. But these still remain unsatisfactory as definitive descriptions for the full range of psychopathology exhibited by these people, which in turn appears to associate with additional clinical syndromes and other diagnostic categories of personality disorder over the lifetime (Coid, 1992). Furthermore, these 'core syndromes' still have an undetermined aetiology and should be seen at this stage to be 'final common pathways' for a series of different psychopathological conditions and for multifactorial predisposing causes.

We are therefore recommending that a multidimensional or multiaxial diagnostic approach be used (see Appendix). This is important as it becomes clearer that each procedure evaluated in this review may have had a bearing on only one or a limited number of components of the overall range of psychopathology to which we are referring.

Criteria for inclusion in this report

Chapter 2 of this book describes the five main contemporary diagnostic approaches to psychopathic disorder. Rather than excluding work which does not fit a given definition of 'psychopathic disorder', we have reviewed any studies which could be considered under the broad terms of psychopathy, psychopathic disorder, sociopathy and antisocial personality disorder (ASPD).

Many research studies include subjects who are described as psychopaths but without elaboration or explanation of how they came to be so defined. Furthermore, many recent studies which have applied suitable criteria, such as the PCL–R (Hare, 1991) or DSM–III–R axis II diagnoses (American Psychiatric Association, 1987), have omitted assessments for the presence or absence of clinical syndromes, such as affective disorders, sexual deviation or alcoholism, in the life histories of their subjects. Comorbidity with other clinical syndromes may well have a profound bearing on the final treatment outcome (Tyrer, 1988). As there is no universally accepted diagnosis or uniform descriptor of psychopathy, whenever possible we have indicated the diagnostic criteria used in each study we have reviewed. When no criteria are applied then the description of the population given by the authors is reported.

Studies which, in the main, concentrate on subjects with a single diagnosis of borderline personality disorder (BPD; DSM–III–R) or borderline personality organisation (BPO; Kernberg, 1975) are not reviewed here. Many features of BPD and BPO are found in psychopathic individuals and there is increasing evidence of the multiple morbidity of personality disorder diagnoses in subjects with severe personality disorder (Dolan *et al*, 1993*b*). However, the majority of those described as having BPD or BPO, in the absence of other personality disorder pathology, fall outside the terms of reference for this review of psychopathic disorder. For similar reasons studies of subjects defined by their history of sex offending or drug addiction (both groups include a high proportion of people with personality disorders) are not included unless the personality disorder dimension was specifically investigated.

Previous authors have noted the need for reviews of work to be as scientific as the work they review by having clearly specified methods of identifying, selecting and validating included information (Mulrow, 1987; Haynes, 1992). However, the vast majority of articles on treatment of psychopathy identified were clinical descriptions or anecdotal reports including little or no objective evaluation. Such anecdotal reports are only incorporated in this review where their inclusion complements the discussion of the evaluative reports. Relevant studies which we considered to come under the remit of 'outcome' studies were any which reported evaluative research findings of changes in behavioural, psychological, psychiatric or social variables during or after a treatment intervention. As noted above, the methods of many studies are flawed. However, rather than applying the criterion of the scientific experimental method for acceptable research (i.e. only accepting the double-blind, placebo-controlled, cross-over, long-term, follow-up designs) – which would exclude every study in this review – we have included studies which are methodologically flawed. Attention is drawn to the merits and shortcomings of each study so that readers can form their own judgement on the quality of research.

The aims of the present review

Even though the available studies of treatment outcome are limited, the current review is wider in scope than previous reports and the intention is to provide something more useful than a simple restatement of the pessimistic sentiments expressed by previous authors. It is hoped that this comprehensive overview of existing research will equip readers with sufficient information to form their own judgements on both the merits and pitfalls of previous research.

The ultimate aims of this review are:

(a) to inform the reader of the current status of research into the treatment of psychopathic and antisocial personaltiy disorder
(b) to suggest possible directions for future investigations of treatment outcome
(c) to promote improved methodology in future evaluations of the effectiveness of treatment
(d) to promote better standards for the assessment and evaluation of psychopathic disorder
(e) to promote the adoption of better, or more comprehensive, measures of outcome of treatment of psychopathic disorder.

Sources of material

The studies considered for this review were assembled from a variety of sources. Firstly, an extensive computerised database search of relevant publications in scientific journals covering the past three decades was conducted using CD ROM *Index Medicus* and *PSYCHLIT*. This list of publications was supplemented by use of *Current Opinion* by 'backward chaining' from existing review work and 'forward chaining' from general articles using the *Citations Index*.

Secondly, researchers with current interest in the treatment of psychopathic disorder were identified through a computerised register of forensic psychiatry research which was compiled for the Mental Health Foundation by the Forensic Psychiatry Department at the Institute of Psychiatry, London. All workers listed as having a major interest in psychopathic disorder were contacted and invited to provide information about any recent or unpublished studies into treatment outcome they could make available. This included workers in Austria, Canada, Denmark, Germany, the Netherlands, the UK and the USA. Information on Dutch research work was also obtained from the Ministry of Justice in Holland.

Personal contact was made with the heads of the psychology or research departments at the three English Special Hospitals, who were invited to provide information on any unpublished or ongoing research into changes during or following treatment of psychopaths in their respective establishments. The Psychology Department of HMP Grendon and the Director of Psychological Services at the Reaside Clinic also provided access to unpublished work.

Format of the review

Following an overview of contemporary diagnostic concepts of psychopathic disorder and a review of natural history studies, the treatment outcome studies selected have been classified by treatment modality and are considered in Chapters 4–10 under the broad headings of pharmacological treatment, physical treatment (including psychosurgery), psychotherapeutic approaches, cognitive and behavioural approaches, Therapeutic Community treatment, long-term hospital admission and 'milieu' therapy, and community supervision. Each of the non-pharmacological or physical treatment modalities is separately considered by setting of treatment, whether in the community, non-secure hospitals, secure units, or Special Hospitals and prisons.

In some senses, the division by treatment modality is an artificial one, as the treatment of psychopathic disorder or severe personality disorder rarely involves one treatment modality or one therapist.

It is usually a multi-agency reshaping procedure extending over a long period. 'Milieu' therapy (often appearing to be a euphemism for long-term hospital treatment employing a variety of treatment modalities) is a particular example of this, where the particular treatment applied is rarely stated. It is arguable that some studies in the 'milieu' therapy section are studies of the accuracy of clinician's discharge decisions rather than of the treatment of psychopathy. They have been included because they underline some of the intrinsic complexities in managing psychopaths, and the ways in which disposal, treatment, containment, discharge and follow-up are necessarily interlinked. This is also evidenced by the final chapter, which considers the issue of community supervision of psychopaths following discharge from secure containment.

Each of Chapters 4–9 ends with a brief summary of the studies of that treatment modality. A criticism of methodologies and outcome measures is made in Chapter 11. There is a more complete summary and evaluation of results in Chapter 12, where suggestions are put forward for future research strategies.

2 Contemporary diagnostic approaches

> "in the context of clinical psychiatry statements about diagnostic validity are essentially statements of predictive power, and hence about practical utility." (Kendell, 1989)

Little progress can be made in assessing the treatability of psychopaths or devising appropriate treatment programmes unless it is clear from the outset exactly what it is that is being treated. Kendell (1989) pointed out that few psychiatric disorders have been adequately validated and that it is still an open issue whether there are genuine boundaries between these syndromes and normality. He believed that in the long term the validation of psychiatric disorder depended on the elucidation of aetiological processes. Although there is nothing pre-eminent about aetiology, modern clinical science is largely focused on the elucidation of underlying mechanisms because experience has shown that this is, almost always, the most effective way of predicting outcome, acquiring new and more effective therapies and, most importantly, preventing the disorder from developing in the first place. Kendell argues that this preoccupation with underlying mechanisms is a "quest for power", the power to predict outcome and the power to prevent or diminish suffering and disability. Unfortunately, reliable diagnostic approaches to the broad group of patients referred to as psychopaths remain in the earliest stages.

Robins & Guze (1970) have described the phases in the validation of a clinical syndrome (see Table 2.1), but none of these has so far been successfully negotiated for this patient group. Thus, although five diagnostic approaches to psychopathic disorder are

TABLE 2.1
Validators of clinical syndromes

	Validator
1	Identification and description of the syndrome, either by 'clinical intuition' or by cluster analysis
2	Demonstration of boundaries of 'points of rarity' between related syndromes to discriminant function analysis, latent class analysis, etc.
3	Follow-up studies establishing a distinctive course or outcome
4	Therapeutic trials establishing a distinctive treatment response
5	Family studies establishing that the syndrome 'breeds true'
6	Association with some more fundamental abnormality: histological, psychological, biochemical or molecular

(After Robins & Guze, 1970; Kendell, 1989.)

currently available to would-be researchers or diagnosticians, each has a different developmental origin and requires some degree of specific training in its use. Each one takes a different perspective of the same individual and is ultimately based on a quite different intellectual framework. It is probable that the approaches also show considerable overlap with each other, but researchers have gone little way in examining this possibility. Thus, although some diagnostic categories show a degree of reliability and internal validity, diagnostic approaches to personality disorder continue to lag behind developments in the major clinical syndromes.

The legal category 'psychopathic disorder'

It is important to differentiate between the clinical construct and legal category of psychopathic disorder. In the UK, the term 'psychopathic disorder' exists in the main as a legal rather than a clinical category. In this context it is a means of detaining patients in secure hospitals under the 1983 Mental Health Act (MHA) because of their "persistent disorder or disability of mind (whether or not including significant impairment of intelligence) which results in abnormally aggressive or severely irresponsible conduct" (MHA, s.1(2)). Although around 25% of patients in the English maximum-security Special Hospitals are detained under psychopathic disorder (Hamilton, 1990), this legal definition was not invented by clinicians and its clinical interpretation is unclear. Chiswick (1992) notes how there has been very little legal explanation of the meaning of psychopathic disorder; nor has there been any authoritative testing of the terms 'abnormally aggressive' or 'seriously irresponsible'. The legal interpretation remains with the particular court concerned with each individual case and thus is an "elastic and ill defined category".

When subjects held in hospital under the Mental Health Act category of 'psychopathic disorder' have been investigated using current clinical concepts of psychopathy, the legal category has not stood up to scrutiny. Coid (1992) reports on the use of Hare's Psychopathy Check-List (PCL–R) and a structured interview for DSM–III–R in 93 women and 86 men detained in English Special Hospitals under the legal category of psychopathic disorder. In all, 28% of the women and 48% of the men scored below 24 points on the PCL–R, indicating that they were not 'psychopaths' in the clinical sense according to this instrument. DSM–III–R antisocial personality disorder was only diagnosed in 44% of female and 38% of male 'legal psychopaths'; in fact, the most frequently diagnosed DSM–III–R category was borderline personality disorder, found in 91% of women and 56% of men. Similar non-concordance of clinical and legal concepts is shown in a questionnaire study of male patients at Ashworth Special Hospital, where 17% of patients legally detained as psychopaths showed an absence of traits of any DSM–III–R personality disorder category, and only 43% scored in a range indicating presence of antisocial personality disorder (Blackburn *et al*, 1990).

Coid (1992) points out that the wide range of psychopathology observed in patients detained under the English legal category 'psychopathic disorder' has never fitted easily into the various classifications of personality disorder. At the same time, as a clinical construct, the condition does not find a suitable place among the major mental disorders. To some extent, 19th-century psychiatrists may have held a more appropriate, broader clinical conceptualisation of psychopathic disorder, corresponding to the legal category, perceiving it as a more wide-ranging and severe entity than a mere abnormality of 'personality'. Nineteenth-century psychiatrists considered psychopathy to be along a spectrum of severity ranging from near normality to near mental illness. At the same time, the condition could not be explained by major mental illness. Preservation of intelligence was observed, but with an impairment in the normal feeling for others, will power and morality. Some early authors observed a predisposition to transient psychotic states, affective reactions, and the *psychopathia sexualis* (sexual deviations). Although the condition was often associated with criminal behaviour, it was not to be discounted as merely due to a criminal disposition. Those who made the clinical diagnosis (according to diagnostic fashions of the time) considered that it warranted psychiatric treatment and care rather than punishment. From the beginning of the 19th century, the disorder was considered to have both constitutional and environmental aetiology. But at various times the idea of a congenital or ideopathic abnormality of personality development was also necessary to explain the apparent absence of any detectable environmental disadvantage in the life histories of a subgroup of psychopaths (see reviews by Lewis, 1974; Pichot, 1978; Coid, 1993*a*).

The following sections examine the current clinical classifications of psychopathic disorder according to five different contemporary diagnostic frameworks.

ICD–10: dyssocial personality disorder

The ICD–10 (World Health Organization, 1989*a*) classification of personality disorders is now considerably closer to DSM–III–R axis II than ICD–9 (see Table 2.2, p. 15) and is an attempt to define categories more on the basis of traits than in previous glossaries. It is recommended that clinicians should generally record as many diagnoses as necessary to cover the clinical picture, but, if recording more than one, then the main diagnosis should be specified. ICD–10 personality disorders include a variety of conditions which indicate that a person's characteristic and enduring patterns of inner experience and behaviour deviate markedly from the culturally expected and accepted range (World Health Organization, 1989*a*). For research purposes, such deviations must satisfy the following requirements (World Health Organization, 1989*b*):

"A. The deviation must be manifest in one or more of

(i) cognition
(ii) affectivity
(iii) control over impulses and needs gratification

(iv) relating to others and manner of handling interpersonal situations.

B. The deviation must be pervasive in the sense of manifesting itself as behaviour that is inflexible, maladaptive, or otherwise dysfunctional across a broad range of personal and social situations.

C. There is personal distress, or adverse impact on the social environment, or both, clearly attributable to B.

D. There must be evidence that the deviation is stable and of long duration, having its onset in late childhood or adolescence.

E. The deviation cannot be explained as a manifestation or consequence of other adult mental disorders, although other episodic or chronic conditions may co-exist or be superimposed upon it.

F. Organic brain disease, injury, or gross dysfunction must be excluded as a possible cause."

Dyssocial personality disorder is intended to include previous diagnostic categories of sociopathic, amoral, asocial, antisocial, and psychopathic personality disorder. ICD–10 defines this condition as usually coming to attention because of a gross disparity between behaviour and the prevailing social norms, and the condition is characterised by:

(a) callous unconcern for the feelings of others and lack of the capacity for empathy
(b) gross and persistent attitude of irresponsibility and disregard for social norms, rules and obligations
(c) incapacity to maintain enduring relationships
(d) very low tolerance to frustration and a low threshold for discharge of aggression, including violence
(e) incapacity to experience guilt and to profit from experience, particularly punishment
(f) marked proneness to blame others or to offer plausible rationalisations for the behaviour bringing the subject into conflict with society
(g) persistent irritability.

For research purposes, three or more of these criteria should be present.

It remains unclear whether the emphasis on personality characteristics rather than behaviour will be an improvement on previous categories. Personality features such as unconcern, specific attitudes, low tolerance, and incapacity to experience certain feelings may ultimately have to be inferred from a patient's behaviour

TABLE 2.2
DSM–III–R and ICD–10 personality disorder classifications

DSM–III–R	*ICD–10*
Cluster A	
Paranoid	Paranoid
Schizoid	Schizoid
Schizotypal	
Cluster B	
Antisocial	Dyssocial
	Emotionally unstable:
	impulsive type
Borderline	borderline type
Histrionic	Histrionic
Narcissistic	
Cluster C	
Avoidant	Anxious (avoidant)
Dependent	Dependent
Obsessive–compulsive	Anankastic (obsessive–compulsive)
Passive–aggressive	Other

patterns rather than a true understanding of underlying personality abnormalities. Furthermore, additional ICD–10 categories of personality disorder may well have to be added to encompass the broad range of psychopathology exhibited by psychopaths (see Coid, 1992). In a review of this category (Coid, 1993*a*), it was concluded that ICD–10 appears to have made an attempt to assemble the core personality traits of the psychopathic personality. But whether this will translate successfully into research and clinical practice remains to be seen.

DSM–III–R: antisocial personality disorder

DSM–III–R diagnostic criteria for personality disorders refer to behaviours or traits that are characteristic of the person's recent and long-term functioning since early adulthood (American Psychiatric Association, 1987). The constellation of behaviours or traits causes either significant impairment in social or occupational functioning or subjective distress. The classification includes 11 categories divided into three 'clusters' (as shown in Table 2.2). These are diagnosed along a separate axis (axis II) from the major mental disorders. Two additional categories, sadistic and self-defeating personality disorders, were proposed but considered in need of further study before formal adoption. The essential features of antisocial personality disorder (ASPD) are patterns of irresponsible and antisocial behaviour beginning in childhood or early adolescence and continuing into adulthood. For the diagnosis to be given, the person must be at least 18 years of age and have a history of conduct disorder before the age of 15 years

TABLE 2.3
Summary of DSM–III–R criteria for antisocial personality

A. Current age at least 18

B. Evidence of conduct disorder with onset before age 15, as indicated by a history of three or more of the following:
   - truancy
   - running away
   - fights
   - using weapons
   - forcing sexual activities on others
   - physical cruelty to animals
   - physical cruelty to people
   - destruction of others' property
   - fire-setting
   - lying
   - stealing without confrontation of a victim
   - stealing with confrontation of a victim

C. A pattern of irresponsible and antisocial behaviour since age 15, as indicated by at least four of the following:
   - unable to sustain consistent work behaviour
   - failure to conform to social norms with respect to lawful behaviour
   - irritable and aggressive
   - failure to honour financial obligations
   - failure to plan ahead, or is impulsive
   - lack of regard for the truth
   - recklessness
   - lack of ability to function as a parent
   - has never sustained a monogamous relationship for more than one year
   - lack of remorse

D. Occurrence of antisocial behaviour is not exclusively during the course of schizophrenia or manic episodes

(American Psychiatric Association, 1987). The criteria for the condition are summarised in Table 2.3, and represent the only personality disorder category that is derived from empirical research (Robins, 1966, 1978). Field trials have shown a higher inter-rater reliability for ASPD than for other axis II categories (Mellsop *et al*, 1982). DSM–III–R ASPD omits the personality traits component of the diagnostic construct of psychopathy and substitutes a framework based on behaviour instead. It is recommended that the present diagnostic concept should change yet again in DSM–IV and align itself more closely to that of ICD–10 (Hare *et al*, 1991).

Several major epidemiological studies have used standardised diagnostic criteria for ASPD, making it the most comprehensively studied personality disorder category in this area of research from any contemporary glossary (see review by Coid, 1993*a*). The Epidemiological Catchment Area study in three US sites surveyed large general population samples and showed a lifetime prevalence rate for ASPD of 2.6% (range 2.1–2.4%) (Robins *et al*, 1984; Robins & Regier, 1991). Lifetime prevalence for males (4.5%) was significantly higher than for females (0.8%), highest in the 25–44-year age groups, no higher in blacks than whites, commonest in those who dropped out of high school, and most commonly found in inner-city populations.

Studies in prison settings have shown a high prevalence of ASPD, varying from 39% to 76% of subjects (Hare, 1983, 1984; Bland *et al*, 1990; Cote & Hodgin, 1990). However, prisons vary in their concentrations of hardened, career criminals who might be expected to have higher rates of ASPD than those found in institutions which contain more petty offenders, such as county jails in the USA or remand prisons in the UK. A study of male prisoners who had posed the most serious disciplinary problems in English prisons demonstrated that 86% had a diagnosis of ASPD (Coid, 1991, 1992). An unpublished survey of 50 women prisoners held in a prison psychiatric wing found that 44% met DSM–III–R criteria for ASPD as measured with the PDQ–R questionnaire (Dolan & Mitchell, 1994). Dolan & Glaister (1994) have used the same standardised assessment instrument to assess personality disorder diagnoses in 50 male 'high tariff' offenders in the community who were attending an intensive probation programme. They found that two-thirds of these men (66%) met DSM–III–R ASPD criteria.

Epidemiological studies have also revealed important characteristics of ASPD individuals. Males and females appear to have differing ages of onset, with males tending to present with conduct disorder at an earlier age than females, who present around puberty (Robins, 1986). Men appear to have a special vulnerability to ASPD. Childhood environments of ASPD females are more disturbed, suggesting that more predisposing factors are required for the disorder to appear in women (Robins, 1985). Similarly, in a child guidance sample, records showed that women later diagnosed as sociopathic had lower IQs, had more frequently been in correctional institutions, more often had parents on welfare or who were chronically unemployed, and more often had alcoholic or sociopathic fathers compared with male sociopaths (Robins, 1966). ASPD appears to predominate in young adulthood and studies have suggested that the symptoms begin to diminish in a proportion during middle age. However, the disorder also involves a higher risk of death during early adulthood. Unfortunately, at least 20% still meet the criteria when aged 45: they constitute 0.5% of the US population, and thus still pose a serious problem for clinicians and for society.

Hare *et al* (1991) have suggested that ASPD should undergo change in DSM–IV, with simplified criteria and the addition of items associated with personality characteristics of the psychopath rather than an emphasis on behavioural disturbance alone. Current DSM–III–R criteria have been criticised as too long and cumbersome, yet ASPD is the only axis II category derived from empirical research and its criteria have obtained the highest inter-rater reliability. There is a substantial association between ASPD and substance abuse (Docherty *et al*, 1986; Tarter, 1988). But the validity of these findings is partly compromised by the questionable independence of the diagnosis in certain individuals (Nathan, 1988; Gerstley *et al*, 1990). However, the inclusion of a longitudinal component within this diagnostic construct considerably improves its descriptive ability, and it could be argued that the addition of other axis II diagnostic categories is all that is necessary to complete a more comprehensive diagnostic picture of the psychopath which cannot be provided by other check-lists and glossaries.

Hare's Psychopathy Check-List

Hare's Psychopathy Check-List (PCL) is a unidimensional scale of psychopathy including both personality traits and antisocial behaviour. Hare (1991) argues that it is a unitary syndrome that can be measured using his scale. During its development, the list of 16 characteristics considered by Cleckley (1976) in his seminal work

The Mask of Sanity were initially taken by Hare to be typical of the psychopath, and he applied them to a series of prisoners (Hare, 1980).

After further studies of prison samples, the preliminary PCL was expanded to a 22-item version, and ratings of 0–2 were applied to each item, which could give a maximum possible score of 44. At a cut-off score of 33, or above, a subject would be designated a psychopath for research purposes. Data are collected both from interview and from institutional files. Two items were subsequently dropped from the 22-item PCL and a further item was modified to create a revised version of the check-list (PCL–R), as shown in Table 2.4. The cut-off for the PCL–R is a score of 30 (Hare, 1991). Hare and colleagues have now demonstrated high inter-rater and test–retest reliability using both PCL and PCL–R on prisoners and forensic psychiatric hospital in-patients when the check-list is used by properly trained raters (Hare, 1991).

More recently, Hare and colleagues demonstrated by factor analysis that the PCL and PCL–R contain two correlated factors that have distinct patterns of intercorrelation with other variables.

TABLE 2.4

Items in the revised (20-item) Psychopathy Check-List (PCL–R)

1	Glibness/superficial charm
2	Grandiose sense of self-worth
3	Need for stimulation/proneness to boredom
4	Pathological lying
5	Cunning/manipulative
6	Lack of remorse or guilt
7	Shallow affect
8	Callous/lack of empathy
9	Parasitic lifestyle
10	Poor behavioural controls
11	Promiscuous sexual behaviour
12	Early behaviour problems
13	Lack of realistic, long-term goals
14	Impulsivity
15	Irresponsibility
16	Failure to accept responsibility for own actions
17	Many short-term marital relationships
18	Juvenile delinquency
19	Revocation of conditional release
20	Criminal versatility

It was suggested that the first factor consisted of core personality traits corresponding to DSM–III narcissistic personality disorder and the second to features of a chronic, unstable lifestyle similar to DSM–III antisocial personality disorder.

The PCL–R items in Table 2.4 are generally consistent with several traditional views of the personality traits and behavioural features defining the construct of psychopathy. Various authors have described psychopaths as selfish, aggressive, feeling no guilt or remorse for their behaviour, lacking in shame, lacking empathy, callous, having a fundamental incapacity for love or true friendship, lacking insight, unable to control impulses or delay gratification, demonstrating pathological lying, thrill-seeking, having poor judgement, having disregard for societal conventions, having social and sexual relationships that are superficial but demanding and manipulative, able to extricate themselves from difficult situations by producing intricate and at times contradictory lies, together with theatrical and convincing explanations and promises, and presenting as two-dimensional people able to simulate emotions and affectional attachment when it is advantageous to do so (Karpman, 1961; Gray & Hutchinson, 1964; Craft, 1965; Buss, 1966; Davies & Feldman, 1981).

Hare (1991) has examined the criminal characteristics of subjects scoring high on the PCL–R in forensic populations. Violence tended to have revenge or retribution as a motive, was often cold blooded and callous, sometimes without understandable motive or in a macho display. Victims were more often male strangers. Overall, the subjects' criminal activities were at a higher level than those of other offenders in the early years. Non-violent offences showed a dramatic drop in mid-life, but violent offences remained relatively constant, and PCL–R scores also appeared predictive of criminal recidivism or violation of parole release.

It remains unclear whether Hare's construct is truly a unidimensional entity. However, PCL–R scores are increasingly used by researchers with criminal populations and many of the more carefully designed treatment studies incorporate this measure. It has been argued that the PCL–R omits a considerable amount of psychopathology that is relevant for descriptive purposes (Coid, 1993*a*). But it is briefer than an extended 11-category DSM–III–R research instrument, has a high inter-rater reliability with suitably trained researchers, and emphasises the obtaining of information from case files as well as at interview – an important factor in subjects who can be adept at presenting themselves in a favourable light at a single interview.

Blackburn's typology derived from MMPI profiles

Dimensional models, using a broad range of personality traits, have been employed most successfully with psychopaths using the Minnesota Multiphasic Personality Inventory (MMPI). Within this framework the psychopath is described and classified along pre-set scales which measure factors of personality abnormality. Despite its basis within a dimensional system, Blackburn's typology is an empirical conversion to a categorical scheme derived from the MMPI. Studies of self-reported personality characteristics using the MMPI in forensic psychiatric hospital samples (Blackburn, 1971, 1975, 1986) and in prison samples (Holland & Holt, 1975; Widom, 1977*a,b*; McGurk, 1978; McGurk & McGurk, 1979; Henderson, 1982) have yielded similar profiles when the variables are subjected to cluster analysis. Typically, four groups have been demonstrated. Types 1 and 2 are considered to represent two subgroupings of psychopaths, whereas types 3 and 4 are considered to be non-psychopathic.

Type 1: primary or 4–9 type. Blackburn considers this to be close to Cleckley's concept. These individuals are highly extroverted, non-neurotic and guilt free; have a high level of impulsivity; and are more violent in terms of previous convictions.

Type 2: secondary or neurotic. These subjects are withdrawn, hypochondriacal, suspicious; prone to depression, tension, and disruptive thoughts; resentful, aggressive, anxious, undersocialised, impulsive, and somewhat introverted. They have a highly abnormal MMPI profile suggestive of paranoid and psychotic disorder, although the samples chosen in various studies tended not to include psychotic subjects. In samples from maximum-security hospitals, type 2 individuals tend to be more aggressive than others and difficult to manage on the wards. The criminal histories of type 2 subjects show more sex offences than those of type 1 individuals.

Type 3: controlled. These tend to show defensive denial about psychological problems; are sociable, slightly extrovert and highly controlled; and deny experiencing anxiety or other negative affect.

Type 4: inhibited. These subjects show defensive denial. They are less controlled than type 3 and more suspicious, but not notably aggressive. They are characterised by social withdrawal and extreme introversion. They show dysthymic characteristics or a profile of depression and social avoidance. They have difficulty in interpersonal relationships but otherwise there is no typical correspondence with the concept of a psychopath. In the hospital samples, they tended to have committed more sex offences.

Blackburn (1982) later argued that despite the advantage of the MMPI in providing the richest available sample of deviant psychological characteristics, most of the substantive information relevant to psychopaths can be obtained with a smaller number of items and scales, but that in assessments of populations in which psychopathic traits and proneness to violence are of interest additional items are required. This led to his development of the Special Hospitals Assessment of Personality and Socialisation (SHAPS) questionnaire. This 10-scale questionnaire is based mainly on the MMPI but with additional items. Most of the variance is summarised by two factors, for which scales have been developed (Blackburn, 1987). The first (belligerence) measures impulsivity and hostility versus conformity; the second (withdrawal) measures shyness and poor self-esteem versus sociability and confidence. 'Primary' and 'secondary' psychopaths are identified in this empirical classification by high scores on the first factor, but opposite extremes on the second. Blackburn describes this new instrument as an advance on the use of the original MMPI clusters, but this instrument requires further research with different populations of offenders.

Psychodynamic classification

The psychodynamic concepts of borderline and narcissistic personality organisation are most relevant to psychopathic patients. These are reflected in the patients' primary characteristics, especially:

(a) the degree of identity integration
(b) the type of defensive operations habitually employed
(c) the capacity for reality testing.

Kernberg (1975, 1984) proposed three broad structural organisations – neurotic, borderline and psychotic – which stabilise the mental apparatus, mediating between aetiological factors and direct behavioural manifestations of illness. Narcissistic personality disorder is seen as a specific form overlapping with, or in some cases part of, borderline organisation. Psychopaths can be placed at the most severe end of a spectrum of severity of borderline and narcissistic personality organisation.

Borderline personality organisation

According to Kernberg (1984) the classical characteristics of borderline personality organisation include the following.

(A) *Descriptive symptoms*

1. Anxiety – chronic, diffuse and free-floating.
2. Polysymptomatic neurosis: two or more of the following–multiple phobias, obsessive symptoms, multiple elaborate or bizarre conversion symptoms, dissociative reactions, hypochondriasis, paranoid and hypochondriacal trends with any other symptomatic neurosis.
3. Polymorphous perverse sexual trends.
4. Classical pre-psychotic personality structures including: (a) paranoid personality; (b) schizoid personality; (c) hypomanic personality and cyclothymic personality organisation with strong hypomanic trends.
5. Impulse neurosis and addiction: chronic repetitive eruption of impulses which gratify instinctual needs.
6. 'Lower level' character disorders: severe character pathology typically represented by the chaotic and impulse-ridden character.

(B) *Lack of integrated identity.* Identify diffusion represented by a poorly integrated concept of the self and of significant others.

(C) *Primitive defence mechanisms.* Primitive dissociation or splitting and the associated mechanisms of primitive idealisation, primitive types of projection (particularly projective identification), denial, omnipotence, and devaluation.

(D) *Reality-testing.* This is retained, in contrast to the psychotic level of functioning.

(E) *Non-specific manifestations of ego weakness.* Difficulty tolerating anxiety without increased symptoms or regressive behaviour.

(F) *Lack of super-ego integration.* The personality organisation characterised by non-integrated super-ego precursors, particularly sadistic and idealised object representations.

(G) *Genetic–dynamic characteristics of instinctual conflicts.* A pathological condensation of genital and pregenital instinctual strivings with a predominance of pregenital aggression.

Gunderson (1984) has suggested a narrower concept of borderline personality disorder in line with the diagnostic category in DSM–III–R, and a stratification of severity of borderline functioning at three levels. Psychopathic patients frequently function at the lowest level, perceiving an absence or lack of any major object. In reaction to this, they can experience brief psychotic episodes, panic states, or impulsive efforts to avoid panic. These can include fights and promiscuity (often assisted by the disinhibiting effects of drugs and alcohol), which reflect desperate efforts to establish contact with and revive the illusion of control over some new object. An alternative reaction can include prolonged dissociative episodes of depersonalisation and derealisation, during which self-mutilation may occur, sometimes accompanied by brief episodes of psychotic depression, hallucinatory phenomena, ideas of reference, or transient somatic delusions.

Narcissistic personality and psychopathy

Certain psychopaths with similar primitive defence mechanisms and highly disturbed super-ego pathology are still able superficially to retain some normal social functioning in many life situations, sometimes for relatively long periods. Narcissistic individuals are protected from the intense intrapsychic conflicts more typical of borderline pathology by the development of the 'pathological grandiose self'. Narcissistic personality organisation usually retains an integrated self-concept, but this self-concept is still pathological and grandiose and its development continues to interfere seriously with super-ego functioning.

Kernberg (1984) describes these patients as having an unusual degree of self-reference in their interactions with others, with a contradiction between their inflated concept of themselves and an inordinate need for positive attention from others. They indulge in grandiose fantasies and envy others. Relationships with others tend to be exploitative and sometimes parasitic. Behind what can be a superficially charming and engaging exterior is coldness and ruthlessness.

Kernberg also described six levels of super-ego pathology in these individuals, ranging from those with neurotic character pathology along a continuum of severity to the practically untreatable antisocial personality proper, or psychopath. At this most severe level the individual is entirely identified with a grandiose self-structure, the stranger self-object. The primary mode of relatedness is aggression, usually experienced as sadistic pleasure. These people cannot experience authentic investment of love in others or appreciate the difference between such investments others may have for them and ruthless exploitation and manipulation. Among this group, Kernberg saw a continuum between the passive, exploitative, parasitic criminal and the frankly sadistic criminal. But in the former, confrontation at this level of superego pathology with their antisocial behaviour can still trigger violent paranoid regression in the transference projected onto the therapist. These individuals are observed to be particularly at home in social conditions or occupations where they can freely express their primitive aggression and cruelty.

Recommendations on the use of diagnostic systems

Each of these five contemporary systems could be employed to assess personality abnormality in future studies of psychopathic disorder. All have their limitations: for example, a full DSM–III–R axis II assessment may be more time-consuming, the MMPI relies entirely on self-report, and a psychodynamic formulation requires highly specialised training. It is likely that there is a considerable degree of overlap between these classifications; indeed, certain DSM–III–R categories are derived from the psychodynamic constructs outlined above. But comparative research remains at the earliest stages. For practical purposes, it is recommended that future clinical assessments or research studies involving psychopaths should employ the PCL–R as a minimum, with a full ICD–10 or DSM–III–R axis II assessment as a preference whenever possible. MMPI profiles and psychodynamic formulations might be added when additional specialist resources are available to clinicians or researchers.

However, alongside the diagnosis of the presence or absence of personality disorder or psychopathy in an individual, issues of severity and comorbidity need to be addressed. Therefore, the following section considers the assessment of the severity of the disorder.

Assessing the severity of personality disorder

Trait approaches to personality disorder

Most classifications of personality disorder are heavily reliant on the use of trait approaches. As defined in DSM–III–R, personality traits are

> "enduring patterns of perceiving, relating to, and thinking about the environment and oneself, and are exhibited in a wide range

> of important and social and personal contexts. It is only when personality traits are inflexible and maladaptive and cause either significant functional impairment or subjective distress that they constitute personality disorders."

Unfortunately, a closer examination of diagnostic criteria within the main classificatory systems, such as ICD–10 and DSM–III–R, reveals that many are in fact features of behaviour rather than true traits of personality, or else can only be inferred on the basis of a patient's behaviour. Furthermore, Tantam (1988) has posed fundamental questions of whether there are traits of personality and whether they contribute much to behaviour. From this must follow the questions of whether personality traits are actually being treated by any single treatment modality, and if so, how treatment effects will be measured. Powell (1984) has reviewed a number of studies which indicate that traits may be individually manifested or correlated in one situation but not another, and that factor-analytic studies do not yield factors that correspond to traits. The problem is therefore compounded because measurements of traits are also weakly predictive of behaviour or attitude and ignore the very important effect of situational factors on determining behaviour (Powell & Stewart, 1978).

Powell has therefore argued the importance of an interactionist approach to personality in an attempt to overcome certain limitations of trait approaches. Thus, individual variation can occur within inherent personality traits and this will affect not only the perception of the situation an individual finds him/herself in but also his/her response to it. Interaction between trait and situational theory assumes that situations and their outcome will result in an individual learning from an emotional experience which in turn changes the individual. Personality is thus not static and has the potential for development throughout life. But this will depend on various factors, such as the individual's capacity to learn and whether or not reactions to situations lead to further novel situations in which new learning can occur, or merely to repeats of previous situations. However, trait approaches comprise only one of several possible intrapsychic explanations for repetitive patterns of deviant behaviour, despite the assumption in most contemporary glossaries that they are the fundamental basis for determining abnormal personality types, a view now strongly voiced in ICD–10. In the clinical assessment of psychopathic disorder, we are therefore promoting an interactionist approach through a multidimensional assessment.

Multiple diagnostic approaches

Coid (1992) has conducted descriptive studies of psychopathic disorder in three different samples using multiple diagnostic approaches. Over 250 men and women from maximum-security hospitals detained under the legal category 'psychopathic disorder' of the Mental Health Act 1983, or admitted to special units in prisons for the containment of highly dangerous and disruptive inmates, were subjected to a battery of research instruments to elicit personality disorder diagnoses, lifetime axis I (clinical syndromes), and a history of potential aetiological factors. Five important findings emerged, with implications for the diagnostic assessment of psychopaths in the future.

Firstly, subjects required multiple DSM–III–R axis II (personality disorder) categories to encompass their broad range of psychopathology. There was an overall mean of 3.6 categories per subject in the series (range 0–9). Less than 10% presented with a single diagnosis of personality disorder using this diagnostic approach.

Secondly, not all subjects were found to have the 'core' features of DSM–III–R antisocial personality disorder, and not all had scores on Hare's Psychopathy Check-List which indicated that they were psychopaths for research purposes. Thus the 'core features' were not necessarily present for clinicians to deem a subject a psychopath. Those with such features were characterised primarily by a history of criminal recidivism. Various subgroups emerged with different diagnostic characteristics but nevertheless presenting with serious criminal and dangerous behaviour.

Thirdly, subjects demonstrated multiple axis I syndromes over their lifetime, with a mean of 2.7 categories. Depressive disorder was the most common, appearing at some time in the lives of 50% of subjects, followed in descending order of frequency by dysthymia, hypomania, substance abuse disorders, schizophrenia, brief psychotic episodes lasting less than a week, and conditions such as phobia, panic attacks, and obsessive–compulsive disorder.

Fourthy, axis I clinical syndromes appeared at specific times over the life-span of subjects. Disordered sexual identity, dysthymia, phobias and somatisation disorder (Briquet's syndrome) presented in late childhood and early adolescence. In later adolescence and early adulthood these conditions were progressively accompanied by deteriorating substance abuse, recurrent episodes of major depression, panic attacks, brief manic episodes, and brief episodes of hallucinosis, sometimes following stress. A subgroup began to manifest schizophrenia and delusional disorder in their mid-20s. Many of these conditions appeared briefly and were recurrent in an individual subject.

Fifthly, potential aetiological factors were divided into three groups:

(a) genetic (including presence of mental disorder or personality disorder in first-degree relatives)
(b) neurological (e.g. a history of birth complications, developmental delay, IQ verbal–performance discrepancy)
(c) environmental factors before the age of 15 (e.g. a history of physical and sexual abuse, loss of parents, witnessing violence in the family home, family criminality, poverty).

Many subjects showed overlap in these three components. Only a small minority presented with no potential adverse aetiological factors.

A recent study of a non-secure sample considered patients referred to the Henderson Hospital for treatment of severe personality disorder (Dolan *et al,* 1993). The study used the Personality Diagnostic Questionnaire (PDQ–R; Hyler *et al,* 1987), a validated self-report measure of the 11 personality disorders described in DSM–III–R. This questionnaire was completed by 275 patients. The number of positive diagnoses of personality disorder per subject ranged from none (in 3% cases) to 11, with an average of 6.0. The most frequent diagnosis was borderline personality disorder, which was found in 87% of cases, but over 60% met criteria for antisocial personality disorder, and even the least prevalent diagnosis, passive–aggressive personality disorder, was present in 43%. There was only limited evidence that these multiple diagnoses clustered in the three subgroups described in the axis II categorisation.

This multiple morbidity of DSM–III personality disorders has been noted previously, but there has been relatively little discussion of the meaning of the finding. When commented on, it is generally explained as due to non-specificity of the instrument or the diagnostic system itself (Tyrer *et al,* 1991; Clark, 1992). In fact, various systems have been used to circumvent the 'problem': the templating diagnostic system of ICD–9, and a general tendency among clinicians to aim for a 'main' diagnosis, lead to reporting of one, or at most, two diagnoses; and many diagnosticians (e.g. Tyrer, 1988) suggest hierarchical classifications in which some diagnoses 'trump' others. Nevertheless, these criticisms of the specificity of diagnosis fail to reflect the importance and potential value of multiple axis II diagnoses.

The multiple morbidity of personality disorder diagnosis is comprehensible if multiple axis II diagnoses are seen as a function of severity. Dolan *et al* (1992*a*) found a significant positive correlation between the number of PDQ diagnoses and score on the impairment distress scale ($r = 0.46$; $P < 0.0001$): a higher number of PDQ diagnoses was positively associated with greater social, psychological and occupational disturbance – i.e. one measure of severity of disorder.

The multiplicity of diagnoses has two important implications for research on personality disorders. Firstly, and positively, whenever systematic interviews or self-report measures of personality disorders are applied, the number of diagnoses per subject forms a crude but useful measure of the range of disturbance. Secondly, and problematically, multiple diagnoses complicate the interpretation of those studies which discuss their subjects in terms of a single diagnostic category (e.g. Gardner & Cowdry, 1986). Such studies will contain a proportion of subjects who have just the one personality disorder diagnosis: however, even out-patient psychiatric samples meet an average of two diagnoses per person (e.g. Nurnberg *et al*, 1991), and to describe such subjects in terms of just the one diagnosis is misleading. A focus on the most crippling or most apparent area of dysfunction may make good clinical sense – hence the use of intuitive or explicit 'trumping' systems – but the breadth of pathology may be as important as that which is seen first. Until there is substantial evidence that personality disorder subcategories are of little or no clinical use, they should all continue to be considered. In the absence of better research knowledge into the aetiology, inter-relationship and treatment response of personality disorder subcategories, we cannot afford to assume that breadth data are redundant.

Taken with the report of Coid (1992), these findings have several major implications for future assessment. Firstly, no single diagnostic approach will encompass all features of a patient's psychopathology and no current system has resolved the problems of comorbidity between or within different diagnostic axes. However, comorbidity may be of considerable importance in assessing treatability, and different categories may well have adverse interactions across and within axes. Secondly, behavioural disorders are included among criteria for most abnormal personality types, and no diagnostic system has so far successfully developed a purely trait-based classification. Assessment of behavioural change will therefore remain the cornerstone of treatment effectiveness. Thirdly, a longitudinal perspective is necessary to take account of the changing presentation of both psychopathology and behaviour over time. Considerable information is available on the development of behavioural disorder from infancy to adulthood, and psychiatric research is providing increasing data on the age of onset and longitudinal course of clinical syndromes. But despite a contemporary emphasis on trait-based classifications of personality disorder, little is known of the longitudinal development of personality traits.

Rutter (1987) identified three unifying features of personality disorder, including:

(a) an onset in childhood or adolescence
(b) long-standing persistence over time without marked remission or relapses
(c) abnormalities that seem to constitute a basic aspect of the individual's usual functioning.

When applied to psychopathic disorders, four additional qualifying features have been applied by Coid (1993*a*):

(a) that the condition is particularly severe, whether measured according to the number of personality traits present, the level of functioning according to a psychodynamic framework, or the number of diagnostic labels finally applied
(b) that the condition is resistant to treatment, as a function either of its severity or of an unwillingness or lack of cooperation in treatment by the individual concerned
(c) that the abnormality of personality leads to dyssocial behaviour (including behaviour harmful to the person concerned)
(d) that the behaviour may be sufficiently socially unacceptable to lead to formal interventions such as criminal proceedings, imprisonment or compulsory admission to hospital, and can also lead to other forms of serious social breakdown such as homelessness or vagrancy.

These four additional features do not separate psychopathic disorder from personality disorder but place it at the far end of a spectrum of severity. An approach to assessment devised from this model is described in the Appendix.

Influence of personality disorder on the course of axis I clinical syndromes

The influence of personality disorder on the course and treatment of clinical syndromes is of particular importance and is a growing area of research interest (Tyrer & Seivewright, 1988). Research on this issue cannot be fully reviewed within this text, but two comprehensive reviews of the impact of personality pathology on treatment outcome of axis I disorders are available (Reich & Green, 1991; Reich & Vasile, 1993). Although many reports in the literature have methodological flaws, these reviews do demonstrate how, in both structured treatment trials and naturalistic surveys of various treatment modalities, the presence of personality disorder has an adverse effect upon outcome of a wide range of disorders. These studies have considered depressive disorders, anxiety and social phobia, panic disorder, obsessive–compulsive disorders, eating disorders and substance abuse or dependence.

Unfortunately, it is still unclear what the mechanism of effect is: perhaps presence of personality disorder reflects a more severe variant of the underlying core disorder (Diguer *et al*, 1993); personality disorder could be a vulnerability factor facilitating onset of axis I disorders; the antisocial behaviour of personality-disordered individuals may precipitate more stressful life events and withdrawal of social supports (Zimmerman *et al*, 1986; Poulton & Andrews, 1992); or the presence of personality disorder may render the patient less likely to comply with treatment for the axis I condition (Conte *et al*, 1991). Whatever the reason for the poorer outcome of patients with comorbid personality disorder, this reduced efficacy of treatment for mental state disorders may in part have added to the increasing therapeutic nihilism on the part of many clinicians regarding personality-disordered people.

The patient who has comorbid personality disorder often begins treatment with worse psychological health than the patient without comorbid personality disorder, and at the termination of treatment does not reach the same state of psychological wellbeing as his/her counterpart without comorbid personality disorder. However, one study of brief psychotherapy for depression has noted that although overall outcome was worse, the improvement of patients with personality disorder, in terms of change between intake and termination of treatment, was statistically similar to the improvement of those without personality disorder (Diguer *et al*, 1993).

Co-occurrence of mental state and personality disorders is also of particular relevance to the clinician, given recent evidence that comorbidity of personality disorder can influence treatment seeking. In a survey of treatment-seeking in 3258 representative general community residents in Canada, the co-occurrence of antisocial personality disorder with major depression or with panic disorder was shown to increase the probability of treatment-seeking to about four times (Du Fort *et al*, 1993).

Although this text focuses upon the treatment of axis II pathology and, to a lesser degree, the co-occurrence of associated axis I morbidity, there is growing evidence to support the view that in both clinical practice and research evaluations prior to treatment studies of clinical syndromes, assessment is incomplete without careful attention being given to axis II psychopathology.

3 Natural history

A longitudinal perspective of the natural history of psychopathy and antisocial behaviour is vital to the evaluation of treatment. This is for three reasons. Firstly, a benchmark is required against which to judge the effects of treatment. The revised Psychopathy Check-List (PCL–R) and DSM–III–R antisocial personality disorder (ASPD), which are thought to comprise the 'core' features, both contain a longitudinal element along which treatment effects could be measured. Thus, an intervention which altered a life course, beginning with the progressive demonstration of conduct disorder in childhood and continuing in adulthood with a range of antisocial behavioural features and accompanying dyssocial personality traits, would be rated as highly effective if the same individual subsequently led a law-abiding life, held a steady job, and could maintain a stable relationship over a prolonged period of follow-up.

Secondly, studying the longitudinal development of psychopathic disorder may in itself provide suggestions for new and more effective methods of treatment. Naturalistic observations of ameliorations and exacerbations – within certain age ranges, after specific life events, etc. – could suggest new interventions. These could take the form of artificial reconstructions of what had been naturalistically observed and could be tested in subsequent empirical trials. This notion fits neatly into the traditional medical model. The history of medicine shows that most new discoveries of effective treatment have been merely fortuitous, the result of clinical or even accidental observations, rather than the outcome of a series of carefully planned research studies.

The third reason is that the longitudinal perspective itself demonstrates that psychopathy is more than just a disease process. This poses a challenge to an exclusive reliance on the medical model and its consequences for treatment. An individual functions and develops as a totality in a way that can be described as a multi-determined stochastic process. This formulation implies that many factors are involved and operate in a probabilistic, often non-linear way. The functioning of an individual is thus characterised by a continuously ongoing, reciprocal interaction among perceptual–cognitive–emotional factors and biological factors in the individual, and social and physical factors in the environment. This interactive process is seemingly complex and chaotic but developmental researchers have begun to demonstrate that it is actually coherent and follows certain laws. Within this research field, the major scientific challenge is to identify the factors involved and the mechanisms by which they operate. To do this, the same individual must be followed across time in order to understand the process of interaction among psychological and biological aspects of functioning and social and physical factors in the environment. Biological factors, while fitting comfortably within the medical model of treatment intervention, are only part of the overall picture, and therefore cannot be the only goal of treatment. Furthermore, the major diagnostic constructs of psychopathy (and indeed most diagnostic categories of personality disorder) will themselves include a major component of the social environment. Intervention in this social environment will also be necessary if psychopathic individuals are to change their way of functioning over their life-span through processes such as maturation and experience. These latter components will themselves imply two additional elements that must be considered within any intervention:

(a) adequate time over which a diagnostic entity defined by dyssocial behaviour, or personality traits leading to dyssocial behaviour, can be expected to change and/or mature
(b) multiple interventions carried out simultaneously on quite different dimensions, including biological, social environmental, physical environmental, and perceptual–cognitive–emotional factors within the individual.

An intervention along one dimension will not necessarily effect change in the individual without an intervention along another.

Faced with these complexities, it is as well to point out at the outset that life-span studies have only begun to piece together the most elementary components of the longitudinal development of what we have termed 'psychopathic disorder'. To review this large area, it is necessary to be selective by covering only the most important studies of the development of conduct disorder, the most relevant studies of the development of delinquency and criminal behaviour, and the findings of authors who have examined 'protective' and 'risk' factors for the development of an adverse social outcome in adulthood. The concepts of 'maturity' and 'burn-out' will be briefly discussed. However, a full examination of the major aetiological factors that shape the development of psychopathy are beyond the scope of this chapter.

Prospective studies of deviant children and adolescents

Several long-term prospective studies of delinquency and behavioural disorder in children have attempted both to learn whether behaviour and associated personality traits have long-term stability, and to identify early predictors of adverse outcomes. There are, however, problems with the long-term study of antisocial personality traits, as these may be expressed differently at different ages. Moreover, continuity of deviant behaviour does not necessarily reflect continuity of underlying causative personality abnormality, as the meaning and motivators of behavioural features may vary with age. Nevertheless, research has demonstrated that a significant proportion of those who

(a) show conduct disorders in childhood
(b) show poor peer relationships
(c) come from disordered and deprived family backgrounds, with parents displaying mental illness, criminality and abusive behaviour

are more likely to have a personality disorder in adulthood (Robins, 1974; McCord, 1982*a,b*; Offord, 1982).

In most cases of adverse outcome these original childhood behaviour problems will have been present, although a subgroup do not display signs of delinquency until middle or late adolescence. Another subgroup display childhood behavioural problems despite a seemingly normal upbringing.

Childhood conduct disorder

The criteria for conduct disorder are met by 4–10% of children in Britain and America, and a third to half of all referrals to child and adolescent clinics (Rutter *et al*, 1975; Robins, 1981; Herbert,

1987; Kazdin, 1987). Conduct disorder is characterised by a persistent pattern of behaviour where the child violates the basic rights of others and the major age-appropriate social norms. Rutter & Giller (1983) suggest that up to 40% of these children will have serious psychosocial problems in adulthood. It is unclear as to whether conduct disorder might be better conceptualised as a phase of a chronic psychiatric disorder which begins in early life and develops into an antisocial personality disorder in adulthood, but which may show improvement at any point along the way (Loeber *et al*, 1991). Robins (1966) recorded the spontaneous improvement of 27% of deviant children in their adulthood, but she also suggests that antisocial individuals who show such improvements may have been given a wrong diagnosis at an earlier stage (Robins, 1970).

The DSM–III–R criteria state that the diagnosis of antisocial personality disorder cannot be given to individuals aged under 18 years. However, Eppright *et al* (1993) surveyed a group of 100 randomly selected incarcerated juvenile offenders aged 11–17 years to examine the possible comorbidity of conduct disorder and personality disorder. By use of a structured interview for DSM–III–R to establish diagnosis, 87% met criteria for conduct disorder. Antisocial personality disorder was 'diagnosed' in 75% of adolescents and was the only comorbid personality disorder significantly associated with conduct disorder. Neither diagnosis was significantly associated with the age, sex or race of the subjects. The authors note that once the age criterion is deleted from antisocial personality disorder, there is great similarity between criteria for the two disorders. They suggest that antisocial personality disorder does manifest at an earlier age than is usually thought.

Certainly the ten other DSM–III–R personality disorder diagnoses, which are not age limited, have been found in school-age children. Golombek *et al* (1986) found that 46% of a sample of 13-year-olds had sufficient personality dysfunction to warrant a DSM–III personality disorder diagnosis. After three years, 44% were free of personality disorder symptoms, suggesting that adolescent personality disturbance is self-limiting in many cases. Bernstein *et al* (1993) carried out a two-year longitudinal assessment of personality disorders (excluding antisocial) in a community sample of 733 adolescents aged 9–19 years. They interviewed both the child and parent and used self-report measures. Overall, 17.3% of subjects received a diagnosis of a severe personality disorder, most often narcissistic disorder (in 6% of subjects). In less than half of cases (42%), the personality disorder persisted over the two-year follow-up period.

Deviant children grown up: a study of psychopathic personality

Robins (1966), in what is perhaps the most famous longitudinal study, followed up a series of 406 children referred to a child guidance clinic for antisocial behaviour, 118 referred for other reasons (primarily with neurotic symptoms), and 100 controls from local schools in the neighbourhood of the clinic. Subjects were traced 30 years later. The original sample of conduct disordered children had parents of low occupational status and only a third were with both parents at the time of referral. A third had spent at least six months in an institution or foster home. Many fathers had deserted their families and/or drank heavily, and many of the mothers failed to keep house or supervise the children. A substantial proportion of the children had siblings with behavioural disorders. Most were behind at school when referred, and 52% of boys and 35% of girls were officially classified as juvenile delinquents. The median age of referral was 13 years and none of the children were above the age of 18 years. Girls were found to have more disrupted lives than boys.

At 30-year follow-up, the antisocial children were more likely to have left their area of origin, 75% of men and 40% of women had been arrested for non-traffic offences, and almost half the males had been arrested for at least one major crime. Arrests for serious offences such as rape and murder in adulthood were found only for the conduct-disordered children. Prostitution was found only in the histories of conduct-disordered females. Of the women referred for antisocial behaviour, 70% were currently divorced, 23% had been divorced more than once, and a third had married before the age of 17. Robins observed that these women tended to choose husbands who were unfaithful, or deserted, or failed to support them. There was a high rate of childlessness in this group, but those who did have children were more likely to have behavioural problems than the two control groups. More than 20% of mothers with antisocial behaviour in childhood had a child who had been arrested. Occupational history in adulthood was characterised by lower social status and more frequent unemployment.

From these findings, Robins devised criteria for the diagnosis of 'sociopathic personality disorder', from which the category 'antisocial personality disorder' in DSM–III–R was ultimately derived (see Chapter 2). The childhood factors that predicted this diagnosis in adulthood included referral to the child guidance clinic for:

(a) theft or aggression
(b) a diversity of forms of antisocial behaviour

(c) many episodes of antisocial behaviour
(d) behaviour involving strangers and organisations other than schools or within the family home.

Girls resembled the boys in their adult pattern but showed more frequent sexual misbehaviour. Unlike the conduct-disordered children (who had a 1 in 5 chance of demonstrating a sociopathic personality in adulthood), children referred with other symptoms of psychiatric disturbance (e.g. fearfulness, withdrawal, tics, speech defects, etc.) were no more likely to have psychiatric disorders as adults than the controls from the local schools.

It was thought that antisocial behaviour in the father was a good predictor for similar behaviour in adulthood for subjects of both sexes. Robins considered that lack of adequate discipline in the family home and the experience of living with a father who drank heavily, was chronically unemployed, arrested, or deserted the family, played an important part. However, early separation from the father did not appear to prevent the child developing later sociopathic behaviour and Robins concluded that taking children from parents was unlikely to help.

Remission and improvement in adulthood could be assessed in the majority of sociopaths. Robins judged that 12% were in remission 30 years later (subjects were then in their fourth or fifth decade), 27% showed a greatly reduced range in severity of antisocial behaviour, but 60% still showed little improvement. The improvement observed in the first two subgroups happened progressively in each decade, most often within the 30–40 age range. It was thought that special life circumstances, sometimes the threat of further punishments following arrest, were a decisive factor. However, Robins believed that neither hospitalisation nor the experience of psychotherapy during the lives of her sociopathic subjects had had any positive association with improvement.

Robins (1978) later replicated her original study with additional cohorts growing up in different eras and living in different parts of the USA. Her original study had included only white subjects. One further cohort consisted of young black males; a third cohort included Vietnam veterans, along with matched non-veterans. Despite considerable differences between samples and in sources of information, there were striking replications of her original study with respect to the childhood predictors of antisocial behaviour. She concluded that all types of antisocial behaviour in childhood could predict a high level of antisocial behaviour in adulthood, and that each kind of adult antisocial behaviour was predicted by the overall number of features of childhood antisocial behaviour.

She argued that her findings indicated that adult and childhood antisocial behaviour both formed syndromes and that the two syndromes were closely connected. She also concluded that adult antisocial behaviour as a pervasive syndrome virtually required a preceding pattern of childhood antisocial behaviour. However, the majority of conduct-disordered children would not go on to become adults with sociopathy or ASPD. It appeared that the variety of antisocial behaviour in childhood was in itself a better predictor of adult antisocial behaviour than any particular individual form of behaviour. Furthermore, the behaviour in childhood was a better predictor for the future than family background or social class.

Wergeland (1980) followed up 39 adolescents (including eight females) referred for treatment of "conduct disorder in a child with weak ego traits and in danger of antisocial development". Personal interviews were conducted an average of ten years after referral (range 4–20 years). Fifteen of these subjects had been hospitalised in a child psychiatry unit, although no description of the treatment is given. The remaining 24 were not treated. On follow-up, 43% of the treated group and 26% of the untreated group were considered free of symptoms; 56% of the treated group were reported as well adjusted to employment, compared with 32% of the untreated sample. However, other measures of social adjustment did not differentiate between the two groups, and it is ultimately unclear from this study whether the natural history of conduct disorder could have accounted for the findings. Thus, the 14 subjects who were untreated and who ultimately had a worse outcome could have been less compliant, from families whose parents were obstructive to treatment, and therefore predisposed to a poorer outcome, rather than a poorer outcome being the result of their not receiving treatment. This important possibility should be considered in all studies of intervention with conduct-disordered subjects and delinquents.

One of the most important observations from longitudinal studies of antisocial conduct in childhood is that behaviour will show different forms at different ages. Loeber (1982) has observed that, from its appearance in early childhood, aggressiveness is the most stable personality characteristic of conduct disorder, although the aggression will be expressed differently at different stages of development. For example, Aschenbach & Adelbrock (1981) found that mothers reported younger problem children to be argumentative, stubborn, and prone to tantrums, while older children had oppositional behaviour. At a later date, these children present with firesetting and stealing, and finally truancy, vandalism, and substance abuse.

Loeber (1982) has reviewed the literature and determined four factors predictive of chronic delinquency following conduct disorder. These are:

(a) frequency of antisocial behaviour
(b) its variety
(c) age at onset
(d) presence of antisocial behaviour in more than one setting.

These factors predispose to adult antisocial personality disorder, substance abuse, and a higher rate of violent death (Hesselbrock, 1986; Rydelius, 1988; Robins & Price, 1991). A small subgroup manifesting conduct disorder will also go on to develop major mental disorder in adulthood (Robins & Price, 1991).

Childhood attention deficit hyperactivity disorder

Attention deficit hyperactivity disorder (ADHD) presents as inappropriate degrees of inattention, impulsivity and hyperactivity in childhood. Although not always well distinguished from conduct disorder, some evidence suggests that it can predict juvenile convictions independent of conduct disorder (Farrington *et al*, 1990). When ADHD and conduct disorder present together they seem to have an additive effect in predicting adult chronic offending.

Prospective studies have examined the continuity of ADHD and shown that the condition usually continues into mid-adolescence, although one-third will show remission by this stage (Klein & Mannuzza, 1991). Those who persist with ADHD through late adolescence have a fourfold higher risk of developing antisocial personality disorder than those who remit. However, it has been suggested that the future development of antisocial personality disorder depends upon the presence of additional risk and protective factors (Hechtman *et al*, 1991).

Studies of the development of delinquency

Previous commentators have criticised the inclusion of criminal behaviour in definitions of psychopathy. Nevertheless, Hare's construct of psychopathy within the PCL–R and the DSM–III–R category ASPD are still heavily reliant on criteria involving criminal behaviour, and the development of this from delinquency in childhood and adolescence. Until an adequate diagnostic classification is based exclusively on personality traits, an understanding of the longitudinal course of psychopathic disorder is still heavily reliant on research into crime and delinquency.

Most Westernised countries have reported increases in crime in recent years and a substantial minority of males can expect to receive a conviction at some time over the life-span. However, convictions are predominantly recorded in the early- and mid-teenage years. Most offenders desist from crime in later teenage and early adult years. But persistence is observed in a subgroup, which in turn associates with other indicators of poor adult adjustment. It is this 'persistence' of criminal behaviour which is considered one of the major findings of longitudinal studies of delinquency, and researchers continue to seek for explanations for this phenomenon.

The Cambridge–Somerville youth study

One of the most ambitious studies of the development of delinquency was the Cambridge–Somerville youth study (Powers & Whitmer, 1951). In 1939 boys from an industrial area of Massachusetts aged 5–13 years (mean 10.5) were selected from schools and welfare agencies as suitable for a treatment programme designed to prevent delinquency. Boys were matched in pairs for predicted delinquency scores and then one of each pair was randomly assigned to a programme of twice-monthly visits by counsellors, to the boy and the family, over the next five years. Detailed case records were kept for both groups.

McCord (1978) reported a 30-year follow-up of 506 men who entered the study after 1942. In total, 480 men from the study were traced (95%), of whom 48 (9%) had died. Official health and criminal records were searched and over half responded to self-report questionnaires. Almost equal numbers in the treatment and control groups had committed juvenile crimes (46% v. 45%), adult crimes (any adult crime, 47% v. 49%), and serious adult crimes (19% v. 17%). Of the men with criminal records, significantly more of those in the treatment group committed at least two crimes (78% v. 67%, $P < 0.05$). A history of treatment for alcoholism was found in 7% and 8% of the groups respectively and 21 (8%) of each group had been hospitalised for other psychiatric disorders. There was little difference in current social demographics of the two groups. Despite the lack of evidence of an effect of the treatment condition, the study does provide a long-term prospective account of delinquency, criminal behaviour and psychiatric morbidity.

McCord (1979) studied the family backgrounds of those men who had offended. She showed that several aspects of the family atmosphere during childhood were related to adult crime: these included father's deviance, parental aggressiveness, mother's lack of self-confidence, parental conflict, and lack of supervision. These family factors were more accurate predictors of crime than those based upon the man's juvenile criminal record.

Although there is an amount of information on the development of disruptive children into delinquent adolescents and antisocial adults, less attention has been paid to the natural history and development of psychopathy once the adult psychopath has been identified. The major reason for this gap in the knowledge base is that, as a rule, psychopaths are not identified as such until their antisocial or self-destructive behaviour brings them to the attention of the mental health or criminal justice systems. At this point there is an obligation upon the professionals involved to intervene. For a proportion, the first and perhaps only intervention will be incarceration.

The longitudinal studies of West & Farrington

In a series of studies of the development of delinquency, West & Farrington systematically surveyed a sample of 411 males recruited aged 8 from a working-class neighbourhood in London (West & Farrington, 1973, 1977; West, 1969, 1982). By the age of 25, one-third had acquired a criminal conviction record. Within the convicted group were different patterns of criminal career, and the authors roughly classified their convicted subjects into four subgroups: juvenile one-time offenders, late-comers to crime, temporary recidivists, and persisting delinquents.

The juvenile one-time offenders differed only slightly in background and behaviour from their unconvicted peers. The late-comers to crime (who also were often one-time offenders) tended to come from unremarkable backgrounds but had been rather more troublesome than the average as schoolboys.

The temporary recividists had multiple convictions in youth, but no more after passing the age of 18. They tended to come from relatively deprived backgrounds and to have been troublesome as schoolboys and significantly deviant in lifestyle up to the age of 18 or later, but subsequently to reform and become socially conformist and non-delinquent.

The persisting delinquents tended to start their conviction careers at a particularly early age, to sustain frequent convictions as juveniles, and to continue to acquire convictions in their 20s. They were generally from the worst, most deprived family backgrounds. They stood out as the most conspicuously deviant group, both during school years and in early adult life.

This fourth subgroup appears to overlap with the sociopathic subjects identified by Robins. However, in this study the repeated follow-up interviews allowed a clearer impression of the developing antisocial character. Thus, adverse features identified at age 10, or earlier, which distinguished persisting recidivists included the following:

(a) very poor parental behaviour, as shown by scoring 6 out of 7 on a rating scale of psychiatric social workers' assessments (up to age 10); the rated features included items such as marital conflict, dominance of one parent over the other in decision making relating to the children, inconsistency between parents in handling the child, attitudes of indifference, positive rejection or neglect, over-strict or erratically varying discipline, and harsh methods of enforcement
(b) IQ in the lowest 10% of the sample (IQ 83 or less at ages 8 and 10)
(c) very large family size (six or more brothers and sisters at subject's tenth birthday)
(d) large family (five or more brothers and sisters) and also low family income at the subject's tenth birthday
(e) both parents convicted before the subject's tenth birthday
(f) at least four of five background adversities on assessments completed at age 10, the five key factors being:

    (i) coming from a low-income family
    (ii) coming from a large family
    (iii) having parents considered by social workers to have performed child-rearing duties unsatisfactorily
    (iv) having below-average intelligence
    (v) having a parent with a criminal record

(g) exceptional troublesomeness (score 20+) on teachers' ratings at age 8 or 10; the questions covered by teachers included the child's application to work, scholastic performance, concentration, cleanliness, obedience, attendance, and relations with other children (perceptions of teachers and the boy's peers that he was an above average nuisance appeared to be the best single predictor of juvenile delinquency in the series.)

At age 18, the 101 subjects who were delinquent (including later persisting recidivists) were compared with non-delinquents: they scored higher on self-reported aggression, were more likely to have tattoos, were more likely to have an unstable job record, spent their leisure time 'hanging about', were involved in anti-social groups of other young men, admitted to having driven while drunk, were more likely to be heavy gamblers, were sexually experienced, were heavy smokers, used prohibited drugs, and were somewhat more likely to have anti-establishment attitudes.

By age 24, the 22 persisting recidivist subjects were more likely to have been unemployed for a period of over two months in the last two years, spent more money on alcohol and tobacco per week, were now living in home conditions which were poor (none lived in homes owned by themselves or by relatives), had unpaid debts, were more likely to be cohabiting rather than married, and were more likely to be separated from their children by other relationships. Within sexual relationships, they were less likely to use contraceptives. More had been involved in at least one fight over the past two years, admitted to at least two items of criminal behaviour during the same period, and had a score of at least 3 out of 6 possible points on an 'antisociality' scale.

The researchers attempted to examine features that might change the course of delinquency careers. They identified the four following major factors which appeared to influence the life course.

Going to the wrong school. There were somewhat more delinquents than expected from schools that had overall high delinquency rates. However, differences between delinquency rates were largely accounted for by differences at intake, those having a high rate having higher proportions of troublesome boys sent to them. West & Farrington were not permitted to pursue research within the boys' schools to find out in more detail what had accounted for these differences. However, they cited other research which indicated that schools themselves had a partial effect on pupil's delinquent behaviour, separate from that determined by the type of pupil admitted.

Getting married. Marriage sometimes appeared to have a restraining effect upon delinquents in the study. To a large extent, marriages took place at the time of life when frequency of convictions in most subjects was decreasing anyway. However, statistical analysis did suggest that marriage had some effect in reducing the chances of delinquency persisting. However, this effect occurred less often than might have been expected, because members of the more delinquent subgroup tended to marry women who were themselves socially deviant.

Getting caught. An increase in deviant attitude and behaviour was observed following first conviction. The delinquents themselves subscribed to the popular belief of a deterrent effect of being caught and convicted. Statistical analysis, controlling for other factors such as an increase in delinquent behaviour leading to the conviction itself, suggested that there was a true effect of getting caught on amplification of subsequent deviant behaviour.

Moving away. There are many possible explanations of why a subgroup of men happened to move away from inner London. However, whatever the explanation in an individual case, it did appear that moving out of the city made the continuation of a delinquency career less likely than would otherwise have been the case. This effect was more substantial than the effect of getting married. The recidivists were particularly frequent movers of address, but this was a quite different phenomenon than the major geographical change which led to increased likelihood of desistence from crime.

The Kauai longitudinal study

A series of surveys by Werner and colleagues, involving a multiracial cohort of 698 children born on the Hawaiian island of Kauai, has provided one of the most important sources of data on longitudinal development and the interaction of social and biological factors on outcome in adulthood (Werner *et al*, 1971; Werner & Smith, 1977, 1982; Werner, 1985). It cannot be assumed that Werner's study has entire relevance for psychopathic disorder, as her main measures of adverse outcome included either a history of arrests or a psychiatric history by the age of 18, measures that only partially overlap with the concept we are evaluating. However, the methodology of her study is superior to that of most others, and the model she employed to measure the interaction of different variables impinging on subjects over the life-span is particularly sophisticated. Her study ranks as a model for future researchers. The original objectives were: to provide a longitudinal perspective on the children's capacity to cope with perinatal stress, poverty, and serious disruptions of the family unit; to examine sex differences in vulnerability and resistance to biological and psychosocial stress; and to identify protective factors within the children and their care-giving environment that discriminated between resilient youngsters and peers who developed serious learning and/or behavioural problems in the first and second decades of life.

Her study was remarkable in collecting its series during pregnancy. Thus, a percentage of potential subjects were spontaneously aborted in the early stages. Data were collected on prenatal and perinatal adversity, and presence of congenital defects at birth; at age two an assessment of physical development was made by a paediatrician. Later, intellectual development was measured, and at age 10 an assessment was made by an interdisciplinary panel to record any evidence of physical, learning or behavioural problems, and to identify need for medical treatment, remedial education, or mental health care. Approximately one out of every three children in the birth cohort had some learning or behavioural problem during the first decade of life, and approximately one out of every five youths had records of serious delinquency or mental health problems in the second decade. Some were exposed to major perinatal insults that prevented normal development. Many more lived in chronic poverty or in a persistently disorganised family environment. Frequently, biological and psychosocial risk factors interacted and exposed these children and youths to cumulative stresses too difficult to cope with unaided. Perinatal complications were consistently related to later impaired physical and psychological development only when they were combined with persistently poor environmental circumstances (e.g. chronic poverty, family instability, or maternal mental health problems). Children who were raised in more affluent homes, with an intact family and well educated mother, showed few, if any negative effects from reproductive stress, unless there was severe impairment of the central nervous system, thus confirming the importance of joint influences of reproductive risk and the quality of the caregiving environment during the child's upbringing.

With respect to most of the problems identified in middle childhood, improvement had occurred spontaneously by the time the cohort reached 18 years, although positive changes in behaviour were noted more often for middle-class than lower-class children. Children with learning and/or behaviour problems that persisted into late adolescence had higher rates of moderate to severe perinatal stress, low birth weight, and "chronic conditions leading to minimal brain dysfunctions" noted by paediatricians in infancy. At the same time, they tended to live more often in chronic poverty or amid parental psychopathology than children whose problems were transient. It was an important finding that those with an adverse outcome had tended to elicit more negative responses from their caretakers, indicating a bi-directionality of the child–caretaker effect. Children with an adverse outcome had infantile temperamental traits which appeared distressing and

TABLE 3.1
Vulnerability and stress factors relating to adverse adult outcome in the Kauai longitudinal study

Major risk factors at birth
Chronic poverty
Mother having little education
Moderate to severe perinatal complications
Developmental delays or irregularities
Genetic abnormalities
Parental psychopathology
Major sources of stress during childhood and adolescence
Prolonged separation from primary care-giver in first year
Birth of younger sibling within two years
Serious repeated childhood illnesses
Parental illness
Parental mental illness
Sibling with handicap, learning, or behaviour problem
Chronic family discord
Father's absence
Loss of job, sporadic employment of parents
Change of residence
Change of school
Divorce of parents
Remarriage and entrance of step-parent into household
Departure or death of close friend or older sibling
Foster home placement
Teenage pregnancy (females)

non-rewarding to their caretakers and may well have contributed to initial difficulties in attachment and bonding seen between parent and child. These disturbed child–caretaker transaction patterns had been observed in the postpartum period and during home visits in the early part of the study.

A number of variables were considered key predictors of serious coping problems in the Kauai study. These are listed in Table 3.1. They can be divided into those which appear relevant at birth and later sources of stress. The presence of four or more of these predictors in the children's records by age two was strongly indicative of those who would go on to develop serious learning and/or behavioural problems at ages 10 and 18.

Having identified the major risk factors, Werner and colleagues went on to examine the characteristics of those children who were resistant to stress during their development. Table 3.2 lists the protective factors which could lead to a good outcome even in the

TABLE 3.2
Protective factors relating to positive adult outcome in the Kauai longitudinal study

Within the child
Integrity of the central nervous system
Birth order (first)
High activity level
Good natured, affectionate disposition
Responsive to people
Free of distressing habits
Positive social orientation
Autonomy
Advanced self-help skills
Age-appropriate sensory-motor and perceptual skills
Adequate communication skills
Ability to focus attention and control impulses
Special interests and hobbies
Positive self-concept
Internal locus of control
Desire to improve self
Within care-giving environment
Four or fewer children spaced more than two years apart
Much attention paid to infant during first year
Positive parent–child relationship in early childhood
Additional caretakers besides mother
Care by siblings and grandparents
Mother has some steady employment outside household
Availability of kin and neighbours for emotional support
Structure and rules in household
Shared values – a sense of coherence
Close peer friends
Availability of counsel by teachers and/or ministers
Access to special services (health, education, social services)

presence of major risk factors in infancy and sources of stress during childhood and adolescence. These are divided into factors within the child and within the care-giving environment. Thus, despite an upbringing in poor conditions and a higher than average rate of perinatal stress, low birth weight, etc., certain children – who otherwise developed normally, appeared good natured and affectionate in the early years, were able to focus attention and control their impulses, etc. – could still develop into normal adults. Similarly, these same vulnerable children – but with protective factors such as additional caretakers besides the mother, structure and rules within the household, ability to make good relations with other children etc. – could still derive considerable support from the care-giving environment which appeared to outweigh the factors of vulnerability. Werner proposed a transactional model of development, noting that as disadvantage through an accumulative number of stressful life events increased, more protective factors in the children and their care-giving environment were needed to counterbalance these negative aspects and to ensure a positive developmental outcome. Optimal adaptive development appeared to be characterised by a balance between the power of the person and the power of the social and physical environment.

It was proposed that interventions on behalf of children and youths might thus by conceptualised as an attempt to restore this balance, either by decreasing a young person's exposure to risk or stressful life events, or by increasing the number of protective factors (competencies, sources of support) that the individual can draw upon within him/herself or his/her care-giving environment. Werner made several important conclusions from her research. These might also guide future interventions in the case of individuals with psychopathic disorder.

(a) There is a need to re-evaluate the present efforts to deal with behavioural problems in the young. Professional and other resources need to be allocated according to the magnitude of needs and critical time periods at which an intervention appears to be most effective.
(b) Development cannot be considered within the narrow context of the individual. The wider context of the family, neighbourhood, community must also be considered.
(c) The time which offers greatest promise of substantially reducing 'casualties' appears to be early in childhood, before the damage is done.
(d) Many key predictors were recognisable in infancy. Every young child should have a thorough medical and developmental examination in early childhood. Children with major risk factors of a physical nature may require increased input in the form of special resources for their families.
(e) Early programmes require cooperation and involvement of mothers. Some of the most effective interventions have focused on enhancing language development and intellectual skills, and on techniques which enhance a mother's sense of control over her own life and that of her child.

(f) Short-term remedial work with identified school 'failures' appeared to be beneficial in middle childhood.
(g) The importance of key 'other persons', such as peer counsellors, alternate care-givers, etc., were identified for vulnerable family units.

This model of interrelations between risk, stress, and sources of support and coping, derived from the Kauai longitudinal study, is of major importance to the future study of treatment for psychopathic disorder. Many of the major risk factors at birth and sources of stress in childhood and adolescence have already been identified in psychopathic subjects (Coid, 1992), but the inter-relationship of these variables requires a more careful future analysis. Considerable similarities can be seen between the longitudinal studies of Robins, West & Farrington, and Werner. But the question of whether an additive effect of multiple vulnerability and risk factors, leading to the development of psychopathy in adulthood, and occurring in the absence of an adequate number of protective factors, will ultimately be found to account for the development of such a severe adult outcome, or whether an alternative model will ultimately be required, cannot be answered at this stage.

The natural history of untreated psychopathic disorder

Reports of incarceration without treatment have overwhelmingly found that recidivism rates are high in psychopaths. Stafford-Clarke *et al* (1951) noted that, on average, criminals diagnosed as psychopaths had already had seven convictions, which was more than twice the rate for non-psychopathic convicts from the same prison. Mohr (1947) in his study of Swiss criminals held in a special prison, including psychopaths, found a recidivism rate of 60% within two years of release.

More recently, studies have indicated that incarceration alone may have a detrimental effect upon behaviour and psychological state. Newton (1980) reports that the rates of homicides committed by psychopaths who served prison terms and were released increased eightfold. Bauer & Clark (1976) found that the 'psychopathic deviance' scores on the Minnesota Multiphasic Personality Inventory became higher the longer a person remained in prison.

Gibbens *et al* (1955) report one of the first follow-up studies of untreated psychopaths released from prison. The study followed

69 men from Wandsworth, Brixton and Wormwood Scrubs prisons who had been described in the earlier study mentioned above (Stafford-Clarke *et al*, 1951). Diagnoses of psychopathy for all these men were made initially by the prison doctor and verified using Henderson's criteria (Henderson, 1939). No specific treatment was offered while the men were in prison. The study included 56 non-psychopathic controls selected from the same prisons, matched for age and for type and severity of present offence, but not for offending history. The criminal record of all subjects over the subsequent five years was studied. All subjects except five psychopaths had been at liberty for more than two years at follow-up. It was found that only 12% of psychopaths (8) were free of reconviction, although a further 15% (10) had only been convicted of one minor offence (i.e. given a sentence of less than a year or probation). In contrast, 57% of controls had no conviction and a further 14% had only one minor offence. However, half of the control group were first offenders, whereas only one-fifth of psychopaths had fewer than three previous convictions, and a quarter had more than eight.

The psychopathic group was subdivided into predominantly 'aggressive psychopaths' and 'immature and inadequate psychopaths'. The aggressive group seemed to have the worst recidivism, in that 50% had three or more reconvictions and only one (4%) remained free of conviction, whereas 13% of the 'inadequate' group had three convictions and seven (16%) were free of reconviction.

In a later paper, Gibbens *et al* (1959) report outcome after eight years for the same subjects. After a minimum of five years at liberty, 10% of psychopaths and 47% of controls remained free of conviction and 14% and 17% respectively had only one minor offence (total 24% and 64%; $\chi^2 = 20.52$, $P < 0.01$). When the pattern of recidivism was considered, it showed that 66% of re-offences by psychopaths were committed within one year of release, whereas only 32% of offences by controls were committed in the first year. Offending by the psychopathic group seemed to tail off over time (possibly because of subsequent incarcerations), with only four offences (4.3%) committed three to eight years after release: controls had a much more even rate of reconviction and committed 22 (41%) of their post-release offences in this period. The re conviction pattern of the psychopathic group resembles the recidivism pattern generally found in serious-crime recidivists, where 90% of new crimes are committed within three years of release from custody (Hoover, 1968).

Much of the difference between psychopaths and controls may be accounted for by the differences in previous forensic histories of the two groups. When only those men with one to four previous convictions were compared, there was no significant difference in subsequent offending behaviour (Gibbens, 1961). On the basis of their findings, Gibbens *et al* (1955) suggest that,

> "the term psychopath should be restricted to seriously aggressive cases, or it should be borne in mind that a spontaneous recovery or a good response to treatment is possible as far as criminal tendencies are concerned."

Guze (1964) investigated recidivism in a consecutive series of 223 male prisoners, stating that the diagnosis sociopathic personality disorder could be applied to nearly all of the men. After an average period outside prison of three years, 217 men were followed up, of whom 68% had been arrested and 41% had been re-imprisoned. The 116 men who were released on parole had a significantly lower arrest and re-imprisonment rate (57% arrested and 28% imprisoned) than those 101 men who were released after serving their entire sentence (81% arrested and 56% imprisoned). However, the paroled men had less serious previous criminal careers, which Guze suggested was the most important factor in determining recidivism rates.

However, in a later report on the same subjects, Guze *et al* (1969) state that only 79% of the 223 men described above were classed as 'sociopaths'. They made this diagnosis if, in addition to criminal activity, they displayed two of the five following manifestations:

(a) a history of excessive fighting
(b) school delinquency
(c) poor job record
(d) a period of wanderlust
(e) being a runaway.

After 8–9 years, 176 men (79% of original sample) were traced and reassessed by interview. Of this group, 78% men were given sociopathic diagnoses at the original assessment and 60% were deemed sociopaths at follow-up. Only 56% were found to be sociopathic on both occasions. This could be taken to indicate improvement for those 14% of men who changed status from sociopathic to non-sociopathic, and deterioration for those 4% who changed status in the reverse direction. However, the criteria used to diagnose sociopathy for this study were rather limited, and in the main were concerned with historical events – which cannot change with time. The authors suggest that failure of memory, misunderstanding of questions, lying or denial may account for the variability between the two assessments. Also, although the same structured interview was used both times, different researchers carried out each assessment and inter-rater reliability is unknown.

In a more recent Canadian study, Hart *et al* (1988) administered Hare's Psychopathy Check-List (PCL) to 231 male white prison inmates before their release from prison on parole or mandatory supervision. The sample was divided into 'psychopaths' (PCL scores of 34 or over; $n = 69$), 'non-psychopaths' (PCL scores 24 or under; $n = 68$) and a remaining 'medium' group ($n = 94$). Subjects were followed up until: they had their release revoked; they reoffended; they successfully reached end date of their supervised release; or the end of the study period (minimum 180 days). It was found that 65.2% of the psychopathic group violated their release conditions compared with 49% and 23.5% of the medium and non-psychopathic groups, respectively. The psychopathic group received more suspensions and presented more supervisory problems than those in the other groups.

Using 'time to event analysis' Hart *et al* calculated that the probability of remaining out of prison for at least a year was significantly lower for the psychopathic group (0.38) than for the medium (0.53) and non-psychopathic groups (0.80). Regression analysis showed that use of the PCL significantly improved the prediction of outcome beyond the use of criminological and demographic variables.

Serin *et al* (1990) also studied release outcome of 93 male prisoners from minimum and medium security prisons in Canada. When psychopathy was measured with the 22-item PCL, 17 men (18%) were rated as psychopaths (score > 31) and 17 (18%) as non-psychopaths (score < 17). Overall, psychopaths were recommitted to prison four times more frequently than non-psychopaths and significantly sooner after release (8 months v. 14.6 months; $P < 0.02$). The PCL scores, analysed as a continuous variable, were predictive of release outcome.

Maddocks (1970) followed up untreated patients labelled as 'psychopaths' after out-patient assessment by psychiatrists. Because of the differing accepted definitions of psychopathy used by clinicians, Maddocks included only those patients who showed at least five core features of impulsivity. Core features included frequent changes of job; several spouses or sexual partners; trouble with the law; telling lies; trouble at school; difficulty keeping friends; inability to manage money; and unreliability. Fifty-two patients were traced

(19 of whom were women) by use of hospital and probation reports and personal contact, and were followed up after an average of five and a half years. Subjects were considered to have settled if they showed reduction in impulsiveness enabling them to stay in a job, stay with the same partner, and generally show a reduction in symptoms that placed them in the category in the first place. Ten (19%, including five women) were considered to have settled; three (6%, including one woman) had committed suicide; the remaining 39 (75%) were classed as 'unsettled'. Of these 39 'unsettled' subjects, 15 were 'frank alcoholics', nine were reconvicted, and two had offended for the first time (conviction rate 21%). No clear pattern of why some had settled could be established, but it was suggested that five had improved after subsequent life history events such as serving a prison sentence, being treated for epilepsy, and having a laminectomy, and after giving up amphetamines.

Maddocks notes that his subjects have less severe disorders than individuals held in special security hospitals, but still holds that maturation is not enough to cure psychopathy and that treatment is needed. The results of this study should be interpreted with caution, as no information is given on the number of psychopaths fitting the criteria who were not traced, and it may be only those most likely to offend or continue to use psychiatric services were followed up. Although no subjects had any specialist treatment for psychopathy, some did have treatment for various conditions in the study period such as drug addiction, alcoholism and following a suicide attempt. However, as a naturalistic study this work does give some indication of the subsequent careers of untreated patients.

In a recent study, Murch & Dolan (1992) have followed up 142 patients (including 40 women) referred to Henderson Hospital (a specialist National Health Service in-patient service for severe personality disorders) for treatment. Subjects were referred between September 1990 and August 1991, but were subsequently not admitted. All patients had at least one DSM–III–R personality disorder diagnosis as measured with the Personality Diagnostic Questionnaire (Hyler *et al*, 1987) and 65% met criteria for antisocial personality disorder.

Approximately one-third (31.5%) were deemed not suitable for admission to the Henderson Hospital; another third (32%) did not attend assessment or admission. The remaining group (37%) had their application for funding of treatment refused by their local district health authority, or withdrawn (Dolan & Norton, 1992). The referrer and general practitioner of each patient were contacted after one year with a brief questionnaire requesting information about the patient's subsequent psychiatric and forensic history. Information was returned for 119 patients (85% response rate); however, 38 referrers (32%) reported that they had not seen the patient since the referral was made to Henderson Hospital.

In the year following referral 81 patients (68%) had been seen and 48 of these (59%) were reported to have had some form of further psychological or psychiatric treatment: 20 (25%) as in-patients, 35 (43%) as out-patients and 9 (11%) in other health care settings; 22 (27%) were taking psychotropic medication; 15 (17%) were known to have been convicted of a criminal offence since referral; four (5%) were currently in prison; and four (5%) had died (three by suicide and one unlawfully killed).

All these figures are likely to be underestimates as they only take account of instances of treatment or offending known to the original referrer. The findings illustrate that some personality-disordered individuals who do not obtain specialist help still have high service usage. It is noteworthy that about a third of referrers had not seen their patient since the referral, despite the patient having been deemed in immediate need of specialist help at the time of referral. This is one indication of how personality-disordered patients can be difficult to hold in treatment and be erratic service users.

Maturity and 'burn-out' in the psychopath

Several authors have held the view that psychopaths would eventually 'burn out' and cease their destructive behaviour. Some say this will happen between 25 and the early 30s (Curran & Partridge, 1963), up to the age of 36 (Henderson & Batchelor, 1962), or in the mid-40s (Davis, 1967), while others have suggested indeterminate incarceration at least until age 50 or over (Morris, 1974). However, in a more careful evaluation of this question, Robins (1966) observed that in 82 subjects with sociopathic personality followed into adulthood (most in their mid-40s), only 12% were judged to be completely in remission, and 27% were found to have a "greatly reduced" range and severity of antisocial behaviour. Perhaps more importantly, 61% showed little improvement even at this phase of the lifespan. Improvement appeared to occur in each decade for the 39%, but most often between the ages of 30 and 40. Robins believed that special life circumstances or the threat of further punishment had been a decisive factor. But neither hospitalisation nor psychotherapy appeared to have conveyed any positive benefit. Similarly, retrospective re-examination of data from the Epidemiological Catchment Area study (Robins *et al*, 1984) demonstrated that those who have at some stage of their life met the criteria for antisocial personality disorder will still present with these features at the age of 45 in 20% of cases (Robins, 1986).

A study of psychopaths defined by high scores on the PCL–R (Hare *et al*, 1988) showed that the criminal activities of psychopaths (observed in the age range 16–45) peaked at a high level – relative to those of other offenders – around the ages of 35–40 and then appeared to decrease sharply. These age-related changes were much more dramatic for non-violent than violent crimes in the psychopathic subjects but not in the controls. Thus, the violent activities of the psychopaths appeared to remain relatively constant even after there had been a sharp drop in their non-violent criminal activities. It appeared that the psychopaths' capacity for violence did not change with age nearly as much as the readiness to engage in other forms of illegal and antisocial behaviour. However, in this series, more than half of the psychopaths were still convicted of crimes after age 40. Even if they received fewer convictions as they got older, this did not necessarily mean that their behaviour was no longer antisocial or amoral. Hare and colleagues speculated that such results could contribute to the age-related decrease in criminality sometimes observed in habitual criminals in other studies. They hypothesised that decreases may have been largely due to the presence of psychopaths in those study samples. Thus the concept of 'burn-out' may be more applicable to psychopathic criminals than to other criminals.

Walters (1990) has pointed out the importance of differentiating between 'maturity' and 'burn-out'. Criminal burn-out does not necessarily imply maturity in the psychopath. Certain people may begin to show greater maturity in their early 40s, with a change in their thinking, values, and motivations accompanying their decline in physical and mental energy. The development of a satisfying relationship, the redefinition of criminal activities as foolish and self-defeating, shifts in aspirations and goals, commitment to legitimate employment and becoming less self-absorbed, rebelliousness and pleasure seeking– all these may be part of the process of maturing. However, many individuals remain on the fringes of crime, still behaving in an irresponsible and self-indulgent manner, but without the same intrusive nature of their criminal behaviour. For these people the stress of continuing a criminal life-style, the gradual wearing down of criminal drive by the accumulation of punishments and incarceration, and fear of further and longer incarceration may have contributed to the process of burn-out.

Reid (1986) suggests that some psychopaths burn themselves out as the physical strength and emotional stamina needed to continue the stimulating, hustling life become too much. Ageing psychopaths have difficulty competing both with younger psychopaths and with their own drive for relief, stimulation, and defence against their inner self. Reid suspects that many ageing psychopaths are still antisocial but less successful. Some will become permanently incarcerated in later life or drift towards 'skid-row', or their efforts at stimulation and psychodynamic defence will turn from outwardly antisocial activity to more passive pursuits such as drug abuse and alcoholism. A small number may also deteriorate into severe depression when no longer able to act out as before or when severe illness or injury creates a sudden enormous barrier of reality between the individual and his/her defensive system.

The twin concepts of 'maturity' and 'burn-out' are of major importance in the longitudinal study of psychopathic disorder. These observations have certain parallels with other important findings from the longitudinal study of mental disorder, such as the appearance of spontaneous dramatic improvement in many chronic schizophrenic people in the fifth decade, and the increasing severity and length of major depressive episodes in patients with recurrent depressive disorder after the fifth and the sixth decade. More recent studies, which have identified a distinct and further phase of change within the life course of antisocial personality disorder in career criminals in their early 40s, do suggest that this could be a distinct feature of the condition which can be expected in a subgroup. Estimates vary from between a third to over a half of subjects, depending on the methodology of the study, the definition chosen for psychopathic disorder, and whether researchers have measured 'maturity', 'burn-out', or apparent desistence from criminal activity. Future research may determine whether individual treatment modalities favour certain life phases, whether the process of 'burning out' and/or 'maturing' can be hastened, and whether those who are likely to manifest these phenomena can be identified at an earlier age.

Psychopathic disorder and mortality rates

Two studies have shown how personality disorder is associated with higher rates of death by unnatural causes than in the general population.

Martin *et al* (1985) carried out a 6–12-year follow-up of 500 male and female psychiatric out-patients with various diagnoses and found that 8.7% had died. This was almost twice the expected frequency based upon a mortality ratio standardised by age, sex and race. Death from unnatural causes was 3.5 times the expected rate. Significant excesses of death by unnatural causes were found for those with primary diagnoses of drug addiction (standardised mortality ratio (SMR) 16.7; $P < 0.01$), alcoholism (SMR 8.9; $P < 0.01$) and antisocial personality disorder (SMR 14.7; $P < 0.01$).

Robertson (1987) followed up a population of 1347 mentally disordered offenders (including those from Walker & McCabe's (1973) study – see Chapter 10). After 23 years, 23% of the sample had died. A quarter of the male deaths were unnatural, with verdicts of suicide and accidental death and open verdicts having been recorded. The proportion of deaths by suicide was 2–3 times the general population rate, although there were no significant differences between diagnostic groups of mentally ill and personality-disordered offenders.

The natural history of offending behaviour and recidivism

Although there have been severe criticisms of the inclusion of criminal behaviour in the medical definition of psychopathy (Scott, 1963; Chiswick, 1992), several constructs and definitions of psychopathy nevertheless remain heavily reliant upon criteria involving criminal behaviour (Hare's PCL–R; DSM–III–R). In addition, criminal recidivism remains one of the major outcome variables reported in treatment studies, therefore some discussion of the natural history of criminal behaviour and prediction of recidivism is presented here to give a context to these outcome studies. It is not within the scope of this report to review those studies which have considered rehabilitation and correctional treatment of non-psychopathic offenders. These issues are covered in a variety of excellent articles (*inter alia*, Grendeau & Ross, 1979; Hollin & Henderson, 1984; Garrett, 1985; Andrew *et al*, 1990; Hollin, 1990).

Research has shown that a small segment of the population is responsible for a large proportion of serious crime. The distribution of offending throughout the population can be likened to that of drinking alcohol: many people do it, but very few do very much. Wolfgang *et al* (1972) report that in a series of all males born in Philadelphia, USA (in 1945) and still living there 10–18 years later, approximately 6% were responsible for 51% of offences by the cohort as a whole. When imprisoned or convicted samples are studied, similar findings emerge (Petersilia *et al*, 1978; Peterson & Braiker, 1980). A study of incarcerated US robbers indicated that their average rate of offending was five robberies per year, but 5% of the sample had committed 180 to 400 robberies each (Blumstein & Cohen, 1979). Another study of 24 000 middle-aged US prisoners found that 14% had been continuously involved in crime since adolescence (Langan & Greenfield, 1983)

Delinquent careers can develop along several trajectories (Smith, 1984). However, for career criminals, persistence through four successive stages can be observed (Walters, 1990):

(a) pre-criminal, 0–18 years
(b) early criminal, 18 to mid-20s
(c) advanced, late 20s to early 40s
(d) criminal burn-out/maturity, from the early 40s.

Pre-criminal behaviour is rarely specialised but larceny, burglary and car theft are the most common offences (LeBlanc & Frechette, 1989). These offences are frequently committed in the company of other adolescents, and thrill-seeking is an important motivator. This stage appears to hold the greatest prospect for change, and a significant proportion of juveniles will not continue their criminality on into adulthood. During the second stage, the number of individuals committing offences steadily declines (Blumstein & Cohen, 1987), but a subgroup move towards career criminality as they find themselves in contact with new criminal associates (often met during incarceration), learn new criminal techniques and gain status in the criminal subculture. The overall number of crimes may decrease, but their seriousness and the value of property stolen will increase, as does the appearance of violent offences (West & Farrington, 1977; Petersilia *et al*, 1978).

Voluntary drop-out from crime is lowest during this advanced criminal stage. Walters (1990) describes these individuals as now having committed themselves to a criminal lifestyle with an associated cognitive style. In the early 40s a further stage is reached which Hirschi & Gottfredson (1983) describe as corresponding to the mid-life transition: some individuals will begin to demonstrate maturity – a change in their thinking, values and motivation – and terminate their criminal behaviour. In others, who remain on the fringes of crime, this period is described as burn-out because of an accompanying decline in physical and mental energy. However, a smaller subgroup will fail to re-evaluate their lives and continue to engage in significant criminal behaviour. The relationship of this subgroup of 'career criminals' to psychopathic personality is unclear, as again the tautological descriptions of psychopathy and persistent criminal activity confuse the picture. Additionally, little is known about how this unrelenting antisocial and criminal activity is related to a range of personality traits. This would be one important aspect for future study.

Predicting recidivism in criminal populations

Kozol *et al* (1972) looked at recidivism in 386 US male violent offenders recommended for release and 49 released despite mental health recommendation of continued incarceration. The overall rate of correct prediction of recidivism by the clinicians was 85.5%. Nevertheless, Holland *et al* (1983) have stated that recidivism is resistant to highly accurate prediction despite numerous and elaborate efforts to accomplish this purpose. However, some statistical composites have performed as well as, or better than, human judges.

Holland *et al* (1983) studied 340 male offenders found guilty of a variety of crimes. The average age of the sample was 28 years. The men had an average of five previous convictions, and 168 had a violent index offence. At sentencing, 142 were incarcerated and 198 given probation orders. After 32 months, 113 (57%) of the probationers had been re-arrested (29 (15%) for violent crimes) and 103 (52%) had been reconvicted (22 (11%) for violence). Evaluation of whether the probation was against clinical advice found that clinical predictions had the greatest accuracy for violent offences, while statistical predictions had greater accuracy for undifferentiated crimes. The authors also point out that the failure rate of their probationer sample can vary between 57% and 10%, depending upon which definition of recidivism is chosen (re-arrest, 57%; reconviction, 52%; reincarceration, 37%; re-arrest for violence, 15%; reconviction for violence, 11%; reincarceration for violence, 10%).

It has been noted how the belief that criminal violence can be best predicted by a history of such behaviour is omnipresent, despite minimal support (Holland *et al*, 1982). Many reports in the literature emphasise the heterogeneity rather than consistency of illegal behaviour patterns. For example, Holland *et al* (1981) analysed the lifetime total criminal convictions of American adult male prisoners and found that the degree of specialisation in violent or non-violent offences was slight compared with the tendency to be involved in both. Holland *et al* (1982) went on to use a longitudinal design with 198 male offenders to investigate whether the occurrence of prior violent offences and the occurrence of prior non-violent offences were the best predictors of recidivism. After 32 months, subsequent offences were classified as violent (involving actual or threatened physical injury to a person or death) or non-violent (against property or public order). Discriminant analysis showed that there was no significant association between prior violent crime and probation performance, although the number of non-violent crimes committed was significantly associated with subsequent offending ($P < 0.05$) and was equally sensitive to non-violent and violent re-offences.

The studies of prediction of recidivism mentioned above are all of general criminal offenders and may not be generalisable to offenders with psychopathic disorder. However, they are presented to give the reader some background to those studies of psychopathic offenders which use recidivism as a treatment outcome measure. They are somewhat relevant in that, for psychopathically disordered offenders, one of the primary considerations is the occurrence of subsequent violent criminal offences after release from detention. Predictive factors for recidivism in psychopathic offenders are considered in the context of the treatment outcome studies reviewed in subsequent chapters; the appropriateness of recidivism as an outcome measure is discussed in Chapter 11.

Conclusions

Considerable space has been devoted to the natural history of psychopathic disorder. This is because a detailed understanding of the life course of this condition is the main starting point for the evaluation of treatment. Studies of crime and delinquency have been included to supplement the poor-quality data on psychopathic subjects. However, individuals who show the core features of psychopathic disorder, as defined by DSM–III–R antisocial personality disorder or high PCL–R scores, make up a varying proportion of subjects in life-span studies of conduct disorder, delinquency, and criminal behaviour. In view of the criteria for these diagnostic constructs, psychopaths are automatically concentrated among subjects who show the most wide-ranging and serious antisocial behaviour and those who persist in antisocial behaviour longer than others. This adverse outcome in adulthood, persisting from conduct disorder in childhood, appears to be related to a complex interaction of vulnerability factors that are present early in life and major sources of stress that can be identified during childhood and adolescence. Improvement and/or a good outcome depends on the counterbalancing presence of protective factors both within the child and within the care-giving environment. Although the disease model of psychopathy would imply a morbid process, this interactive model suggests a much more complex entity. Psychopathic disorder can also be finally reached along a series of quite different pathways over the life-span. The significance of this broader conceptualisation of psychopathic disorder and its implications for treatment is returned to in Chapter 12.

This complex model of psychopathy, based on a series of interactive processes, suggests:

(a) that a range of treatment approaches may have to be applied in a single individual
(b) that it is important to choose the right time over the life-span for the application of a single modality
(c) that different prognostic indicators can be identified at different ages, and that these may individually influence the effectiveness of treatment
(d) that the severity of the condition (and by implication its resistance to treatment) may be partially determined by the addition of both vulnerability and stress factors, with a corresponding reduction in the risk of an adverse outcome according to the presence of certain protective factors
(e) that more complex mathematical models could ultimately be developed, based on these interactions, which will determine both prognosis and suitability for individual treatment modalities
(f) that future naturalistic studies may identify which individual protective factors or beneficial life events will result in major positive change.

From these observations it may be possible to replicate the same factors as treatment interventions on an empirical basis.

4 Pharmacological treatment

There are two major questions posed by the pharmacological treatment of psychopathic disorder:

(a) whether a condition that is composed of abnormal personality traits, rather than symptoms, can actually respond to medication
(b) whether any observed treatment response is confined exclusively to associated symptomatic conditions rather than core personality traits.

If personality disorder is conceptualised as a deeply ingrained, maladaptive pattern of perceiving, relating to, and thinking about the environment and oneself, exhibited in a wide range of important social and interpersonal contexts (American Psychiatric Association, 1987), this will imply that it is a condition that has developed over time, has become relatively constant, and is resistant to change. It is therefore unsurprising that treatment methods promoting inner change within an interpersonal context, or the alteration of social factors which impinge upon the individual, have received more attention that pharmacotherapy. These would logically appear to hold out more hope for developmental change over a patient's lifetime than a treatment modality whose effects would be expected to be relatively rapid. Furthermore, the psychodynamic idea that many behavioural disturbances and syndromes of mental disorder exhibited by patients with character disorder are in fact epiphenomena (see review by Coid (1993*a*)) previously tended to relegate pharmacotherapy to a supporting role to dynamic psychotherapy. In this context, medication would only be employed when a patient began to show decompensation during psychotherapy or as a result of external life stress. But if a more flexible view is taken of psychopathic disorder (see Chapter 1), it becomes clear that no easy demarcation can be found between abnormal personality traits and certain features of the major clinical syndromes of mental disorder.

This poses four additional questions when the drug treatment of patients with psychopathic disorder is considered.

(a) Are the core features of psychopathic disorder (as defined according to the Hare's Psychopathy Check-List (PCL–R) or DSM–III–R antisocial personality disorder (ASPD) resistant to pharmacotherapy in all cases?
(b) Is there a spectrum of psychopathology, varying from abnormal personality traits at one end to clinical syndromes at the other, along which, at some point, pharmacotherapy will be effective? (This may vary to a considerable degree between different individuals and be influenced by additional variables such as a history of deprivation, cerebral dysfunction, and comorbidity between axis I and axis II disorders.)
(c) Are certain forms of psychopathology which are currently characterised as DSM–III–R axis II disorder misclassified, leading to a failure to give an adequate trial of treatment to what is in fact a drug-responsive axis I disorder?
(d) Are certain forms of behavioural disorder demonstrated by psychopaths responsive to treatment irrespective of the associated axis I and axis II psychopathology?

These questions cannot be entirely answered from the current state of pharmacological research. But each could partially explain the wide range of responses found in the different pharmacological trials which that are summarised below. The first question will not be answered to any degree of satisfaction in this chapter. No clinical trial has specifically addressed the question of the treatment response of PCL–R criteria or the criteria for ASPD. In general, reports of drug responsiveness have not been published even on subjects described as 'psychopaths', apart from a small number of early, uncontrolled observations with psychostimulants. It is therefore necessary to divert from our original intention to examine only those studies which included subjects with these 'core' features of psychopathy. We justify this diversion for the following three reasons.

Reason 1. A study of legally detained 'psychopaths' in maximum-security hospitals and prisoners in special units for the control and containment of difficult and dangerous inmates revealed that the majority received a diagnosis of borderline personality disorder (BPD) and that only approximately one half received a diagnosis of ASPD. Furthermore, subjects with ASPD showed comorbidity with BPD and there appeared to be an adverse interaction of the two conditions (Coid, 1992). Thus, treatment of BPD in the latter subjects could have an ameliorating effect on the overall condition and consequent behavioural disorder.

Reason 2. Despite the identification of 'core' features and the development of constructs such as Hare's PCL–R and ASPD, many psychopaths show additional neurotic, affective, organic and, at times, psychotic symptoms while not manifesting clinically recognisable diagnostic syndromes classified as axis I disorders. In a review of this complex area, Docherty *et al* (1986) pointed out that the relationship between axis II personality disorder and axis I clinical syndromes becomes increasingly complex the closer it is examined. Dimensional models of classification are suggested by such observations, with the inevitable question of where the dividing line should be drawn between the axes. In an earlier review of the treatment of personality disorder, a multi-author American Psychiatric Association (1989) publication included a small section examining the affective, anxiety, and organic 'spectrum' in an attempt to deal with this nosological dilemma. Thus, in view of the multiple aetiological factors and considerable axis I and axis II comorbidity observed in psychopaths, it remains probable that these associated symptomatic components may show considerable potential for response to pharmacological agents. The rationale for this view is briefly summarised below for the affective spectrum, the anxiety spectrum and the organic spectrum.

Weiss *et al* (1983) observed in a large in-patient series that psychopaths with dysphoric and affective symptoms constituted a distinct subgroup. Many showed symptoms of depression, anxiety, agitation, irritability, suicidal thoughts, difficulties in intellectual functioning, and sometimes other neurotic traits. They appeared to stay longer in hospital than the non-dysphoric group and many other non-psychopathic patients. It is possible that many of these individuals had a comorbid BPD diagnosis. Subjects who had BPD, the most common axis II diagnosis in one study of psychopaths (Coid, 1992), had a high lifetime prevalence of major affective disorder and the diagnostic construct itself contains a strong affective component. Similarly, BPD subjects have a raised prevalence of both BPD and major affective disorder in their first-degree relatives (see Docherty *et al*, 1986).

Several authors have identified or attempted to identify affective syndromes presenting in a variety of subjects with personality disorder (usually BPD). These affective syndromes overlap with psychopathy in that either the studies include psychopathic subjects or the diagnostic criteria overlap with some core features of psychopathic disorder. A full discussion is beyond the scope of this chapter but the syndromes include:

(a) dysphoria (Berner *et al,* 1987)
(b) emotionally unstable character disorder (Rifkin *et al,* 1972)
(c) character spectrum disorder (Akiskal, 1983; Akiskal *et al,* 1983)
(d) intermittent brief depression (Dobler-Mikola, 1985; Montgomery *et al,* 1989; Angst, 1990)
(e) affective spectrum disorder (Hudson & Pope, 1990)
(f) hysteroid dysphoria (Leibowitz & Klein, 1981)
(g) affective syndrome of psychopaths with borderline personality disorder (Coid, 1993*b*)

There is a degree of overlap between the affective and anxiety spectrum, in that Weiss (1983) noticed symptoms of anxiety as well as affective symptoms in his series of dysphoric psychopaths. Similarly, many personality-disordered subjects with a history of panic attacks, phobias and generalised anxiety show comorbidity with BPD and lifelong affective disorder (Docherty *et al,* 1986). Moreover, the Epidemiologic Catchment Area study in three US sites found that in a series of 524 patients with ASPD, 17.5% had some type of phobia. Similarly, Coid (1992) found that one in five of his psychopathic subjects had an avoidant personality disorder. In a subgroup of difficult and dangerous prisoners with high PCL–R scores, a quarter had a history of panic attacks. Furthermore, clinical observation of these subjects revealed a considerable degree of interpersonal sensitivity in certain cases, leading to avoidance of social interaction, sometimes with violent or disruptive behaviour to effect removal to sheltered or solitary conditions within an institutional setting.

Subtle neurological dysfunction may also underlie some syndromes thought to be personality disorders. A study of psychopaths has shown higher levels of reported birth complications than in schizophrenia, and higher levels of developmental delay and other neurological soft signs than in the general population (Coid, 1992). There have been attempts to construct diagnostic categories based on intermittent, explosive, and aggressive outbursts or behavioural dyscontrol. These are presumed to have some degree of underlying organic dysfunction and partially overlap with constructs of psychopathic disorder. These include 'intermittent explosive disorder' (American Psychiatric Association, 1987) and 'episodic dyscontrol syndrome' (Monroe, 1970).

Psychodynamic theory has suggested a relationship between severe personality disorder and psychotic symptoms in the context of vulnerability to psychotic decompensation when primitive defences are breached, usually by stressful circumstances. It is believed that an unstable and underdeveloped personality organisation maintains a fragile homeostasis, often maintained only through acting-out behaviour. However, clinical research has suggested that the presence of psychotic-like symptoms in personality disorder are associated with a diagnosis of schizotypal or paranoid personality disorder. In a prison setting, paranoid personality disorder in a series of subjects with additional high PCL–R scores frequently resulted in serious assaults on other prisoners and staff, where everyday situations had been misconstrued, and where the individual had believed that others were talking about him/her, planning an attack, or where grudges had been rigidly held for long periods (Coid, 1991).

Reason 3. Certain studies of pharmacological response have demonstrated that different forms of serious behavioural disorder, such as assaultiveness and self-injury, may be ameliorated in quite different psychiatric conditions by the same medication. This would suggest either serious diagnostic shortcomings, in that the true underlying conditions that have been treated in different subjects have not been correctly identified, or that the behaviour itself is responsive to the drug. This chapter shows that there is some evidence for the latter proposition. As a consequence, psychopaths with unresponsive 'core' features may nevertheless show an improvement in their behaviour as a direct response to pharmacological treatment.

Studies discussed

The following discussion will examine the response of personality-disordered subjects according to different categories of medication, focusing on the recent major drug trials. These include: studies where the effects of a drug on a specific personality disorder have been examined (most of these have included BPD); studies that focus on a specific syndrome or behaviour in subjects with a personality disorder; and studies relevant to psychopathic disorder on the effect of drugs on DSM–III–R axis I disorders. Inclusion criteria were the same as those of Stein (1992): the study should describe the effects of the pharmacological agent on a patient or group of patients with a primary diagnosis of personality disorder. In this review, studies have been chosen which relate to psychopathic disorder. In addition, some studies where the prevalence of severe personality disorder or psychopathy was known to be high, such as studies of prisoners, have also been included.

Neuroleptic medication

There are no systematic trials of neuroleptic medication with patients diagnosed as psychopaths on the basis of the core symptoms of DSM–III–R antisocial personality disorder or Hare's Psychopathy Check-List. It is possible that researchers have been deterred by accusations that tranquillising drugs would be used merely to control difficult behaviour, particularly for psychopaths in a penal setting. Neuroleptics have both tranquillising effects on disturbed behaviour and a specific antipsychotic effect. Many clinicians will have had personal experience of administering neuroleptics to a range of disturbed and aggressive patients in hospital settings to control crises. But the question of whether treatment programmes involving major tranquillisers, prescribed over the medium or long term, should apply to psychopaths has not received careful consideration.

As most clinical trials have involved subjects with a diagnosis of borderline or schizotypal personality disorder, it is even more surprising that psychopaths have not been systematically investigated. The majority of these subjects receive a diagnosis of borderline personality disorder in the UK (Coid, 1992). However, it is possible that multiple axis II categories could lead to certain interactions and altered therapeutic effects through comorbidity. Most trials have involved subjects receiving a single diagnostic category. But it cannot be assumed that multiple labelling might not have occurred had a more rigorous diagnostic assessment been applied. Until trials specifically targeted at samples of psychopaths have been undertaken, the following survey of hospital-based in-patient and out-patient trials of neuroleptic therapy must be considered only as directions for future research.

Low-dose neuroleptic therapy (uncontrolled studies)

Early observations by American psychoanalysts suggested that low-dose neuroleptic therapy could be helpful in the treatment of patients with borderline personality disorder. During the course of analysis, certain patients would demonstrate severe anxiety, aroused by the treatment process, which appeared to be controlled with neuroleptics. Primary process material would then seem less threatening and was more amenable to interpretation (Winkleman, 1955; Schmideberg, 1959; Kernberg, 1968; Mandell, 1976). Stein (1992) observed a second, and quite independent, impetus to the role of neuroleptics in personality disorders coming from Belgium after the synthesis of pimozide by the pharmaceutical company Janssen. Global improvement occurred in 69% of a large series of personality-disordered subjects with mixed diagnoses in a study described by Reyntjens (1972) (see Table 4.1). In this study it appeared to take up to three months for beneficial effects to be shown. But between three and nine months there was little further improvement in a replication by Collard (1976).

Table 4.1 summarises the major uncontrolled trials of neuroleptics in personality disorders, mostly borderline personality disorder. All showed some improvement in symptoms and behaviour when subjects were given neuroleptic medication in dosages lower than would normally be prescribed for schizophrenics or depressed patients. However, when these studies are examined more carefully, patients with schizotypal symptoms or psychotic-like episodes appear to benefit most of all. Some studies also indicate a reduction in anger and hostility, and occasionally behavioural disturbances such as suicidal gestures or aggression. Neuroleptic side-effects resulted in poor compliance in certain studies, along with a high drop-out rate.

Steiner *et al* (1979) described an adverse reaction of “behavioural toxicity” in nine subjects with a diagnosis of DSM–II ‘borderline schizophrenia’. The limited case material suggests that six probably had schizoid rather than a schizotypal personality but three had pure borderline personality disorder. None was initially psychotic, but higher doses of chlorpromazine (150–500 mg daily) or haloperidol (7–10 mg daily) resulted in precipitation of psychotic symptoms and ‘behavioural toxicity’ characterised by agitation, conceptual disorganisation, paranoid delusions, depersonalisation, and derealisation. The authors postulated either a psychodynamic mechanism or that the drugs had precipitated an atropine-like psychosis. No other study has specifically observed the effects of high-dosage neuroleptics on personality-disordered patients. This study is important in suggesting that if neuroleptics are to be given they should probably be administered only in low dosage.

TABLE 4.1

Uncontrolled trials of neuroleptics in personality disorders in adults and adolescents

Author	*Subject*	*Method*	*Results*
Reyntjens (1972)	120 mixed DSM–III patients (schizoid, paranoid, obsessive–compulsive, hysterical, borderline, inadequate, sexual deviation)	Open trail 2 months; 2–8 mg pimozide (mean 3 mg); 36 psychiatrists participated	Global outcome excellent 30 (25%), good 53 (44%), moderate 27 (33%), poor 10 (3.5%). Best in schizoids and paranoids, but not statistically significant
Brinkley *et al* (1972)	5 psychotherapy-resistant BPD subjects	Open; low dosage; various neuroleptics	2 responded to 2.6 mg daily perphenazine, 2 responded to 25 mg nocte thioridazine. Important predictors; : regressive psychotic-like symptoms and paranoia
Soloff (1981)	97 in-patients with BPD (Spitzer's criteria)	Uncontrolled retrospective case-note study (variety of psychotropics)	5 of 11 (45%) borderlines good outcome on neuroleptics; no significant difference between medications

Leone (1982)	80 BPD subjects	Double-blind random; loxapine v. chlorpromazine (no placebo)	Loxapine more effective in early stage; no difference at 6 weeks; reduced anger and hostility; high drop-out due to side-effects
Montgomery & Montgomery (1982)	Twice attempted suicide; no axis I; most borderline, histrionic, dependent personality-disordered subjects	Flupenthixol 20 mg i.m. monthly v. mianserin 30 mg daily v. placebo	No difference at 3 months; at 6 months, reduction in suicide attempts with flupenthixol; mianserin no benefit
Cole *et al* (1984)	17 BPD subjects	Uncontrolled; retrospective case-note study	10 (58%) good outcome (coexisting schizophrenic symptoms and depression did best on neuroleptics)
Serban & Siegel (1984)	52 consecutive walk-in patients; borderline schizotypal, or both all with previous mild, transient psychotic episode	Blind parallel; thiothixene (mean 9.8 mg) v. haloperidol (mean 3 mg) (no placebo)	55% marked improvement, 28% moderate, 12% no change; one worse; best for cognitive disturbance, ideas of reference, anxiety, depression, low self-image; thiothixene improved borderline syndrome index score in schizotypals

Placebo-controlled trials

Table 4.2 summarises the results from four placebo-controlled trials of neuroleptics. Three studies were able to identify the specific effects on borderline personality disorder, two examined the effects on schizotypal or both conditions, a fourth examined the effects on a mixture of personality disorder diagnoses. The study by Goldberg *et al* (1985) demonstrates why a placebo control is so important for drug treatment studies of borderline and schizotypal patients. The placebo had large effects on self-rated anger, hostility, and interpersonal sensitivity; observer-rated suspiciousness; and overall borderline and schizotypal scores. There were no differences between drug and placebo groups for overall global improvement or total borderline or schizotypal scores. However, interviewer-rated scores on delusions and ideas of reference, and self-rated scores on psychoticism, obsessive–compulsive symptoms, and phobic anxiety, showed greater improvement with the active medication.

Soloff *et al* (1986*a*) compared haloperidol with placebo and amitriptyline. They chose an in-patient group who may have been more disturbed than the community-based subjects studied by Goldberg and colleagues. Haloperidol was found to be superior to amitriptyline, with large drug–placebo differences for haloperidol on a broad spectrum of neurotic and psychotic symptoms, as well as measures of behavioural dyscontrol. Depression improved only according to the self-rated Beck Depression Inventory and not according to the observer-rated Hamilton scale. Haloperidol also led to a significant improvement in scores on the Schizotypal Symptom Inventory, which had been developed to measure the core features of schizotypal personality disorder.

Cowdry & Gardner (1988) examined the effects of medication, including neuroleptics, on 16 subjects with pure borderline personality disorder using a complex design. Patients were repeatedly challenged with four different drugs and a placebo for consecutive six-weeks periods in a longitudinal cross-over trial. Only ten patients started with trifluoperazine and three dropped out in the first three weeks, a further two dropping out between weeks 3 and 6, indicating that only half the subjects were able to tolerate the neuroleptic. Those who completed showed a significantly reduced tendency to suicide attempts and behavioural dyscontrol, although these improvements were less than with carbamazepine in the same patients.

In an earlier study, Barnes (1977) compared the effects of mesoridazine (a low-potency neuroleptic structurally similar to thioridazine) and placebo in 30 adolescents with diagnoses of some form of personality disorder. Included in the group were patients who were passive–aggressive, antisocial, schizoid, explosive, hysterical and paranoid, and patients who had inadequate personality. The study lasted six weeks and in this trial there was a significantly greater drop-out rate in the placebo group than in the group receiving mesoridazine. Statistical analysis revealed superiority for the neuroleptic on a variety of measures relevant to personality-disordered patients, such as a tendency to blame others, rage outbursts, verbal aggressiveness, low frustration tolerance, conflict with authority, as well as on measures of anxiety, hostility, and depression. Unfortunately, Barnes did not elucidate whether treatment was helpful for any specific personality disorder and the study indicates the potential problem of maintaining a true double-blind trial with a neuroleptic versus placebo. In this study statistical comparisons included some of the drop-outs, which may have made the mesoridazine look better than if these had been excluded.

As would have been expected, placebo-controlled trials of neuroleptics have consistently indicated greater improvement of symptoms considered to be on the 'borderline' of schizophrenia, in particular the schizotypal features. This was until a recent study by Soloff *et al* (1993). There had also been observations of reduction in behavioural disturbances including aggression and a tendency to self-harm. Nevertheless, in the Cowdry & Gardner (1988) study, with pure borderline subjects, the effect of the anticonvulsant carbamazepine on behavioural dyscontrol was more impressive than that of trifluoperazine.

A more recent study which examined the effect of haloperidol on a larger series of subjects than any previous study with neuroleptics has failed to reveal an improvement compared with placebo, and showed an overall inferiority on measures of depression, borderline psychopathological symptoms, and anxiety compared to phenelzine (Soloff *et al*, 1993). The authors concluded that they had failed to replicate prior results (including their own) of the efficacy of this neuroleptic on a broad spectrum of affective, schizotypal, and behavioural symptoms. In this study, the effectiveness of haloperidol was limited to observed measures of hostile belligerence and impulsive–aggressive ward behaviours; for these measures the results were similar to previous reports. On the self-reported scales of hostility and anger, phenelzine was clearly superior, suggesting that haloperidol may be more useful for overt, hostile and aggressive behaviour in these patients, whereas phenelzine may have a direct effect on the affective disturbance itself. However, two factors may have influenced the overall negative findings. Firstly, significantly more subjects with a history of

TABLE 4.2

Placebo-controlled trials of neuroleptics in personality disorders

Author	*Subjects*	*Method*	*Results*
Barnes (1977)	30 adolescents (13—18 years) (several axis II diagnoses)	Double-blind; placebo v. mesoridazine (mean 44.7 mg); 6 weeks	Improvement in rage, verbal aggression, blaming others, frustration, authority conflicts, measures of anxiety, hostility, depression c.f. placebo
Goldberg *et al* (1985)	50 borderline or schizotypal personality-disordered out-patients (major psychosis excluded)	Double-blind; placebo v. thiothixene (mean 8.67 mg); titrated by patient	Improvement on delusions, ideas of reference, anger, hostility, obsession; smaller improvement on suspicion, paranoia, somatisation, depersonalisation c.f. placebo; no effect on hallucinations, depressive hostility, rejection sensitivity

Soloff *et al* (1986*a*)	62 in-patients; (43% BPD, 6% schizotypal personality disorder, 51% both)	Double-blind, placebo v. haloperidol (mean 7.24 mg) v. amitriptyline (mean 147 mg)	Haloperidol superior to amitriptyline for schizotypal symptoms, behaviourial dyscontrol, hostility, paranoia, interpersonal sensivity; no significant difference for amitriptyline v. placebo
Cowdry & Gardner (1988)	16 BPD, females	Double-blind cross-over, 6–8 weeks; alprazolam (1–6 mg) v. trifluoperazine (2–12 mg) v. tranylcyp-romine (10–60 mg) v. carbamazepine (200–1200 mg) v. placebo; only 10 started trifluoperazine	Trifluoperazine; 4 dropped out in 6 weeks ; best improvement on psychotic symptoms. Tranylcypromine: subjects showed improvement as to suicidal tendency and behaviourial dyscontrol but less than same on subjects carbamazepine
Soloff *et al* (1993)	108 BPD in-patients	Random double-blind, allocation; 5 weeks; 36 haloperidol (mean 4 mg), 38 phenelzine (mean 60 mg), 34 placebo (mean 4 tablets)	Significant improvement all groups; no overall superiority of haloperidol over placebo

depressive disorder were allocated by chance to the group receiving haloperidol. Secondly, the daily dose of haloperidol received by this treatment group was low (mean 4 mg) compared both with the usual clinical use of this preparation and with the dose used in the researchers' previous study (Soloff *et al*, 1986*a*), which had shown superiority over amitriptyline when a mean daily dose of 7 mg haloperidol was prescribed.

Comment

Trials suggest an indication for low-dose neuroleptic therapy in psychopaths with schizotypal features, including conceptual disorganisation, ideas of reference, illusions, paranoid ideation, and a history of short-lasting psychotic episodes. There is some evidence that symptoms such as anxiety, interpersonal sensitivity, depersonalisation, and derealisation will show a mild to moderate improvement in certain patients, as will a tendency to aggressive outbursts and self-harm. The effect of neuroleptics on patients' mood appears less certain at this stage. Future research will need to parcel out the effects on different groups of target symptoms and diagnostic categories of personality disorder according to whether the type of neuroleptic administered has a high or low sedative effect. There is some clinical indication that neuroleptics are primarily indicated for those demonstrating overt motor agitation and aggressive behavioural disturbance, rather than those who demonstrate only schizotypal features, but this remains to be established.

Antidepressants

The response of patients with severe personality disorders to antidepressant medication is a confused and uncertain area of pharmacological research. This is for three main reasons. Firstly, it is not always clear from available studies exactly what the major goals of treatment have been. More specifically, has the treatment been directed towards a separate affective disorder manifesting in a patient with personality disorder, an integral affective component of the personality disorder itself, or a separate component of behavioural disorder? Secondly, studies suggest that patients with a combination of affective disorder and personality disorder have a poorer response to antidepressant treatment than patients with affective disorders alone. Thirdly, a paradoxical worsening of both affective symptoms and behaviour has been observed in a subgroup of personality-disordered patients in response to antidepressants.

No trials of antidepressant medication have been specifically applied to psychopathic subjects. However, the response of BPD (which has an affective component among its criteria) has been studied in a small number of open and placebo-controlled trials.

Naturalistic chart-review studies of tricyclics

Soloff (1981) carried out a study involving two chart reviews (40 and 50 subjects respectively) of BPD patients admitted to hospital. He pointed out that this method had the limitations of being an indirect and uncontrolled method to study drug response, with uncontrolled assignment to treatment groups depending on the clinical approach of individual clinicians. There was also differing use of medications and a subjective assessment of outcome by the clinicians concerned. Patients were treated with neuroleptics alone, tricyclics alone (all on amitriptyline at doses of 150–250 mg), a combination of neuroleptics and tricyclics or other drug therapy, or no medication. Patients benefited more from receiving some form of medication than from hospital in-patient treatment alone. However, there was no significant overall superiority of one form of medication over another. There was also a variation of responsiveness within each treatment modality, presumably reflecting the heterogeneity of BPD. Thus, both antidepressants and neuroleptics showed a subgroup of non-responders. Similarly, a small number of those who had received in-patient treatment alone also showed a clear response.

Cole *et al* (1984) reviewed the charts of 60 patients meeting criteria for BPD who received a trial of antipsychotics, tricyclic antidepressants, or a combination of both in adequate dosage. Diagnostic criteria for major depression and schizophrenia were also applied to the BPD subjects. Assessment of global improvement was made blind to diagnosis. Fifteen of the 60 patients were 'pure' BPD, having no diagnosis of schizophrenic-like symptoms or major or minor depression. Almost half of all subjects ($n = 28$) received a trial of drug therapy as in-patients. However, another six were considered to have had inadequate trials as they had refused to continue medication after a relatively short period. It was not possible to assess differences between medicated and non-medicated groups. But it was concluded that subjects meeting criteria for both BPD and major depressive disorder showed improvement on tricyclic antidepressants and on antipsychotics. Patients with schizophrenia or with certain schizophrenia-like symptoms responded to antipsychotics. Patients in the 'pure' group, without additional axis I disorder, tended not to improve on either type of drug therapy. This study was of interest in that patients with a marked affective component to their condition appeared to make as good a response to neuroleptic medication as to tricyclic antidepressants.

Open trials of selective serotonergic reuptake inhibitors

Several studies have suggested that depression, suicidal thoughts, and impulsive aggression are linked to deficiency of available serotonin (5-hydroxytryptamine) (Coccaro *et al*, 1989a,*b*, 1990*a*; Moss *et al*, 1990). In patients with personality disorders but without concurrent affective disorder, low levels of CSF 5-HIAA have been correlated with syndromes of impulsive aggression and criminal violence (Virkkunen *et al*, 1989). Patients with BPD also appear to have diminished central serotonergic activity as demonstrated by low levels of 5-hydroxyindole acetic acid (5-HIAA) in cerebrospinal fluid (CSF) and blunting of the prolactin response to fenfluramine challenge, a serotonin-mediated response (Brown *et al*, 1979, 1982; Brown & Goodwin, 1986; Coccaro *et al*, 1989*a*; Gardner *et al*, 1990). Blunting of the prolactin response to fenfluramine correlates with suicidal behaviour in both depressed and borderline patients, but correlates with impulsive aggression only in borderline patients compared with depressed controls (Coccaro *et al*, 1989*a*). This research suggests that a drug that enhances central serotonin neurotransmission could demonstrate effects against both depression and impulsive aggression.

Four open trials have reported the effects of fluoxetine on patients with BPD, and a further open trial has examined the effects of fluoxetine on patients with major depression exhibiting anger attacks (Table 4.3). Norden (1989) followed 12 out-patients with BPD, but without comorbid major depression, in a private practice setting, for periods of 5–26 weeks; these patients were on 5–40 mg fluoxetine daily. The author used his own severity scale to demonstrate improvements in rejection sensitivity, anger, depressed mood, mood lability, irritability, anxiety, obsessive–compulsive symptoms, and impulsivity, including substance abuse and overeating. Improvement was reported to occur rapidly, in 2–5 days, before attainment of steady-state plasma levels could have been expected. Discontinuation resulted in a deterioration within 4–8 days.

Cornelius *et al* (1990) studied five refractory borderline patients who had failed to respond to other psychotropic agents. After a one-week wash-out period they were given fluoxetine for eight weeks, starting with 20 mg and increasing to 40 mg within two weeks if clinically indicated. Research ratings indicated significant improvement on global symptom severity, depression, and impulsive ward behaviour. Self-report measures of hostility, paranoid ideation, psychoticism, somatisation, and obsessive–compulsive symptoms also showed improvement.

Markovitz *et al* (1991) studied 22 out-patients, eight with BPD, ten with both BPD and schizotypal personality disorder, and four schizotypal subjects. Thirteen had a comorbid diagnosis of major depression and 12 a significant history of self-mutilation. Several other treatment modalities were reported to have failed with these subjects. Patients received fluoxetine, 80 mg daily for 12 weeks. Significant improvements were observed on all scales of the Symptom Check-List (SCL–90), with no differences between subgroups and patients according to schizotypal personality disorder or BPD, and also presence or absence of major depression. Self-mutilation ceased in ten patients and improved in the other two.

Coccaro *et al* (1990*b*) reported the effects of an open trial of fluoxetine on impulsive aggressive behaviour in three out-patients with DSM–III–R personality disorder. One met the criteria for antisocial personality disorder, the other two for BPD. Patients were rated by use of a modified overt aggression scale. Other medication (nortriptyline for one patient, lithium/lorazepam for another – the third was medication-free) was held constant for the six-week trial. Patients initially received "at least" 20 mg of fluoxetine daily for the first two weeks, building up to "at least" 40 mg by weeks 5 and 6. Treatment was initially associated with clinician-reported and self-reported reduction of impulsive–aggressive behaviour in the subjects. However, the patient with antisocial personality disorder showed a rise of physical aggression above baseline scores in weeks 5 and 6, which corresponded with a break-up of a close relationship and discontinuation of fluoxetine, unbeknown to the researchers. A subject with BPD also showed an increase in self-reported aggression in the final two weeks of the trial, corresponding with her parents (with whom she was enmeshed) leaving her at home during holiday time. The authors argued that the early temporal response to fluoxetine was consistent with the observation of Norden (1989). However, they also questioned whether the occurrence of clinically significant life events and stressors could still over-ride the anti-aggressive effects of the fluoxetine. Nonetheless, it is equally possible that the apparent rapid response on impulsive aggressive behaviour observed in both these open studies was merely a placebo response.

Fava *et al* (1993) examined the effect of fluoxetine, 20 mg daily, over an eight-week period, in an open trial with patients with diagnoses of major depression. A subgroup of subjects reported

Table 4.3

Open trials of selective serotonergic reuptake inhibitors in personality disorder

Author	*Subjects*	*Method*	*Results*
Norden (1989)	12 BPD out-patients. No comorbid depression	Open trial. Fluoxetine 5–40 mg daily. Followed for 5–24 weeks	75% gobally improved. Improved rejection sensitivity, anger, depression, lability, irritability, anxiety, substance use, overeating
Cornelius *et al* (1990)	5 refractory BPD in-patients (1 with depression, 2 with dysthymia)	Open trial. Fluoxetine 20–40 mg daily for 8 weeks	Improved global symptom severity, depression, impulsive ward behaviour. No effect on anxiety or inter-personal sensitivity

Markovitz *et al* (1991)	22 out-patients (8 BPD, 10 BPD/schizotypal, 4 schizotypal; comorbid depression in 22, self-mutilation in 12)	Open trial. Fluoxetine 80 mg daily for 12 weeks	Improvement on SCL-90 scales. No differences according to BPD or schizotypal. Major improvement in self-mutilation
Coccaro *et al* (1990*b*)	3 out-patients (2 BPD, 1 antisocial)	Open trial. Fluoxetine "at least" 20–60 mg daily for 6 weeks	Rapid improvement in impulsive aggression. Slower response on self-report. 2 destabilised after life events
Fava *et al* (1993)	85 out-patients with major depression (34 with history of anger attacks and significantly more ASPD, BPD, narcissistic, histrionic, passive–aggressive personality disorder)	Open trial. Fluoxetine 20 mg daily for 8 weeks	Anger attacks disappeared in 71%. Greater overall improvement in depressed subjects with anger attacks

having major anger attacks associated with a surge of autonomic arousal, including tachycardia, sweating, flushing, and a feeling of being out of control. Significantly more of this group had diagnoses of antisocial, borderline, narcissistic, histrionic, and passive–aggressive personality disorders than those without anger attacks. Furthermore, they scored higher on self-reported hostility than the other group. Among the 85 depressed out-patients who completed at least eight weeks of treatment with fluoxetine, 24 (28%) reported having anger attacks at baseline but not after treatment, 10 (12%) reported anger attacks at both baseline and after treatment, 48 (56%) reported no anger attacks either before or after, and only 3 (4%) (two of whom otherwise responded to treatment) reported anger attacks after treatment but not before. There was a significant improvement in the subjects with anger attacks on self-reported hostility and scales of the Symptom Questionnaire. There was also a non-significant improvement on the Hamilton Rating Scale for Depression in comparison with subjects who did not have anger attacks. The authors argued that they had identified a subgroup of highly irritable and hostile depressed patients who reported anger attacks and had a psychological profile distinct from that of subjects without anger attacks. They concluded that fluoxetine appeared to be beneficial in reducing their anger and hostility. In a further study, the same group of researchers administered the thyrotropin-releasing hormone (TRH) test to a subgroup of 25 subjects, 12 of whom described experiencing anger attacks (Rosenblaum *et al*, 1993). Those with anger attacks had a blunted prolactin response to TRH stimulation compared with depressed patients without anger attacks. However, fluoxetine was followed by an overall increase in prolactin response to TRH among the depressed patients with anger attacks. The prolactin response to TRH also tended to predict the degree of response to treatment, suggesting that the subset of depressed patients with anger attacks may have had a greater central serotonergic dysregulation than the depressed patients without such attacks.

Before the uncontrolled findings on serotonergic reuptake inhibitors described above can be accepted, double-blind, placebo-controlled trials of fluoxetine and other serotonergic reuptake inhibitors are needed in patients with borderline, antisocial, and other personality disorders. Correlation of the clinical response with baseline assessment of central serotonergic function, using methods such as fenfluramine challenge, examination of CSF 5-HIAA, and examination of prolactin response to TRH stimulation, may further elucidate the role of serotonin in mediating the affective and impulsive aggressive behaviour of patients with BPD and other personality disorders.

Controlled trials of tricyclic antidepressants

In two early studies, Klein (1967, 1968) administered placebo, chlorpromazine (up to 1200 mg plus procyclidine), and imipramine (up to 300 mg daily) in a randomised, double-blind fashion to 295 randomly assigned consecutive hospital admissions, who included 32 with a "pseudoneurotic" schizophrenia; this subgroup are now thought to have BPD, as pseudoneurotic schizophrenia was a nosological forerunner of BPD. For the pseudoneurotic group, a significant difference from placebo was found for imipramine but not chlorpromazine. Global improvement was demonstrated in 69% compared with 25% of placebo controls. As might be expected, there was a differential response within the subject group. The pseudoneurotics improved with imipramine whereas the schizophrenics responded to chlorpromazine.

Akiskal (1983) has attempted to develop a new nosological framework for understanding the psychopathology of low-grade chronic depressions. He carried out several studies with large series of subjects with affective disorders lasting two years or more. He was able to separate out three main groups:

(a) patients having late-onset primary depressions with residual chronicity
(b) patients having chronic secondary dysphorias, having a variable age of onset and considered part of the symptomatic picture of non-affective neurotic disorders or reactions to long-standing incapacitating medical diseases
(c) patients having early-onset characterological depressions.

The third group is believed to contain a substantial number of patients who would be given diagnoses of BPD. But it is important to point out that Akiskal was approaching his subjects from a quite different nosological viewpoint, perceiving them as suffering from a subclass of chronic affective disorder rather than personality disorder as a primary condition. He collected a series of patients from this third subgroup having chronic affective disorder for a trial of antidepressants. These subjects included 65 given diagnoses of "characterologic depression" who fitted the criteria of:

(a) a history of mild depressive symptoms for five or more years
(b) onset before the age of 25 years

(c) depressive symptoms for most of the year
(d) a condition that did not represent the residuum of a well defined depressive episode requiring hospital admission.

Treatment was initially with a tricyclic antidepressant with mainly noradrenergic properties (desipramine or nortriptyline) in full dosage. If this failed, a serotonergic drug such as amitriptyline or clomipramine was prescribed. In all cases this was in full therapeutic dosage (150–200 mg daily). Of the original 65 subjects, 20 (31%) responded well to tricyclic antidepressant medication. From this approach, Akiskal subdivided his subjects with characterological depression into two further subgroups, depending on their responsiveness to treatment. One subgroup comprised patients classified as having subaffective dysthymic disorders: these patients responded and were characterised by a history of a major depressive episode, hypersomnia, a mild hypomanic episode in response to tricyclics, and female sex. The other subgroup comprised patients classified as having character spectrum disorders: two-thirds of these subjects did not respond, and the subjects were more likely to be male, to have an unstable personality, to have a history of abusing hypnotics, alcohol, or psychostimulants, and to have a poorer social outcome; in this subgroup there were high rates of familial alcoholism and parental assortative mating (i.e. both parents ill with alcoholism or personality disorder), but not affective illness.

Akiskal believed that parental loss and broken homes seemed to provide the developmental roots of the characterological disturbance in many of these patients. He concluded that the character spectrum dysphoric pattern appeared as formes frustes or alternative expressions of alcoholism, sociopathy, and somatisation disorders, indicating some degree of overlap with psychopathy.

Only one prospective double-blind trial has carefully compared amitriptyline with placebo and haloperidol in subjects with BPD or schizotypal personality disorder (Soloff *et al*, 1986*a*). Some of the subjects also had major depression. Overall, the depressed subjects treated with amitriptyline did only marginally better than those receiving placebo, whereas patients on haloperidol did markedly better measured with the Hamilton and Beck scales. Again, heterogeneity within the patient group was demonstrated by the observation that individual cases showed differing response. Some treated with amitriptyline responded well whereas others became much worse, demonstrating that a paradoxical deterioration in certain cases may obscure positive findings for responders.

Adverse effects of comorbidity

Although many clinicians have long believed that personality pathology may interfere with the effectiveness of treatment of axis I disorders, until recently there were no empirical studies on the subject. In a review of the literature, Reich & Green (1991) concluded that studies published in the last two decades have indicated that there is indeed an adverse interaction between axis I and axis II psychopathology with regard to the outcome of treatment. Stein (1992) also concluded that in antidepressant studies, where the primary aim is the treatment of depression, tricyclics are less successful among those with coexisting personality disorders than among those whose premorbid personality is normal.

In a retrospective case-note study, Black *et al* (1988) compared 75 subjects with major depression and coexisting personality disorder with 152 subjects with pure major depression. A good response to adequate tricyclic treatment was shown by 64% of subjects in the pure depression group compared with only 27% of those with an additional personality disorder. Pfohl *et al* (1984), using a similar retrospective design, also demonstrated that response to antidepressants was worse among patients with personality disorder (16%) than among patients with pure depression (50%). However, as the main outcome measure was made after only two weeks' treatment, these figures may well be unreliable and unduly pessimistic. Charney *et al* (1981) retrospectively reviewed the charts of 160 patients with major depressive disorder. Subjects both with and without an additional personality disorder received psychosocial treatment. However, medication was received by 71% of those without a personality disorder but only 28% of those with a personality disorder. For the subjects on medication, 76% of those who had no personality disorder had a good response to tricyclic antidepressants, compared with only 36% of those who had personality disorder.

Paradoxical response to antidepressants

Paradoxical effects and rage reactions were observed in an early study of emotionally unstable adolescents receiving imipramine (Klein & Fink, 1962). This reaction was also reported in four depressed subjects who experienced severe aggressive outbursts within a few hours of taking a tricyclic (Rampling, 1978). The most detailed examination of this phenomenon was carried out by Soloff *et al* (1986*b*) in the course of their work on the efficacy of amitriptyline and haloperidol on patients with BPD (see section above on controlled trials of tricyclic antidepressants). They observed a disturbing clinical worsening among some of the patients who had received amitriptyline. These patients appeared progressively more hostile, irritable, and behaviourally impulsive than they were at baseline. It appeared to the researchers that the symptoms were qualitatively different from the patients' initial complaints and became progressively worse with longer duration and higher doses of medication. They therefore used weekly outcome measures up to 42 days to compare: 15 borderline subjects who were amitriptyline non-responders with 14 placebo non-responders; and 13 amitriptyline responders with 10 placebo responders. Treatment responders, both to amitriptyline and placebo, improved in global functioning, depression and psychoticism but not in self-rated hostility. Amitriptyline responders improved in all areas of impulsive behaviour on the ward scale, significantly so in temper tantrums, assaultive threats, and manipulative behaviour. In contrast, the non-responders became progressively worse in global functioning, paranoid ideation, and impulsive ward behaviour. The increases in demanding behaviour and assaultive acts demonstrated by this group were statistically significant. These amitriptyline non-responders were also more demanding, made more suicidal threats, and were more physically assaultive than the placebo non-responders. It was thought that this paradoxical effect reflected a true disinhibition of impulsive behaviour independent of the antidepressant effect of amitriptyline. The authors did not believe that their subjects were undermedicated, overmedicated, or clinically hypomanic as a result of the study and therefore cautioned that "clinicians should be aware of the potential for paradoxical effects in 'borderline patients'".

Since the late 1980s and early 1990s, lawsuits have been pending in the USA with regard to the effects of fluoxetine. Reports have linked its use to suicidal thoughts and violent behaviour, with some patients complaining that they have become obsessed with urges to harm themselves or others. However, unfavourable reports in the media have been based largely on anecdote (O'Donnell, 1991). A meta-analysis of 17 double-blind trials comparing fluoxetine with a tricyclic antidepressant, or with a tricyclic antidepressants plus fluoxetine, in seriously depressed patients concluded that fluoxetine improved existing suicidal ideation in comparison with placebo, and did not increase the emergence of suicidal ideation or precipitate suicidal acts. A commentary in the *Drug and Therapeutics Bulletin* (1992) concluded that this meta-analysis had serious defects, but as far as could be judged the data available were reassuring about the suicidal risk of fluoxetine. However, the question of violent behaviour had not been addressed. The possibility thus remains that patients with psychopathic disorder may also show a differing response to fluoxetine, possibly with paradoxical reactions in a small subgroup.

Comment

Studies of response to antidepressants in patients with personality disorder have been restricted almost entirely to BPD. The studies available do not demonstrate a dramatic response. There is a suggestion that the response observed is more often seen with symptoms of depressed mood. Certain authors have argued that the behavioural improvement which may follow antidepressant treatment is not a direct result of the antidepressant effect: this possibility clearly requires further study. There are problems with borderline patients who demonstrate marked mood disturbances for periods of several days to weeks, which can then be followed by periods of relative stability. This fluctuating pattern reflects the natural history of the condition. Carefully controlled trials are therefore required to avoid the possibility that an apparent benefit is not merely a reflection of the natural course of the disorder. Moreover, in view of the suggestion that core borderline features are not improved to a greater degree by antidepressant medication than by neuroleptics, the latter drugs should also be included in any future trials.

Caution should also be exercised when antidepressants are prescribed in view of the possibility of behavioural deterioration in a subgroup of patients. However, as major depression is observed in a substantial proportion of psychopaths (Coid, 1992), this should not necessarily deter clinicians from administering antidepressant medication for an axis I condition. This has a good chance of success and treatment may sometimes be life-saving. It remains unclear whether there is a risk of serious behavioural deterioration in patients with severe personality disorder and concurrent major depression. However, in such a situation ECT could be substituted for the antidepressant.

Monoamine oxidase inhibitors

Monoamine oxidase inhibitors (MAOIs) act by inhibiting monoamine oxidase, thereby causing an accumulation of amine neurotransmitters. The metabolism of some amine drugs, such as sympathomimetics, and tricyclic and related antidepressants is also inhibited and their pressor action may therefore be potentiated. The pressor effect of tyramine present in certain foods may also be dangerously potentiated with these compounds. MAOIs are used much less frequently than tricyclic and related antidepressants because of these dangers of dietary and drug interactions and the fact that it is easier to prescribe MAOIs when tricyclic antidepressants have been unsuccessful rather than vice versa. Tranylcypromine is considered the most hazardous of the MAOIs because of its stimulant action. Phenelzine and isocarboxazid, which are less stimulant and therefore safer, are considered preferable. Phobic patients and depressed patients with atypical, hypochondriacal, or hysterical features are thought to respond best to MAOIs. But MAOIs can also be tried in patients who are refractory to other antidepressants, where there is occasionally a dramatic response. The high prevalence of atypical depressions such as dysthymia, panic attacks, and mood swings over the lifetime of psychopathic subjects (Coid, 1992) suggests that MAOIs could be beneficial for certain patients.

Unfortunately, optimism for a dramatic effect of MAOIs in patients with personality disorder was somewhat dampened by the observations of Shawcross & Tyrer (1985) in a retrospective study of 50 depressed neurotic out-patients. They found that 68% of their non-responding group had an additional diagnosis of personality disorder (mainly anankastic and passive–dependent), compared with only 18% of the phenelzine-responsive group. In this study, subjects had been treated with both MAOIs and tricyclic antidepressants and the response of depressive symptoms was measured using the Montgomery–Asberg scale (Montgomery & Asberg, 1979). There was some evidence to support the view that patients who improved on MAOIs showed fewer abnormal personality traits, particularly for sensitivity, pessimism, and hypochondriasis, than those who improved on tricyclics. Only five of the subjects were given diagnoses of sociopathy using the Personality Assessment Schedule (Tyrer *et al*, 1979). But four of this sociopathic subgroup were unresponsive to either drug; the other subject responded to tricyclic antidepressant medication.

The methodology of Shawcross & Tyrer's study cannot be considered satisfactory in that it involved an unusual out-patient sample whose response to treatment may not apply to a psychopathic sample. Table 4.4 summarises the three placebo-controlled trials of MAOIs in subjects with BPD and atypical depression. Hedberg *et al* (1971) compared the effects of tranylcypromine, trifluoperazine, and a combination of both in a double-blind, placebo-controlled cross-over trial of 96 subjects with diagnoses of schizophrenia, although 28 had diagnoses of pseudoneurotic schizophrenia, a nosological precursor of BPD. Pseudoneurotics responded best to tranylcypromine, which was superior to trifluoperazine alone and in combination with tranylcypromine in this subgroup. The non-pseudoneurotic schizophrenics tended to deteriorate when no longer receiving trifluoperazine.

Liebowitz & Klein (1981) administered phenelzine in doses of up to 75 mg in an open trial to subjects fulfilling the criteria for hysteroid dysphoria, of whom 14 fulfilled criteria for BPD. A positive response to medication was shown by 11 women; this occurred within the first three months of treatment and was observed in several areas, including symptoms of depression and anxiety (emotional and somatic) as well as a number of labile personality and hysteroid dysphoric features. Borderline features, measured by eight criteria, fell from a mean of 4.5 to 3.9 out of 8 possible criteria. When the 11 improved patients were entered into a double-blind, placebo-controlled withdrawal trial, subjects on the placebo developed more borderline features and showed increased behavioural disturbance, including angry outbursts, self-harm, and the break-up of relationships, along with feelings of chronic emptiness, problems of being alone, and impulsivity. Identity disturbance and affective lability were borderline features showing little response. The authors concluded that their findings suggested drug responsiveness for some of these "so called personality traits".

Parsons *et al* (1989) collected a large series of subjects who met Research Diagnostic Criteria for major depression or intermittent depressive disorder and who presented with symptoms of atypical depression. Borderline status was established in a group of 171 according to DSM–III criteria. Improvement was measured with the Clinical Global Impression Scale (National Institute of Mental Health, 1985) and the Hamilton Depression Rating Scale (Hamilton, 1967). Phenelzine showed a significant effect over imipramine in a double-blind, placebo-controlled, random-assignment study and response was virtually identical whether subjects had four or five or more borderline criteria. However, with lower borderline scores, the phenelzine–imipramine difference disappeared, indicating a specific response of atypical depression in BPD to MAOIs compared with imipramine. The authors noted that some subjects with BPD did respond to tricyclics, but overall the response to phenelzine was significantly greater.

Liebowitz and colleagues later confirmed these findings with an expanded series of 119 patients (Liebowitz *et al*, 1988). Overall response rates were 71% with phenelzine, 50% with imipramine,

TABLE 4.4

Placebo controlled trials of monoamine oxidase inhibitors in borderline personality disorder and atypical depression

Author	*Subjects*	*Method*	*Results*
Hedberg *et al* (1971)	96 schizophrenics (28 'pseudoneurotic' schizophrenic) in-patients	Double-blind cross-over, 8-week phase; placebo v. trifluoperazine, tranylcypromine (max. 30 mg) v. MAOI and antipsychotic combined	Pseudoneurotics: 50% responded to tranylcypromine, 28% to combination, 22% to trifluoperazine (global assessment and Minnesota–Hartford Personality Assay)
Liebowitz & Klein (1981)	16 female hysteroid dysphoric out-patients (14 BPD)	Open pilot trial, phenelzine (15–74 mg daily) plus thrice weekly psychotherapy; double-blind v. placebo withdrawal trial of 11 responders	For pilot 11 (68%) good response, 5 no response (1 depressed, 1 grand mal seizure, 2 alcohol abuse, 1 delusional parisitosis), 6 no longer BPD; for withdrawal trail, 8 (73%) relapsed on placebo (self-injury, relationship breakdown increased BPD features)

Cowdry & Gardner (1988)	16 BPD females	Double-blind cross-over 6–8 weeks; alprazolam (1–6 mg) v. trifluoperazine (2–12 mg) v. tranylcypromine (10–60 mg v. carbamazepine (200–1200 mg) v. placebo (17 started, 9 completed tranylcypromine)	Tranylcypromine: improved anxiety, depression, sensitivity to rejection; behaviour dyscontrol improved, but less than on carbamazepine
Parsons *et al* (1989)	171 out-patients with atypical depression (40 (23%) with 5 or more BPD criteria, 61 (36% with 4 or more)); sociopaths excluded	Double-blind random assignment; 14 days; phenelzine 60 mg v. imipramine 200 mg v. placebo	Clinical Global Impression scores for BPD: 89% responded to phenelzine, 38% to imipramine, 20% to placebo; for low BPD scores, no imipramine/phenelzine difference
Liebowitz *et al* (1988)	119 out-patients with atypical depression, rated for BPD criteria; sociopaths excluded	As for Parsons *et al* (1989); different data analysis for overlapping sample	Comparison of baseline v. outcome scores on BPD criteria: imipramine v. placebo, NS; phenelzine v. placebo, $t = 2.5$, $P < 0.01$; phenelzine v. imipramine, $t = 2.4$, $P < 0.02$
Soloff *et al* (1993)	108 BPD in-patients	Random double-blind allocation; 5 weeks; 36 haloperidol (mean 4 mg), 38 phenelzine (mean 60 mg), 34 placebo (mean 4 tablets)	Significant symptom improvement in all groups; no overall superiority of haloperidol over placebo

and 28% with placebo. Phenelzine was "widely superior" on most measures to imipramine and this superiority was even greater after a six-month continuation phase. However, the superiority of phenelzine and imipramine over placebo was largely confined to patients in subsets of the overall sample who were prospectively judged to have a history of spontaneous panic attacks and/or showed 'hysteriod dysphoric' features. In this second phase of the study, the overlap between hysteroid dysphoria and BPD was recognised and a separate analysis of results according to BPD scores was carried out. Only the phenelzine group ($n = 33$) showed a fall in borderline features, from a mean of 2.6 to 1.4 ($n = 30$ at end of study) when re-measured after treatment (see Table 4.4 for subgroup comparisons according to treatment).

In their multi-compound, double-blind cross-over study, Cowdry & Gardner (1999) examined the effects of tranylcypromine in 17 subjects, 9 of whom completed the trial of this compound. The MAOI improved anxiety, depression, and sensitivity to rejection. There appeared to be some moderate improvement in behavioural dyscontrol, but this was less than with carbamazepine.

In a recent study comparing phenelzine, haloperidol, and placebo (see Table 4.4), phenelzine was found to be superior to both haloperidol and placebo on measures of depression, borderline psychopathology, and anxiety after five weeks of treatment (Soloff *et al*, 1993). Phenelzine was also superior to placebo on subjective measures of anger and hostility. However, when its efficacy in atypical depression and hysteroid dysphoria were examined, there was no significant effect in this study. The authors argued that phenelzine was useful for self-perceived anger and hostility in patients with BPD, a finding complementing that of Cowdry & Gardner (1999) with tranylcypromine on behavioural impulsivity.

The results of this study illustrated many of the difficulties of treating acute symptom presentations of patients with BPD with pharmacotherapy. Response to time and in-patient milieu alone (placebo effects) were both powerful and non-specific. All three groups, including placebo, showed significant falls in most symptom measures merely as a result of being admitted to hospital to take part in the trial. Furthermore, Soloff *et al* (1993) conceded that quantitative change within the groups on measures used was modest. Thus, although significant improvement was shown on depression scores as a result of the phenelzine, many subjects were still clinically impaired. Although the study improved on the methodology of several previous trials by having a one-week washout period before the random allocation, there were still two major limitations: firstly, the length of time over which subjects were studied (five weeks), and secondly, the mean levels of phenelzine and (in particular) haloperidol administered to the experimental subjects. Soloff and colleagues argued that a mean level of 90 mg phenelzine, administered over a longer period, might have been preferable to demonstrate more clearly whether the drug had an effect on atypical depression.

Comment

Stein (1992) has pointed out that there are divergent views as to whether the beneficial effects of MAOIs on personality disorder are due to their antidepressant effects, as in the case of atypical depression, or to their psychostimulant effects. Studies of MAOIs have largely included subjects with features of atypical depression or the overlapping construct of hysteroid dysphoria. Within these subject groups, MAOIs have been shown to be significantly more effective than placebo, and in most cases also more effective than tricyclic antidepressants. Thus, in psychopathic subjects with atypical depression, or with features of hysteroid dysphoria, MAOIs may be the treatment of choice. However, it is important that MAOIs should be prescribed in adequate dosage and probably for a minimum of eight weeks before their effectiveness is evaluated. In subjects with BPD, there may also be a reduction of certain core features, including anger control, interpersonal sensitivity, impulsivity, and feelings of emptiness. However, in view of the potential seriousness of side-effects and the unreliability of patients with severe personality disorder, a trial of MAOIs may only be appropriate after lithium and carbamazepine have failed.

Benzodiazepines

Two major reviews of the drug treatment of personality disorder have concluded that benzodiazepines are contra-indicated in these patients because of reported cases of disinhibition resulting in rage reactions and the risk of drug dependency (Tyrer, 1988; Stein, 1992). However, re-examination of these studies suggests that this warning may have been applied too broadly and that in specific cases the judicious use of benzodiazepines may be helpful.

Unfortunately, judgement of the usefulness of these compounds has to be based on only two studies carried out in a careful and double-blind manner, one by Lion (1979) and the other by Cowdry & Gardner (1988). Table 4.5 summarises the trials of benzodiazepines in patients with personality and behavioural disorder.

TABLE 4.5

Trials of benzodiazepines in patients with personality and behavioural disorders

Author	*Subjects*	*Method*	*Results*
Kalina (1964)	52 male prisoners (schizophrenic, schizoid personality disorder, epilepsy); behaviourally disturbed and aggressive	Open trial, 6 months; diazepam 20–30 mg daily	Violence, destructiveness, belligerence resolved in 33 (63%), improved in 3 (6%), unchanged in 16 (13%)
Goddard & Lokare (1970)	16 epileptics, long-stay in-patients due to aggression and disruption of families	Open trial, 6 months; diazepam 6–30mg; additional anticonvulsants	Anecdotal report of improved aggression and personality functioning (3 subsequently discharged)
Lion (1979)	65 out-patients (20 drop-outs); temper outbursts assaults, impulsive, belligerent; mixed explosive, anti-social, passive–aggressive features	Double-blind trial, random allocation; oxazepam 120 mg daily v. chlordiazepoxide 100 mg daily v. placebo. Doses doubled at 2 weeks; measures at 2 and 4 weeks	Significant improvement in hostility and anxiety on oxazepam compared with chlordiazepoxide and placebo; significant improvement in irritability, on oxazepam compared with placebo

Bick & Hannah (1986)	10 in-patients; "different diagnoses"; "chemically restrained" for violence	Retrospective open pilot trial; haloperidol 10 mg v. lorazepam 2 mg; single i.m. admistrations	Mean time in seclusion after i.m. administration; lorazepam 1.9 h; haloperidol 6.1 h (for total sample)
Cowdry & Gardner (1988)	16 BPD females	Double-blind cross-over trial, 6–8 weeks; alprazolam (1–6 mg) v. tranylcypromine (10–60 mg) v. carbamazepine (200–1200 mg) v. placebo (12 administered alprazolam)	Alprazolam: 2 subjects showed better response than on other compounds; 7 subjects serious dyscontrol compared with 2 on placebo; overall mood unchanged

Lion (1979) concluded that despite the small size of the subgroups studied in a random-allocation trial (14 on oxazepam, 16 on chlordiazepoxide, and 15 assigned to placebo), differences emerged in the analysis of the scales used to measure both anxiety and aggression. Oxazepam appeared somewhat better in reducing anxiety than chlordiazepoxide and was superior on one subscale of the tests used to measure hostility. Lion believed that anti-anxiety drugs did play a significant role in the treatment of explosive personalities who were prone to temper outbursts with underlying paranoid suspiciousness and mood lability. No rage reactions were observed among his subjects.

Unfortunately, Cowdry & Gardner (1988) observed serious dyscontrol in 7 of the 12 subjects who were administered alprazolam in their double-blind cross-over trial (see below). Overall, the mood of their subjects was unchanged, although a small subgroup of two subjects showed a better response to alprazolam than to the other compounds employed in the study.

Kalina (1964) showed apparent improvement in violent, destructive, and belligerent behaviour in 63% of a group of 52 male prisoners with a history of behavioural disturbance and aggression. Subjects had various diagnoses including schizophrenia, schizoid personality disorder and epilepsy and were administered diazepam in an open trial over six months. Similarly, Goddard & Lokare (1970) anecdotally reported improvement in aggression and personality functioning in an open trial of diazepam with 16 epileptics who had been in hospital for at least a year because their aggressive and disruptive behaviour had rendered their families unable to cope with them. However, both of these uncontrolled trials were carried out at a relatively early stage in the introduction of diazepam, when there was considerable optimism for its anti-anxiety properties and lack of side-effects, and when the risk of dependence had not been properly identified. These factors may well have influenced the optimistic comments of these authors.

Bick & Hannah (1986) examined the case-notes of a series of patients with different diagnoses, most probably acutely psychotic, who had been admitted to hospital and at some time had had to receive intramuscular sedation to control their aggression. The authors had encouraged colleagues to administer lorazepam as an alternative to neuroleptics and the authors had examined the case-notes subsequently to compare the time spent in seclusion following an administration of haloperidol or lorazepam (intramuscularly) on different occasions. It appeared that there was a marked reduction in the amount of time spent in a seclusion room after the administration of lorazepam compared with haloperidol. There was no greater incidence of disinhibition observed following the administration of the benzodiazepine. However, the nature of this trial must give some cause for concern as to whether seclusion was always necessary. The measures used to assess the drug effect also cannot be considered satisfactory.

It is possible that opinions regarding the benzodiazepine alprazolam, which was increasingly prescribed in the USA in the early 1980s, were influenced by the same optimism for effectiveness that diazepam had enjoyed over a decade earlier. Faltus (1984) reported on three subjects who had BPD, with histories of substance abuse, multiple admissions to hospital, and failure to respond to a variety of other drugs, including tricyclics, neuroleptics and lithium, who responded well to a small dose of alprazolam. The author observed that it appeared to relieve anxiety and also certain features of the character pathology of BPD. Such reports may have influenced the choice of alprazolam in the more elegant study later carried out by Cowdry & Gardner (1988), where a double-blind procedure showed a less favourable response.

Griffith (1985) described two patients who had diagnoses of episodic behavioural disorder whose condition appeared to benefit from rapidly absorbed short-acting benzodiazepines. The first patient, suffering from intermittent explosive disorder and atypical psychosis, and having diffuse brain damage, had suffered for many years from outbursts of rage preceded by anxiety, hallucinations, irritability, racing thoughts, and hyperactivity. The patient had not been helped by carbamazepine or thiothixine and it was observed that the ensuing rage outbursts reduced symptoms of tension. Triazolam (0.05 mg) taken at the onset of the prodromal symptoms aborted an escalation to rage in 80% of episodes. However, occasionally the rages would reappear three hours later (presumably after the effects of the benzodiazepine had worn off). Substituting chlorazepate (7.5–15 mg) brought control with no recurrence of the symptoms. However, when administered on a regular basis, this was ineffective, and increasing the dosage brought with it sedation and ataxia. It was of some interest that "family and social interventions" later eliminated the propensity to rage attacks and the benzodiazepines were continued. In the second case, triazolam (0.5 mg) was administered to a woman with poorly controlled complex partial seizures, pseudoseizures and explosive behaviour secondary to chickenpox encephalitis suffered in childhood. In adulthood this patient also presented with mixed personality disorder and episodic dyscontrol. Administration of triazolam prevented escalation of angry outbursts and pseudoseizures and was followed by a brief sleep, in 90% of episodes. Behavioural intervention also facilitated the cessation of triazolam administration at a later stage, except on rare occasions.

Reactive behavioural dyscontrol

There have been several reports that benzodiazepines increased the incidence of behavioural dyscontrol, including hostile outbursts, aggressive behaviour, and suicidal ideation and acts, in a variety of patients and normal controls (Ingram & Timbury, 1960; Ryan *et al*, 1968; Gardos *et al*, 1968; Hall & Joffe, 1972; Gaind & Jacoby, 1978). Gardner & Cowdry (1985) carried out the most careful examination of dyscontrol in patients who had been prescribed alprazolam in their previous double-blind controlled trial (Cowdry & Gardner, 1988). Among their seven subjects who showed dyscontrol during the trial, two took overdoses, one made deep cuts to the neck, one made transverse wrist cuts, and one variously attempted to break her own arm, threw a chair at her own child, and jumped in front of a car. The last subject also jumped in front of a car while on placebo, and another patient on placebo took an overdose. It was necessary to terminate four of the alprazolam trials early because of the severity of the dyscontrol. The authors advised caution in treating subjects with a previous substantial history of behavioural dyscontrol with alprazolam but noted that among the other benzodiazepines, oxazepam had not been found to increase hostility or disinhibition in controlled studies.

Comment

The available literature on the effect of benzodiazepines on behaviour and personality disorders is not of high quality. What is available does not strongly promote the use of these compounds in this group of patients. Benzodiazepines are highly effective in controlling anxiety, but in recent years it has been increasingly recognised that there is a risk of dependence if they are prescribed over a prolonged period. This is likely to deter most clinicians from sustained trials of treatment of patients with severe personality disorder.

Rage reactions have been noted along with other forms of behavioural dyscontrol. It is believed that the former are relatively rare but in borderline personality disorders the risk may be increased and therefore could be a further contraindication. However, a single administration of benzodiazepine for a disturbed and aggressive patient may be helpful during episodes of severe disturbance or when anxiety is overwhelming. The administration of single doses of short-acting compounds prior to behavioural disturbance, when it can be predicted by a patient on the basis of mounting symptoms of tension, irritability, etc., warrants further study.

Anticonvulsants

It is now recognised that anticonvulsant compounds have an important spectrum of clinical activity in both neuropsychiatric syndromes and behavioural disorder, in addition to their effect on epileptic disorders. But whether these compounds are working through their anticonvulsant effect on the behavioural disorder or through quite separate therapeutic properties remains unresolved. There is general agreement that, on rare occasions, aggression can occur during epileptic attacks. But in unselected populations of epileptics, there is no evidence of increased interictal violent behaviour (Treiman & Delgado-Escueta, 1983). Epileptics who do demonstrate interictal violence are more likely to be young, male, and personality disordered, and to have lower IQ, a higher level of neurological deficits, and an early onset of severe epilepsy consisting of partial seizures or generalised convulsions (Dam & Dam, 1986). In a review of the association between aggressive behaviour and epilepsy, Fenwick (1986) concluded that aggression is more likely to be associated with brain damage than epilepsy in these patients. But gross brain damage is not thought to be an appropriate model for psychopathic disorder, despite major personality change sometimes being observed following head injury (McClelland, 1988). On the other hand, studies of 'minimal brain damage', the postulated syndrome of 'episodic dyscontrol' (both of these are considered on the border of what is conventionally regarded as psychopathic personality), and clinical presentations that with more definite clinical evidence would be diagnosed as temporal lobe epilepsy (Lishman, 1978) suggest that anticonvulsants might be helpful in a subgroup of patients.

Further encouragement to use anticonvulsants emerges from electroencephalography (EEG) studies of psychopaths. Several forms of mental disorder show different levels of EEG abnormality. But the incidence is thought to be highest in patients with personality disorder and behavioural abnormalities, particularly 'aggressive psychopaths' and those with a history of habitual aggression or explosive rage, who show the highest incidence of all (Hill & Waterson, 1942; Hill, 1944*a*; Williams, 1969). In most cases, the abnormality reflects cerebral immaturity, the patterns being more usually associated with a very much younger age group. However, in those with antisocial behaviour the abnormality is more commonly localised in the temporal lobes, particularly the posterior temporal area. Williams (1969) concluded that the disturbed behaviour and EEG findings were "constitutional" in origin and reflected a disturbance of cerebral physiology in habitually aggressive individuals. Similarly, it has been argued that violent behaviour may be the only overt symptom of brain disease in certain subjects who manifest the syndrome of 'episodic dyscontrol' (Mark & Ervin, 1970; Bach-y-Rita *et al*, 1971; Maletsky, 1973). Most of these subjects are male, from disturbed family backgrounds, and have a history of repeated outbursts of violence since adolescence or childhood, usually with minimal provocation, again showing a degree of overlap with the construct of psychopathy. They show a high incidence of abnormal EEGs and some evidence of minor neurological dysfunction, many also having symptoms reminiscent of epileptic phenomena even in the absence of diagnosed epilepsy. Clinical observation suggests that outbursts of violence may be preceded or followed by features similar to temporal lobe epilepsy.

Carbamazepine

Carbamazepine (CBZ) has been in use as an anticonvulsant since the 1960s and is especially valuable in the treatment of partial or focal seizures. But it was noticed that the psychological problems of epileptic patients also seemed to improve. More recent studies have demonstrated that it is effective in a range of different psychiatric conditions. In a detailed review, Elphick (1989) concluded that there is considerable evidence to support its use in the acute treatment of mania and in the prophylaxis of bipolar affective disorder. In addition, overactivity, aggression, and poor impulse control also appear to improve in a variety of different diagnostic categories: borderline personality disorder, organic brain disorders and post-traumatic stress disorder.

Borderline personality disorder

Carbamazepine (200 mg three times daily) was prescribed to 11 women with BPD in a six-week double-blind cross-over trial with placebo and three other active medications (Cowdry & Gardner, 1988). There was decreased severity of behavioural dyscontrol. This was especially marked in comparison with the placebo administrations, where 11 of the trials had to be discontinued due to clinical deterioration in the patients. Overall, there was no improvement of mood in comparison with placebo. However, three patients on CBZ developed depression and four had allergic skin reactions which resulted in discontinuation of this preparation (Gardner & Cowdry, 1988). However, Gardner & Cowdry observed that in the patients who did respond, the CBZ appeared to allow them to reflect on their actions rather than immediately act on impulse as before.

Organic brain disorders

Table 4.6 summarises the positive effects of CBZ in a series of reports of (mainly single cases) of different forms of organic brain disorder. Although it might at first be assumed that the CBZ had a direct effect, possibly through its anticonvulsant properties, one study of severely learning-disabled patients indicated that their overactivity was most likely to respond when accompanied by elevation of mood (Reid *et al*, 1981).

Post-traumatic stress disorder

Hodge (1992) has postulated that psychopathic disorder may have its origins in post-traumatic stress consequent upon childhood sexual and physical abuse. He has proposed that psychopaths may be "addicted" to violence through developmentally mediated post-traumatic stress disorder (PTSD). However, in the UK psychopaths study (Coid, 1992), 20% of subjects denied any history of adverse early environmental experience, indicating that if PTSD applies to these subjects, it is not necessarily relevant to every case. Nevertheless, studies of pharmacological treatment of PTSD in war veterans could be relevant to a subgroup of psychopaths. Lipper *et al* (1986) found that nightmares, flashbacks, and intrusive recollections were improved in seven out of ten patients with CBZ. Wolf *et al* (1988) found improved impulse control and decreased violence in an open trial with eight Vietnam veterans, but without reporting formal ratings.

Diphenylhydantoin

Diphenylhydantoin contrasts with CBZ in showing little positive effect on behavioural disturbance and hostility. Lefkowicz (1969) found a better response to placebo in 50 disruptive delinquents when rated by staff for disruptive behaviour. A fall in ratings was shown by 40% taking placebo compared with only 26% taking

TABLE 4.6
Effects of carbamazepine on affective and aggressive symptoms in organic brain damage

Reference	*No. of subjects*	*Psychological or behavioural components*	*Organic component*	*Outcome*
Reid *et al* (1981)	12	Overactivity	Severe mental handicap	Improved overactivity
McAlister *et al* (1985)	5	Primary psychiatric disorder	Frontal lobe disease	Reduced affective lability
Anton *et al* (1986)	1	Bipolar illness	Multi-infact dementia	Improved cognition and psychotic symptoms
Buck & Harvey (1986)	1	Violence	Mental retardation	Synergism with lithium
Essa (1986)	1	Hyperactivity	Dementia	Reduced hyperactivity
Gupta *et al* (1979)	1	Explosive aggression	Prader–Willi syndrome	Reduced aggression
Hellekson *et al* (1979)	1	Bipolar disorder	Seizure disorder	Improved
Stewart (1985)	1	Rage attacks	Kluver–Bucy syndrome	Improved rage attacks
Stone *et al* (1986)	1	Episodic dyscontrol	Midtemporal discharges	Improved dyscontrol
Tunks & Dermer (1977)	1	Dyscontrol disorder	Right temporal dyscontrol	Improved seizures

diphenylhydantoin, with some subjects rated worse on the active preparation on measures of distress, unhappiness, negativism, and aggressiveness. Similarly, a placebo cross-over trial of diphenylhydantoin administered to child-abusing parents which showed some beneficial effects on anxiety, depression and somatic symptoms, showed none for the core symptoms of aggressiveness, impulsivity, and hostility (Rosenblatt *et al*, 1976).

Phenobarbitone

Studies with child subjects suggest that phenobarbitone should be given with caution and may therefore be contraindicated in subjects with psychopathic disorder. Several authors examined the use of phenobarbitone in prophylaxis for febrile convulsions and commented on its undesirable effects on behaviour. Wolf & Forsythe (1978) found that 43% of 109 children given phenobarbitone for febrile convulsions developed a reversible behavioural disorder – especially hyperactivity, but also including irritability, tantrums, disobedience, lethargy, or insomnia – compared with only 18% of those not given prophylaxis. The drug-induced behavioural disturbance usually appeared in the first month of therapy and did not relate to drug levels. The only significant correlation was with behavioural abnormality preceding the initial febrile convulsion, suggesting that the child's personality was an important factor in determining whether or not behavioural changes would be precipitated by the drug. Heckmatt *et al* (1976) also noted that 16 out of 88 patients developed behavioural problems, which improved in 12 after treatment was stopped. Similarly, in a comparative trial of monotherapy with four major anti-epileptic drugs in previously untreated children with epilepsy, 5 of the first 10 (50%) randomised to phenobarbitone developed hyperactivity or aggressive behaviour, or difficulty coping with school work, necessitating withdrawal of the drug from the patient and abandonment of the drug from the study (McGowan *et al*, 1983).

Comment

It is possible that other anticonvulsants may have a beneficial effect in certain specific cases, but only CBZ has been shown to improve overactivity, aggression, and poor impulse control. However, this does not appear to be restricted to individual diagnostic categories, so the prescription of CBZ is more appropriately applied to these target symptoms and behaviour patterns rather than as a treatment for any particular axis II category. Thus, CBZ may be as effective in reducing behavioural disorder in a subgroup of psychopaths as it is in a subgroup of individuals with organic brain damage, schizophrenia, etc. Although there is a strong theoretical basis for the administration of CBZ to patients with psychopathic disorder (on the basis of a high incidence of EEG abnormality and indicative of possible neurological abnormality), it still remains possible that the therapeutic effect is mediated more strongly through a mood-stabilising or other psychotropic effect, rather than its anticonvulsant properties.

Psychostimulants

The possibility of a relationship between overactivity in childhood and syndromes of antisocial behavioural disorder in adulthood have been considered likely for several years. However, the association between DSM–III–R attention deficit hyperactivity disorder and the development of antisocial personality disorder in adulthood is now considered to be complex and to require additional intervening factors for the one to lead to the other (see Coid, 1993*a*). Nevertheless, observations of the apparently 'paradoxical' effect of psychostimulants in certain individuals, such as overactive children, have led to various theories; for example, that the behavioural disorder is a reaction to 'cortical underarousal'; this is linked with the proposal that such a mechanism could lead to similar problems in adulthood, especially in subjects with minimal brain dysfunction.

More recently, doubt has been cast on whether the effects of psychostimulants are necessarily 'paradoxical'. Dosages used in clinical practice tend to be smaller than those taken to induce euphoria or excess activity. Within this dose range the behavioural effects of a single dose are similar in normal adults, normal children, and hyperactive children – in kind, even if not in degree (Rapaport *et al*, 1978). These are thought to be characteristic effects of the drug on human behaviour at this dose level (Robbins & Sahakian, 1979). Furthermore, although phenothiazines will also result in improvement in the behavioural problems of overactive children, the consequent reduction in overactivity appears to be less selective upon these target symptoms than is seen with psychostimulants. This could account for the failure of stimulants to produce significant effects in conditions such as autism or severe mental handicap. This important observation holds out the promise that, within a broad range of antisocial adult subjects, a syndrome of behavioural disorder could ultimately be recognised that is specifically responsive to psychostimulants.

There are more than 100 controlled trials of stimulant drug effects in overactive children of normal intelligence (Barkley, 1977; Cantwell & Carlson, 1978; Rapoport, 1983). The short-term results are unequivocal: drugs such as amphetamine and methylphenidate are more active than placebo in reducing ratings of behavioural disorder. In addition, the action is substantial and in certain cases may be dramatic. However, it is important to pay specific attention to certain target symptoms in children. Thus, the main effects should be expected on the chaotic, restless, inattentive overactivity that is severe enough to constitute a handicap to the child's development. There should not be evidence of severe, overt emotional distress or other contraindications such as tics, or stereotypes. Stimulants are recommended for children only when psychological treatment methods are inadequate or impractical. Aggression and antisocial behaviour at home is moderately responsive to medication. Greater response is noted in classroom behaviour and off-task restlessness. However, there is no convincing evidence that stimulants are effective in reducing aggression in non-overactive children. Psychometric tests show improvement in what appears to be a dose-dependent effect, with increasing dosage worsening scores. However, the improvement is not paralleled by significant improvement in overall academic performance. Mood does not appear to be affected within the therapeutic range, although at high dosage euphoria will appear in most cases, with dysphoria seen in a small subgroup. Children with primary conditions of mood disorder are not helped by this medication. With time, some overactive children will be found to require stimulants no longer, although others may require years of treatment to prevent a relapse of their symptoms (Taylor, 1986).

Family and cross-fostering studies have indicated a possible genetic link between attention deficit disorder in childhood and adult personality disorders, alcoholism, sociopathy, and hysteria (Morrison & Stewart, 1971; Cantwell, 1972). Follow-up studies of hyperactive children show that a proportion demonstrate behavioural disturbance and personality disorder in adolescence and adulthood (see Coid, 1993*a*). However, three possible explanations still remain for the observation that some adult subjects with personality or behavioural disorder improve with psychostimulants. The first is that there is a direct relationship between these individuals and children with attention deficit hyperactivity disorder (ADHD) in the sense that the treatment-responsive group are merely the same children now grown up. The second is that

TABLE 4.7

Psychostimulant trail in adults with residual attention deficit disorder

Authors	*Subjects*	*Method*	*Results*
Wood *et al* (1976)	11; minimal brain dysfuction in childhood and several axis I diagnoses in adulthood	Double-blind, placebo-controlled, 2 weeks; 20–60 mg methylpenidate followed by pemoline and tricyclic antidepressant	Improved calmness, energy, concentration, temper; effect methylphenidate > pemoline > tricyclic
Wender *et al* (1981)	26 with ADD since childhood; 60 with ADD symptoms adulthood only	Double-blind, placebo controlled, 6 weeks; pemoline, max. 150 mg daily	No significant difference for whole sample; but for 26 with ADD since childhood, improvement on hyperactivity, concentration, talkativeness, temper, impulsivity

Mattes *et al* (1984)	26 residual ADD with hyperactivity; 35 no childhood symptoms	ADD double-blind cross-over; methylphenidate 48.2 mg mean daily	No overall benefit; childhood history irrelevant; 25% entire sample improved, but not significantly
Wender *et al* (1985)	37 ADD residual type	Double-blind cross-over, 2 weeks; methylphenidate max. 90 mg daily	Moderate to marked response methylphenidate 21 (57%), c.f. placebo 4 (11); improved attention, overactivity, affective lability, impulsivity
Shekem *et al* (1989)	18 ADD residual type (8 males, 10 females)	Open trial; nomifensine maleate max. 300 mg daily	All 8 males, 7 females improved on attention, hyperactivity, impulsivity; 3 females no response (drug later withdrawn)

conditions such as ADHD and personality disorder are multifactorial but show a similar or, to some degree, an overlapping genetic component while being phenotypically different clinical conditions. It could be hypothesised that in the treatment-responsive group this 'overlap' is greater. The third explanation is that there is a subgroup of stimulant-responsive individuals with personality disorder whose conditions have no relationship to ADHD. It remains possible that all three explanations apply in the case of those psychopaths who respond to treatment in what is clearly a highly heterogeneous group of conditions.

Table 4.7 summarises the studies on the effect of stimulants on adult subjects having diagnoses of attention deficit disorder, residual type. All studies but one are double blind, and placebo controlled, and all but one have shown both a statistically significant improvement in patients on active medication when compared with those on placebo, and a significant clinical improvement noted by the researchers. Subjects chosen were classified as showing features of affective lability, inability to complete tasks, explosive temper outbursts, impulsivity, inability to tolerate stress, motor restlessness and difficulty paying attention. Some subjects had additional clinical syndromes such as depressive episodes and anxiety disorder in adulthood, but all studies excluded major psychosis. However, Wender and colleagues also excluded subjects with borderline and schizotypal personality disorder, in contrast to Mattes and colleagues who included these conditions. Wender *et al* (1985) argued that it was important to exclude these conditions, but, more importantly, that it was important to get observer ratings from parents of the subject's behaviour in childhood. They observed that a proportion would rate themselves as previously hyperactive even though this had not been observed by their parents. This latter group did not respond well to psychostimulants. It is possible that the more rigorous process of separating subjects into those with and those without childhood symptoms on the basis of their parents' observations resulted in the positive findings of studies by Wender and colleagues compared with that of Mattes *et al* (1984), who used self-report measures

Psychopaths and amphetamine

There are two early reports of positive effects of amphetamine in uncontrolled studies with adult psychopaths (Hill, 1944*b*; Shorvon, 1947). Hill described experience of administering amphetamines to a large series of psychopaths in clinical practice. For eight subjects on whom he could maintain close observations over a four-year period, it was observed that those who tended to respond had "an aggressive, bad tempered and generally hostile tendency to interpersonal relationships, which is manifested wherever frustration is met". Response was most satisfactory in those capable of making warm interpersonal relationships, even if they usually wrecked them by their impulsivity and irritability. Other positive indicators for treatment included very deep sleep, nocturnal enuresis after the age of 11, excessive sexual appetite, and a family history of epilepsy or history of infantile convulsions. Hill observed that the best test was the subject's tolerance of amphetamines without affecting their sleep. Non-responsive patients included paranoid and schizoid personalities and "inadequate, passive, hysterical or neurasthenic personalities," where amphetamine would usually increase irritability, anxiety, and insomnia.

Influenced by Hill's clinical experience, Shorvon (1947) reported making "extensive use of the drug, in varying dosage, for adult psychopaths of the predominantly aggressive and predominantly inadequate types whose persistent abnormality of character generally showed itself in pathological emotionality, pathological or excessive sexuality, or asocial or amoral trends". He described uncontrolled studies with three subjects, an inadequate male psychopath and aggressive male and female psychopaths, who responded to 20–40 mg of benzedrine. In each case, mood swings, rage attacks, and irritability improved. Bed-wetting ceased in the inadequate male; and the female, who had become a prostitute, self-reported a reduced libido; Shorvon described her as previously "unable to control her sexual impulses and masturbation". The author recommended 20–45 mg, divided into twice-daily doses, and observed that sleep was rarely affected in those who responded to treatment. He also observed that although the depressive moods of psychopaths appeared to respond to benzedrine, there was little effect in true manic–depressives. However, he also reported a subgroup of psychopaths for whom the beneficial effects appeared to fade with time.

Amphetamine challenge

The possibility of a subgroup of personality disorders, unrelated to childhood ADHD but responsive to psychostimulants, is suggested by Schulz *et al* (1988) in an amphetamine challenge test with borderline personality disorder. Eight subjects were entered into a double-blind placebo-controlled trial. Five received amphetamine and placebo, three amphetamine alone. By measuring change according to global improvement and ratings on the Brief Psychiatric Rating Scale, it was concluded that some borderlines improved while in others the condition worsened, supporting the idea of considerable heterogeneity within BPD. Subjects with an additional schizotypal personality disorder responded adversely by showing more psychotic symptoms, suggesting that for this group psychostimulants may be contraindicated.

Stein (1992) has suggested that amphetamine challenge may be useful to identify patients' responses to other medications. This whole area appears unclear and undeveloped, but he cites studies which predict a response of depression to tricyclics (Deykin & Dimascio (1972), but not found by Akiskal *et al* (1980), imipramine (Fawcett & Siomopoulou, 1971; van Kammen & Murphy, 1979), and lithium (van Kammen & Murphy, 1979), and in schizophrenia to pimozide (van Kammen *et al*, 1982).

Comment

Psychostimulants prescribed at low dosage for behaviour disorders appear to be largely free of unwanted side-effects such as euphoria and the overactivity seen at higher levels. The widespread concern that giving stimulants to psychopaths will inevitably lead to problematic behaviour and increasing demands for more medication may have been exaggerated. More experience is clearly needed with psychostimulants on both an in-patient and an out-patient basis to provide clinical guidelines for the future. However, despite the clear-cut benefit that this medication conveys on children with overactivity, psychostimulants may only be useful in a small group of psychopaths. In those with schizotypal features it is probably contraindicated.

Experimental studies with borderline and schizotypal personality disorder indicate that there is heterogeneity within these conditions. Patients within the same diagnostic categories may show quite different responses. It is therefore important to recognise at an early stage of any study which patients are in fact showing a deterioration in their condition so that any benefits which are occurring in the responding group are not ultimately obscured in the final analysis. There is now strong evidence that adult subjects with attention deficit disorder, residual type, show a good response to psychostimulants. But subjects with these features appear to be relatively rare in clinical practice. The response of subjects with severe personality disorder, but without a history of overactivity in childhood, is an important area for future research.

Lithium

Aggression is sometimes a prominent feature of mania and will subside when the manic episode responds to lithium. However, it has become clear that lithium has additional and special anti-aggressive actions. Animal studies showed that lithium has an action on aggression when it is spontaneous or provoked by environment, drugs, or electrical stimuli, leading to considerations of its use for human subjects. There are reports suggesting that there will be a response in subgroups of people with personality disorder, emotionally unstable adolescents, some violent criminals, aggressive learning-disabled subjects, alcoholics, and patients with borderline personality disorder or who show borderline features. Table 4.8 summarises the major studies of lithium on behavioural disorder within a wide range of non-learning-disabled subjects.

Sheard and colleagues carried out two studies with prisoners. In an open, multiple cross-over study with 12 male delinquents, characterised by personality disorder and repeated impulsive aggressive behaviour, aggressive episodes decreased when sufficient lithium was prescribed for a high serum level (Sheard, 1971). But when this was allowed to drop below the therapeutic range the effect disappeared. An interesting finding in this study was that in delinquents whose aggressive behaviour appeared to be an integral part of their personality, reduction in aggression was associated with a concomitant increase in anxiety and depression. But in four individuals whose destructive behaviour was a source of anxiety to them, the reduction in aggression occurred without any increase in depressive affect or anxiety.

Tupin *et al* (1973) examined the effect of lithium on 27 male prisoners with patterns of recurrent violence who reacted rapidly to slight provocations. Several had a history of brain injury and non-specific abnormal EEGs. They had various psychiatric diagnoses. The largest group were explosive personalities, followed by a group having diagnoses of "schizophrenia" or "possible schizophrenia". It had been noted that phenothiazines had in the past reduced psychotic symptoms in the schizophrenics but had not controlled their violent behaviour. Observations of drug effect were based on reports from prison guards on rule infractions, changes in security classifications, reports from the prisoners themselves, and observations by psychiatric staff. There was a significant decrease in the number of disciplinary actions for violent behaviour on lithium compared with an equivalent time period before

Table 4.8

Trials of lithium for behavioural disorder in adults and adolescents (not mentally handicapped)

Authors	*Subjects*	*Method*	*Results*
Tupin *et al* (1973)	27 male prisoner; various diagnoses (most schizophrenia and explosive personality disorder); recurrent violence	Open study; lithium, 1800 mg (mean plasma level 0.82 mol/l)	15 (56%) marked decrease in prison interactions, 3 (11%) increase, 4 (14%) no change, 2 psychosis worsened
Sheard (1971)	12 aggressive delinquents in correctional institution	Open cross-over study; 12-month follow-up after release (4 weeks 0.6–1.5 mol/l, 4 weeks < 0.6 mol/l)	Serious aggressive incidents decreased only at higher dosage (no effect if non-serious incidents included)
Sheard *et al* (1976)	66 prisoners; serious offenders, chronically assaultive in prison	Double-blind placebo-controlled; 1 month drug-free then 3 months on lithium or placebo infractions – no change	Major infractions (assaults or threats) reduced to zero on lithium; rebounded on stopping lithium; minor
Rifkin *et al* (1972)	21 female adolescents; "emotionally unstable character disorder"	Double-blind, placebo; 6-week cross-over	14 improved on lithium, 4 on placebo, 3 no improvement (only within-day mood fluctuations significant)

the drug was started. Non-violent disciplinary actions decreased, but not by a significant amount. Of the 21 subjects who were judged to have improved, 16 had an abnormal EEG or a history suggestive of brain damage. In this study the dosage of lithium tended to be higher than is usual for the maintenance of manic–depressive illness, although the mean plasma level was only 0.82 mmol/l, leading Tupin and colleagues to comment that this group may handle lithium differently, or else be less cooperative about taking medication. They noted that the prisoners seemed subsequently better able to reflect on their potentially violent behaviour, but also observed that a reduction of aggression seemed to create significant psychic turmoil in many of their subjects.

In their second study, Sheard *et al* (1976) carried out a double-blind study in a correctional institution with young delinquent inmates with severe personality disorders. The main criteria for selection were convictions for serious aggressive crimes such as manslaughter, murder and rape, and a history of either chronic assaultive behaviour or chronic impulsive antisocial behaviour. Ages ranged from 16 to 27; and of 80 inmates starting the study, 66 completed it. Drug administration was preceded by a one-month drug-free period, followed by a random allocation over a three-month period to either lithium carbonate or placebo. Change during the study was assessed by the number of infractions of institutional rules – and divided into major infractions (which would consist of threats or actual assaults) and minor infractions (which were less serious institutional offences such as being in the wrong place or having contraband items). The decrease in number of infractions was significantly greater in the active drug group, but was restricted to major infractions. After discontinuation of lithium there was a rebound effect in the formerly aggressive subjects, who showed a resurgence of violent behaviour. The results of this impressive study confirmed those of open trials which have shown that lithium may be effective in reducing aggression in certain individuals with severe personality disorder.

In a study of female subjects, Rifkin *et al* (1972) administered lithium in a six-week, double-blind, cross-over trial to 21 adolescents having diagnoses of "emotionally unstable character disorder". The characteristics of this condition included mood swings, chronic maladaptive behaviour patterns, poor acceptance of authority, poor work record, manipulativeness, sexual promiscuity, and abuse of drugs. Mood swings were often reactions to environmental or interpersonal events. Of the 21 patients, it was judged that 14 were better on lithium, four on placebo, and three showed no improvement. However, the only significant observed change was that

TABLE 4.9

Trials of lithium on aggression in adult mentally handicapped

Authors	*Subjects*	*Method*	*Results*
Worrall *et al* (1975)	6	Double-blind cross-over trial	3 (50%) improved (2 neurotoxicity)
Dale (1980)	15	Open trial	11 (73%) improved, 3 (27%) no change, 1 (7%) worse
Tyrer *et al* (1984)	25	Double-blind cross-over	17 (68%) improved (socially withdrawn males less likely to improve)
Craft *et al* (1987)	42	Double-blind parallel group trial	73% of group treated with lithium improved

lithium was more effective than placebo in reducing the severity of mood swings.

Aggression in the learning disabled

Table 4.9 summarises the effects of lithium on aggressive behaviour in learning-disabled subjects, demonstrating that 50–73% of subjects show an improvement in aggressive episodes and self-mutilation. The cause of the behaviour in this group is unknown, but is presumed to be a mixture of brain damage and character pathology rather than affective disorder. Pooling the results of the three controlled trials in Table 4.9, Wickham & Reed (1987) found an overall response rate of around 70–75%, compared with a placebo response rate of 30%.

Craft *et al* (1987) concluded that lithium therapy is worth a two-month trial in any learning-disabled patient whose repeated aggression or self-mutilation is proving difficult to control. As virtually all such patients would be in hospital, the authors argued that the danger of lithium intoxication should be minimal when patients are carefully supervised. They recommended that serum lithium concentrations of 0.7–1.0 mmol/l should be aimed at for a clinical effect. Higher levels were associated with tremor and uncoordination in their subjects, and with neurotoxicity in the earlier trial by Worrall *et al* (1975), although Worrall and colleagues attributed the signs in their two patients to the combination of lithium and underlying brain damage. It was observed that most aggressive patients (possibly because they tend to be hyperactive) need more than 800 mg/day of lithium carbonate as a single daily dose to achieve therapeutic levels, and sometimes require as much as 3000 mg/day (Dale, 1980). Once therapeutic levels are reached, the clinical response is usually evident within 2–8 weeks. A controlled-release formulation, suitable for once-daily dosage (e.g. Priadel), is easier to administer to these difficult patients, and in long-term use is less likely to cause side-effects or renal changes (Plenge *et al*, 1982). Although Tyrer *et al* (1984) noted that male subjects who were socially withdrawn and had a high level of assaults were less likely to respond, Craft and colleagues cautioned against identifying subgroups of responders or non-responders within the current level of knowledge in case spurious findings should become accepted as dogma and patients who might respond to lithium should not be considered for such treatment.

Comment

Maintenance treatment with lithium is a promising development in the treatment of personality disorders, particularly where patients are explosive, impulsive, and emotionally unstable. This suggests that future trials should be carried out with selected groups of patients with borderline personality disorder. Lithium may also hold out some hope for the treatment of those with an antisocial personality disorder or high PCL–R score who show frequent aggressive outbursts. But the effective serum levels appear to be similar or occasionally higher than that which is required to prevent affective episodes in patients with manic–depressive psychosis. It is also possible that the optimum serum level will vary among individuals and will have to be determined for each patient. There are disadvantages in that lithium has side-effects which are poorly tolerated by some impulsive and emotionally unstable patients, although for many these will not persist. It may therefore be easier to stabilise such patients initially on an in-patient basis. For out-patients, additional education for family or supporters will be necessary. Furthermore, difficulties may arise with certain borderline patients who tend to form intense and sometimes oscillating feelings of idealisation and hostility towards a clinician, sometimes sabotaging the clinical trial. At the present time, the prediction of a good response in any individual or any category of personality disorder cannot be made with accuracy. However, patients with personality disorder who show impulsiveness, instability of mood, or unpremeditated aggressive outbursts should be given a trial of lithium, particularly if the effects of other treatment have been inadequate.

Towards a rational strategy for pharmacological treatment

As the pharmacological trials surveyed in this chapter have not demonstrated an effect on the 'core' features of psychopathic disorder, it is essential to have clear goals of treatment for these patients. Nevertheless, studies reviewed indicated that several compounds may convey considerable benefit on these patients. Certain goals of pharmacological treatment for psychopaths can also be derived from the data we examined. These include:

(a) treatment of associated axis II (personality disorder) comorbid conditions
(b) treatment of associated axis I (clinical syndromes) comorbid conditions
(c) treatment of associated syndromes and symptoms within the affective, anxiety, psychotic, or organic 'spectrum'
(d) the decrease of a specific vulnerability to symptomatic or cognitive decompensation, usually observed as a result of stress
(e) enhancement of the capacity for pleasure, normal social functioning, etc., in psychopathic patients.

Liebowitz *et al* (1986) have recommended that a careful clinical evaluation of patients with personality disorders should be carried out before any strategy of pharmacological treatment is formulated. They recommended that an initial out-patient assessment (or in-patient evaluation) should be scheduled to last at least 90 minutes. During this consultation, the mental health professional must take a very active role in obtaining the history of the present illness, psychiatric history, medical history, family history, personal history, and mental status. We have proposed that a full axis II evaluation should be carried out and that the Hare PCL–R should be completed as a minimum. Detailed questioning concerning possible affective episodes and fluctuations must be undertaken, with emphasis on whether the patient experiences unprecipitated mood shifts (either highs or lows), excessive mood reactivity (into dysphoric or hypomanic states), vegetative symptoms when depressed, or chronic hypersensitivity to criticism or rejection. It is also important to ask about spontaneous panic attacks and transient psychotic symptoms, and about minimal brain dysfunction and attention deficit disorder in childhood. A significant other in the patient's life should be interviewed, with the patient out of the room, to obtain another perspective. The biological work-up should always include an assessment of thyroid status to rule out occult thyroid disease and, where indicated, an EEG. If facilities permit, nasopharyngeal leads should be used to rule out temporal lobe epilepsy. Very careful attention to criminal history and previous behavioural disorder should be applied. Some impression should be gained of the extent to which behavioural disturbance follows fluctuations in mood or other symptoms, the extent to which the patient is able to exert control over the behavioural dysfunction, and the general attitude and perceived rationale for antisocial behaviour.

If a possible indication for pharmacotherapy is present, the patient should be started on an appropriate medication and the dose should be raised systematically. It is important that any medication is given a thorough trial before it is abandoned. If possible, medications should be increased to the maximum dose unless the benefit is outweighed by the appearance of side-effects. Trials should be carried out for an adequate length of time. Preparations which can be measured according to serum level should have these tests carried out when there is uncertainty over adequate dosage. Patients may need to be seen at short intervals in the initial stages of treatment, depending on their cooperation, to monitor progress and adjust dosage.

While the goals will vary according to an individual patient's particular problems, it is important in all cases to specify treatment targets prospectively. For example, goals could include the reduction of transient psychotic episodes, relief of agitation with low-dose neuroleptics, and reduction of autonomous mood shifts with lithium. However, given the current state of knowledge, it must be accepted that pharmacotherapy for psychopathic patients should be considered largely empirical or, as Liebowitz and colleagues have suggested in the case of personality disorder, "a mini experiment in which therapist and patient participate".

Table 4.10 summarises several proposed strategies that might be employed according to individual personality-disorder categories and associated behavioural and symptomatic syndromes. This table assumes that any individual patient will have had a full diagnostic

TABLE 4.10

Proposed pharmacotherapy for individual personality-disorder categories and associated syndromes

Category of personality disorder or associated syndrome	*Indication from research or diagnostic criteria*	*Empirical trial*	*Additional related circumstances*
Antisocial; PCL–R scores 30+	–	Psycho-stimulants	Carbamazepine or lithium for episodic behavioural dyscontrol
Borderline and affective spectrum	Low-dose neuro-leptic; lithium; carbamazepine; MAOI	Tricyclic; SSRI	Antidepressant for associated major depression
Schizotypal, paranoid and psychotic spectrum	Low-dose neuroleptic or neuroleptic with low sedation	–	Neuroleptics at recom-mended dosage for major psychotic episodes. Benzodiazepines for brief espisodes of psychotic anxiety
Schizoid	-	–	Low-dose neuroleptics for explosive reactions, intolerance of change, or dangerous fantasy life
Passive–aggressive	-	–	–
Narcisstic	-	–	MAOI for associated hysteroid dysphoric features
Avoidant and anxiety spectrum	MAOI; tricyclic; SSRI	–	Benzodiazepine for acute episodes of anxiety
Histrionic	-	–	MAOI for associated hysteroid dysphoric features
Obsessive–compulsive	-	–	Clomipramine for symptomatic obsessions and compulsions
Organic spectrum	Carbamazepine; lithium	Psycho-stimulants; low-dose neuroleptics	–

assessment of both axis I and axis II disorders. In column 2 of the table, the basis for inclusion of compounds is either the research that has been summarised above or the criteria inherent within the diagnostic category itself (e.g., the criteria for paranoid or schizotypal personality disorder which include psychotic-like features). Column 3 of the table indicates compounds that are not strongly indicated on this basis but where research or case reports in the literature have suggested that an empirical trial might be helpful in certain cases. The last column recognises that in certain circumstances additional psychopathology and behavioural disorder typically associated with the personality-disorder category may warrant a trial of an individual drug. Where more than one compound has been listed in a column according to an individual personality-disorder category, the order is according to preference based on the results of the studies surveyed above.

Conclusions

Measurement of change in the studies reviewed in this chapter could have been improved by more careful assessment of personality features and behavioural changes both before and after treatment rather than global assessments of whether the experimenter thought the subject had improved or not. Counting the frequency and severity of episodes of behavioural dyscontrol rather than attempting to measure subjective states such as impulsivity and aggressiveness, would have been preferable. Certain axis II categories such as borderline personality disorder lend themselves more easily to pre- and post-trial assessments, but few studies attempted to include such measures. Most importantly, Stein (1992) has argued that "the era of uncontrolled studies has passed and only placebo-controlled trials should now be undertaken" with personality-disordered subjects. Placebo effects may be substantial in psychopaths, some of whom may be highly suggestible and reactive to environmental circumstances.

Despite a paucity of studies on which to assess the potential pharmacological effect on 'core' features of psychopathic disorder, pharmacotherapy is one area of treatment that does show some considerable promise for the future. However, within the current state of knowledge this must still be seen as somewhat peripheral in the sense that the major treatment goals are largely directed towards associated axis II comorbidity, or symptomatic disturbance and associated behavioural disorder, that is not necessarily part of the 'core' condition. At the same time, however, the difficulties of carrying out future trials with psychopaths cannot be over-emphasised. Ethical difficulties of giving medication to detained subjects, collecting adequate numbers of subjects, deciding on the appropriate length of time for studying these unstable and unpredictable individuals, and difficulties in choosing suitable measures of change, have all deterred would-be researchers in this field. As many of the studies reviewed in this chapter have been carried out on out-patients or in-patients in ordinary psychiatric hospitals, it is likely that the conditions suffered by many of the subjects were not as severe as the conditions of the subjects in the studies which used different techniques and which we have reviewed in other chapters.

5 Physical treatment

Since the first attempts at a diagnostic description of psychopathy, some workers have asserted that brain abnormality is a major aetiological factor in psychopathic behaviour (Spellacy, 1978; Miller, 1988). Such views have supported the investigation of physical treatment of psychopathy, such as electro-shock therapy and psychosurgery.

Electro-shock therapy

Green *et al* (1944) reported on 24 "criminal psychopathic" prisoners (mean age 22 years) who were given petit mal electro-shock therapy on an average of 11 occasions. No diagnostic criteria for psychopathy are presented and no other treatment was given. Green *et al* reported that although patients volunteered for the treatment they "exhibited some uneasiness and apprehension". Immediately after treatment patients were described as "sleeping better and less nervous with emotional tone and rapport slightly improved". However, at six-month follow-up, objective clinical assessment rated only four patients as improved, seven as slightly or "doubtfully" improved and 14 as unimproved; thus the majority were unchanged by the experiment. In addition, electroencephalographic readings showed increased abnormalities for up to three months after treatment, although all returned to pretreatment level after six months. Although their experiment shows little effect of electro-shock therapy, rather than suggesting alternative methods of treatment, the authors recommended that further experimentation should be made with grand mal electro-shock.

More recently, research has shown how the comorbidity of personality disorder can obviate the efficiency of electroconvulsive therapy (ECT) for treatment of axis I disorders. Zimmerman *et al* (1986) reported on the use of ECT in 25 depressed patients, 40% of whom had DSM–III personality disorder diagnosed using a structured interview. These authors found a much poorer six-month outcome for depressive symptoms for those patients with personality disorder, although short-term response to ECT was similar in those with and without comorbid personality disorder. Patients with personality disorder were also eight times more likely to be readmitted to hospital in the following six months.

McCord (1982*b*) has reviewed electro-shock studies from the 1940s and notes that those which reported "beneficial" effects included many obviously non-psychopathic people among their subjects. McCord concludes that the lack of clear positive results is unsurprising, as the electro-shock therapy served only to reduce anxiety, which is not a problem for many psychopaths. However, despite McCord's conclusions, ECT may be useful in certain circumstances, such as when a psychopath develops a severe depressive illness, which may respond. Perry (1985) found that certain subjects with borderline personality disorder experienced "double depression" – discrete episodes of major depression superimposed upon chronic dysphoria. These episodes have been clinically observed in psychopaths by one of the authors (JC). During these phases there is an abrupt and apparently inexplicable regression, and the patients enter a phase of severe and frequent behavioural dyscontrol, with daily or almost daily suicide attempts and self-mutilation. Alternatively the regression can take the form of refusal of food and drink, cessation of any social interaction, and lying curled in a foetal position for long periods. ECT is often beneficial in breaking this cycle. Even though the effect may be short-lived, it can be life-saving, enabling the development of alternative treatment strategies.

Cold wet sheet packs

In one recent uncontrolled study, reported in the *American Journal of Psychiatry*, and carried out in a renowned American general psychiatric hospital between 1984 and 1986, therapeutic use was made of cold wet sheet packs, as an alternative to seclusion (Ross *et al*, 1988). The procedure consisted of wrapping the disturbed patient in a sheet soaked with cold water so that he/she is immobilised. Patients initially felt cold but warming was rapid due to vasomotor change. The patient was supervised throughout and could ventilate whatever was on his/her mind. The procedure might last up to two hours.

Of the 46 patients who received this therapy, 31 had diagnoses of DSM–III personality disorder. The authors claimed that 38 patients (83%) "benefited" in terms of an instant calming effect and facilitation of subsequent psychotherapeutic work. The authors suggested that the technique was preferable to drug sedation or seclusion as it had no side-effects. However, there remains the question of the punitive nature of this treatment when one reads that six patients (13%) needed more than 20 applications and one patient "showed no benefit although she had more than 50 packs during her stay".

Psychosurgery

Since the 1940s it has been frequently claimed that psychosurgery will successfully reduce aggressive behaviour in psychopaths. Most early reports are of single cases. Darling & Sandall (1952) reported that 17 of 18 "antisocial" maximum-security hospital patients "improved" one year after lobotomy, although no standard for improvement was given. However, there is a lack of consensus over the specificity of the approach, nor is it clear which procedures should be followed and which brain areas are the most effective targets for psychosurgery and which patients benefit. Kelly (1976), in a review of psychosurgery, argues that patients who have poor impulse control, psychopaths, alcoholics and drug addicts should not be considered for operation. However, there have been some uncontrolled studies claiming amelioration of aggressive or assaultive behaviour following psychosurgery.

Poblete *et al* (1970) reported follow-up of thalamotomy in 25 "aggressive patients in whom medical treatment proved unsuccessful". Five of these patients were suffering from a psychotic disorder; no diagnosis is given for the others. A "good" outcome at follow-up (after an average period of three years seven months) is described in seven patients (28%) as reintegration into home environment, lack of aggression, and independent productive social and personal activity. Six (24%) showed a minor improvement. However, 12 patients (48%) showed no change or had not been evaluated.

Balasubramanian & Rammamurthi (1970) reported on 100 patients with "behaviour disorders" mainly consisting of "uncontrollable destructive tendencies and acts of aggression". Features included assault (72%), breaking objects (31%) and self-harm

(16%). Following amygdalotomy, only 6% of patients were considered to have a good outcome in that they needed no further drugs and were able to mingle easily with others; 69% were described as "docile but given to occasional outbursts" or needed management with drugs; 16% showed no improvement; and 9% had died.

The most successful results of psychosurgery are claimed in patients whose psychopathy was clearly related to brain damage. Andy (1975) reported thalamotomy for six "psychopathic" patients who all had brain abnormality, either congenital or acquired through seizures or trauma. Follow-up was for between 1 and 11 years, during which time four subjects showed marked "sociologic improvement" in that they were maintaining jobs and three had married. Five had not needed medication since the operation. It is stated that there were no psychological changes in these patients, although the only assessment reported is IQ. However, the six patients reported are heterogeneous in terms of age, aetiology and length of their disorder. The six operations were carried out over a ten-year period, between 1961 and 1971, and no control groups were studied.

MacKay (1948) reported the results of leucotomy for the "treatment of psychopathic feeble minded patients" at Rampton Hospital. The 20 patients (14 women) were all classified as psychopathic by Cheney's criteria (Cheney, 1934): these include emotional immaturity, defect of judgement, not learning from experience, impulsive reactions and emotional instability. All these patients exhibited violent behaviour and emotional tension. At six months after leucotomy, 35% are described as markedly improved, 35% as improved and 25% as showing little or no change (one patient had died). However, the criteria upon which these judgements are based are not presented and the study was not controlled.

Summary

Cleckley (1952) suggested that, although lobotomy results in some irreversible loss of functioning, "the hopeless prognosis and severe disability of these cases justifies and indicates drastic therapeutic measures".

However, Falconer & Shur (1959) reviewed studies of psychosurgery and concluded that no generalisations could be made until long-term follow-up studies were available. Since then, there have been no long-term controlled trials of psychosurgery as a treatment for psychopathy or for aggressive behaviour and there is still no clear justification for its use. High mortality rates and the ethical dilemma of patients undergoing such operations involuntarily have restricted the use of this treatment and led to discontinuation of research into outcome of these approaches

Despite the inefficacy of physical treatment, there remains considerable discussion and investigation of the proposition that some antisocial behaviour is related to underlying abnormalities of brain function (Elliot, 1978; Tancredi & Volkow, 1986). The most commonly held view is that for some specific subgroups of patients the neurological impairment interacts with other psychosocial factors to place patients at risk for certain forms of antisocial behaviour (Mullen, 1984). Lewis (1988) has reported high rates of neurological deficits in American juvenile offenders sentenced to death for murder, and Schalling (1978) and Gorenstein (1982) have implicated frontal lobe and limbic system damage in some psychopathic behaviour. Nestor (1992) looked at neurological correlates of murder and extreme violence in 40 forensic in-patients, and found that younger patients were more likely to have a history of childhood conduct disorder and to have developmental disabilities on neuropsychological tests, whereas older patients were more often psychotic, with less neuropsychological disability.

Sellars (1992), in a preliminary study, compared ten personality-disordered male Broadmoor in-patients, of whom five scored as impaired and five as non-impaired on the Luria Neuropsychological Battery (Luria, 1980). At one-year follow-up, all of the impaired group were in a Special Hospital (including some transferred or readmitted), whereas four of the non-impaired group had been discharged and remained outside the Special Hospital system.

However, despite the continuation of neuropsychological research into psychopathy, most recent studies suggest that their findings offer implications for assessment of risk and of dangerousness rather than having major implications for treatment approaches.

6 Psychotherapeutic approaches

The psychodynamic approach to psychopathic disorder emphasises personality structure and development, and views antisocial behaviour as an expression of the underlying personality disturbance. Therapy aims to provide insight for patients, allowing them to understand their feelings and address maladaptive defence mechanisms. Increased self-esteem and self-control come about from enabling the patient to accept responsibility for his or her own actions. The therapeutic relationship plays an essential part in this process and forming a trusting alliance with patients is an essential factor if they are to remain in therapy.

Many therapists have suggested that psychotherapy is contraindicated in psychopathy and in antisocial personality disorder (ASPD), and that its presence is indicative of a poor treatment outcome. As early as 1947, Bender stated that "psychopaths' inability to enter into any relationship makes therapy or even education impossible," while Kernberg (1975) has noted how "there is nothing new in mentioning the absolutely hopeless prognosis for the analytic treatment of antisocial personality disorders". Conte *et al* (1991) have shown how the presence of personality disorder affects compliance with psychotherapy, focusing on the lack of capacity to form a therapeutic alliance. However, others disagree with this view. For example, Gerstley *et al* (1987) have shown that some patients with antisocial personality disorder are able to form a therapeutic alliance and benefit from therapy. They suggest that within the category of antisocial personality disorder, patients are not uniformly lacking in the ability to benefit from therapy.

Psychodynamic therapies have been used in treating psychopathic disorder both in individual and group settings. However, the difficulties of dealing with a personality-disordered client on an individual basis, particularly the client's ability to manipulate the therapist and feign improvements, have led most therapists to suggest group therapy as the most pragmatic approach. In group settings defensive tactics are more readily confronted by the therapist and other patients, and the group may have less toleration of attempts at manipulation (Carney, 1972; Borriello, 1979).

Many psychotherapists consider that holding a psychopathic or personality-disordered person in out-patient therapy is extremely difficult. Drop-out rates are high; therefore, therapy in a residential setting is often the treatment of choice (Frosch, 1983; Marcus, 1987). As discussed in Chapter 9, psychodynamic therapies are often an important component of the 'milieu' therapy approach, and a variety of psychotherapeutic approaches within a treatment milieu have been described (Cox, 1986; Gallwey, 1992). In addition psychodynamically oriented group therapy is often a major element of the Therapeutic Community model.

However, there are very few reports of the efficacy of the independent use of psychotherapy for psychopathic patients. Those independent psychotherapeutic treatments which have been studied are discussed below.

Out-patient psychotherapy

As noted above, engaging personality-disordered patients in out-patient therapy is a difficult task and often only achievable when clients are on probation or under court orders of treatment (Sadoff *et al*, 1971). The paucity of literature on the subject is one indication of how infrequently out-patient work is attempted. However, Lion & Bach-y-Rita (1970), in a clinical report, described how a good outcome of out-patient group therapy resulted from self-referred male voluntary patients with "impulse character disorders" and "borderline individuals with paranoid and/or psychopathic features".

In an uncontrolled study, Reckless (1970) reviewed the psychotherapeutic out-patient treatment of 21 young women who presented with problems of antisocial and disturbed behaviour. These were middle-class women of above-average intelligence treated with combinations of individual and group psychotherapy in a Canadian private practice. Thirteen patients were in 'enforced' treatment and were required to move to the local area and obtain jobs or training while attending the treatment programme. The women's living expenses were subsidised by their families on condition that attendance at therapy sessions was maintained. Reckless describes the women as either true 'sociopaths' or 'pseudosociopathic' with a degree of emotional maturity and capacity for growth, although this is an unsupported clinical judgement. He reports that the 16 pseudo-psychopathic women tended to remain in individual therapy longer, gave up their antisocial activities and maintained their jobs or studies after treatment. The five sociopathic women stayed in group therapy as long as the other subjects, but tended to drop out of the individual sessions sooner.

Despite the lack of empirical follow-up measures, Reckless's study does demonstrate that it is possible to maintain some sociopathic types, namely middle class, intelligent women, in out-patient therapy. Although a degree of 'enforcement' was necessary, it seems that group therapy had a better holding effect than an individual approach. However, these tentative findings should not be generalised to other subject groups.

Carney (1977) described an uncontrolled follow-up study of out-patient group therapy for aggressive personality-disordered male offenders. Patients were on probation with a condition of treatment and attended the group for an average of 13 months. At nine-month follow-up there were significant improvements on the probation officer's ratings of the men's community adjustment, and the recidivism rate was 28%. However, no significant changes were found on psychological tests, including the Minnesota Multiphasic Personality Inventory (MMPI). Carney suggests that even though the therapy did not alter personality it did control violent behaviour in these men.

In one of the largest controlled trials of sociopathy and psychotherapy outcome, Woody *et al* (1983) randomly assigned 110 non-psychotic male opiate addicts, 45% of whom met DSM–III criteria for antisocial personality disorder, to individual sessions of (a) drug counselling alone, (b) supportive–expressive psychotherapy and drug counselling, or (c) cognitive–behavioural therapy and counselling. A variety of psychological questionnaires were completed (SCL–90, BDI, Maudsley Personality Inventory) and measures of substance abuse, criminal behaviour, medical problems and employment were devised. Therapy continued for six months. At one-month follow-up, all subject groups had improved on some measures. There were no significant or pervasive differences between the two psychotherapy groups but both had improved significantly more than the group who had only had drug counselling, and both psychotherapy groups had used less medication than the other group in the study period.

Woody *et al* (1985) went on to investigate the effect of DSM–III antisocial personality disorder diagnosis and depression on outcome of psychotherapy in 62 subjects from their earlier study (age range

18–55 years). Improvement following therapy was greatest for the subjects with opiate addiction alone, who showed positive changes on 16 of 22 criteria (11 of which were significant at $P < 0.05$). Positive changes on all measures were shown by the group with depression and opiate addiction (nine of these changes were significant), and by those with concomitant antisocial personality disorder. Changes in the latter group were related to drug use and psychiatric symptoms (anxiety and depression). The group with antisocial personality disorder and opiate addiction but no depression had the worst outcome, with significant improvement on only three measures, which were related to drug use and illegal activity.

Woody *et al* conclude that although drug counselling may reduce drug use, it is not beneficial to employ psychotherapy to treat opiate-dependent patients who have antisocial personality disorder only. However, it should be noted that on average each patient had only 11 psychotherapy sessions. Most clinicians who advocate psychotherapy for ASPD patients would recommend a much longer course of treatment, and so these results cannot be generalised to longer-term psychotherapy.

Group psychotherapy has been used in community settings with specific offending categories such as sex-offenders. Cook *et al* (1991) report their experience of a group for non-violent recidivist adult sex offenders subject to probation orders in the community. Over a ten-year period, 55 men attended the group; of these, 33 'completed' treatment (median 22 months), 11 attended for some time (median 6 months) but dropped out against advice ('default' group) and 11 never engaged, attending only a few times. The authors found that, after a median follow-up time of over four years, significantly more of the 'default' group committed further offences (72% v. 27% of 'completed' group and 18% of 'non-engaged' group). However, the three groups were not comparable on criminological variables. The 'non-engagement' group seemed to be less severe offenders, having fewer juvenile and adult convictions, and fewer men who had served a prison sentence. The 'default' group had committed significantly more previous sexual offences and non-sex-related crimes than the other two groups, which suggests they would be more likely to reoffend. However, if only those 26 men who had previously served a prison sentence are considered, the 16 men in the 'completed' group had a significantly better outcome in terms of recidivism than the ten who did not engage or dropped out ($P < 0.05$).

Sadoff *et al* (1971) investigated whether American offenders' attitudes to enforced group psychotherapy were related to outcome.

As a condition of probation, 43 convicted sex offenders were ordered to have group therapy and attended weekly sessions for an average of 40 weeks. To evaluate the programme, the patients were asked about their attitudes towards the group experience. The treating psychiatrist and an independent psychiatrist were asked to predict recidivism. Contrary to expectations, it was those offenders who expressed most favourable attitudes towards the group therapy who were most often re-arrested in the following two years. The independent psychiatrists did not predict this recidivism, as the prognosis they made was positively correlated with the offenders' attitude to therapy, which was in turn negatively related to outcome. The treating psychiatrists did accurately predict recidivism and this prognosis was negatively correlated with patients' positive statements about the groups ($P < 0.05$). Sadoff *et al* suggest that offenders who fail may not have sufficient capacity to express critical or negative attitudes to therapy and that the group therapists could see through any false kudos attributed to therapy. In contrast, the independent psychiatrists, with no experience of the patients, were easier to 'con'. These findings may have some implications for forensic psychiatry settings where evaluation of treatability is based on an individual interview.

In-patient psychotherapy

Some authors are pessimistic about the use of psychotherapy, even within structured hospital environments. For example, Stein & Brown (1991) report on group therapy with forensic patients who had committed violent crimes and were serving indeterminate sentences in a Canadian maximum-security hospital. They noted the inability of their patients to form a cohesive group or to develop the group dynamics which help other types of patient (Yalom, 1975). However, although 23% of their patients had a diagnosis of DSM–III–R antisocial personality disorder and 16% had other personality disorders, 53% of the group also had a diagnosis of psychosis. It may be that the heterogeneity of the sample diminished the possibility of group cohesion.

Other reports of psychotherapeutic treatment of psychopathic personalities in hospitals are limited to single case studies or descriptions of the regime. For example, Kaila (1972), in a clinical report, documents the case of a young woman with antisocial personality disorder who was successfully treated with intensive psychotherapy in a secure hospital ward in Finland.

Psychotherapy with delinquent adolescents in secure institutions

There are several reports on the efficacy of psychotherapeutic approaches with adolescent 'delinquent' subjects in secure institutions. Persons (1966) considered 82 young male offenders (aged 15–19) in a reformatory. These were 41 pairs pre-matched for age, intelligence, race, social class, current offence, previous convictions, and length of time in institutions. Boys were randomly assigned to no treatment or a combination of twice-weekly group psychotherapy and once-weekly individual therapy for 20 weeks. All subjects were tested with the MMPI and an anxiety scale and delinquency questionnaire at the beginning and end of therapy time. There were no significant group differences at initial testing. After 20 weeks, the treated group had improved significantly more than the untreated group on the anxiety and delinquency scales and on 9 of the 13 MMPI subscales. In addition, the therapy group had significantly fewer disciplinary reports in the study period ($P < 0.01$) and they obtained passes giving them more freedom sooner than the untreated group ($P < 0.01$). No long-term follow-up is reported and so it is unclear how long these improvements were maintained.

In another randomised controlled study, Truax *et al* (1966) assigned 70 institutionalised delinquent girls (aged 14–18 years) to twice-weekly group therapy for three months, or to a no-treatment condition. Success was measured by changes in attitude and social functioning, using the Minnesota Counselling Inventory (MCI), and a Q-sort technique, and also by the girls' subsequent ability "to get out and stay out of an institution" during a one-year follow-up period.

Results showed significantly better outcome for the subjects receiving group therapy, in that they spent significantly more of the subsequent year outside institutions (55% v. 40%; $P < 0.001$) and showed a significantly greater improvement on the MCI family relationship scale ($P < 0.01$) and the emotional stability scale (which indicates the delinquency-prone response) ($P < 0.05$). However, the mean post-therapy scores of the treated group would still classify them as delinquency-prone on this measure. On the Q-sort tests, the treated group showed greater improvement in self-esteem and self-adjustment.

Another evaluation of group psychotherapy for adolescent girls was carried out at a borstal in New Zealand (Taylor, 1967). Forty weeks before their discharge date, 22 girls were randomly assigned either to weekly psychoanalytically oriented group therapy sessions or to no treatment. Another group of 11 girls who were already having counselling, within the institution, was also used for comparison. Self-ratings, staff ratings and personality tests were used alongside data on recall and reconviction after discharge. On follow-up, 26 weeks after discharge, Taylor found some significant improvements in all groups. However, the group therapy subjects had improved significantly on more personality, attitudinal, and behavioural measures than the other two groups. There was no difference in the number of girls reoffending in the groups: Taylor notes that this was partially due to two girls in the experimental group carrying out their frequently stated intention of returning to crime, and that these two would have been excluded from therapy had this been a clinical and not an experimental study. However, the members of the experimental group who were reconvicted committed less serious offences than those for which they had been sentenced to borstal. The recidivists in the other two groups carried out more serious offences. Overall, it seems difficult to claim any great success of group therapy from this study, given the psychological improvements in the untreated sample, the lack of difference in recidivism and the very short follow-up period of only six months.

Redfering (1972) compared attitudes of female delinquents who had 11 weeks of brief group counselling with those who had the usual institutional treatment. The counselling group showed significantly greater positive effects in terms of attitudes towards self, peers and parents. At one-year follow-up (Redfering, 1973) attitudes to the self and parents continued to be significantly more positive in the counselling group. In addition, more of the counselling group had been released from the institution (94% v. 40%), although there were no differences in the proportions of each group who had gained employment after release.

Psychotherapy with adults in prisons and secure environments

Persons (1965) randomly assigned 12 male offenders (age 22 years) "with a record of a diagnosis of sociopathic personality" to 20 sessions of individual 'eclectic' psychotherapy over a ten-week period. Self-report questionnaires measured psychopathy (Personal Experience and Attitudes Questionnaire, PEAQ; Applezweig *et al*, 1958), delinquency (Peterson's Delinquency Scale; Peterson *et al*, 1959) and anxiety (Taylor Manifest Anxiety Scale; Taylor, 1953). Post-treatment results were compared with results from 40 untreated controls. Initial scores of the two groups did not differ, but a significant effect of therapy ($P < 0.001$) was shown on all outcome variables (PEAQ, delinquency and anxiety) after treatment. The therapy group had significantly fewer disciplinary reports during therapy but no long-term analysis of the psychological or behavioural changes was made.

Gough (1948) has presented a sociological theory of psychopathy in which it is postulated that manifest behaviour symptoms are due to defective socialisation processes – deprivation in close emotional relationships, which provide little opportunity for identification with others and development of appropriate social roles. Maas (1966) suggested that modification of developmental defects would not necessarily arise from the use of verbal media, but that participation in new behaviour accompanied by emotional involvement might bring about change. She developed a group treatment programme which combined action procedures, such as psychodramatic techniques, with more conventional group psychotherapy. Maas reported on the use of this 'actional group psychotherapy' with a group of 46 'sociopathic' women prison inmates (aged 25 years) in California who scored below the cut-off point on Gough's socialisation continuum. Women were randomly divided into two groups, one of which had a three-month course of twice-weekly group therapy. At the end of therapy, the treated group showed significantly greater improvement on the Block Ego-Identity index, a measure of consistency in reactions to other people (Block, 1961). Maas suggests from her clinical experiences that actional procedures are a useful adjunct to group psychotherapy, but the study does not report any long-term follow-up of her subjects.

In one of the largest psychotherapy outcome studies with adults, Jew *et al* (1972) evaluated group therapy with 257 male personality-disordered offenders in an American prison who were treated between 1958 and 1962. All subjects were given psychoanalytically oriented group therapy for a minimum of a year (average 18 months) for eight hours a week. These men were matched on criminological and demographic factors judged to relate to recidivism with 257 men also in the prison at the same time, who did not receive therapy. The groups were not matched for psychological characteristics, as the treated men were chosen for treatment primarily because of their psychological disturbance. The rate of parole revocation during their first year on parole for treated men was significantly lower than for the untreated offenders (24% v. 40%; $P < 0.05$). However, on four-year follow-up, the difference in number of returns to prison disappeared (54% v. 40%). Jew *et al* suggest that the lack of support facilities for paroled men may have been critical for the reoffending. They refer to two unpublished studies which support this assertion, and they suggest that more follow-up treatment programmes for parolees could be instigated to help prevent relapse.

Kozol *et al* (1972) report on combined group and individual treatment of "dangerous psychopathic offenders" in a special diagnostic and treatment centre in the USA. Firstly, 592 convicted male offenders were assessed. Of these, 304 (51%) were judged not dangerous and released to the community after their sentence, while 226 (38%) were considered dangerous and were ordered by the courts to attend treatment on an indeterminate sentence. A further 49 (9%) were released by the courts against the advice of the assessment staff. The treatment involved an "individualised approach", with a specific psychotherapeutic treatment plan for each inmate: 65% attended group therapy; 85% received individual therapy, and 67% had both. Some men had more 'intensive' treatment than others, and half had more than two hours per week of therapy sessions over an average of 43 months. Outcome data on new offences of serious assaultive crimes were considered after an average post-release follow-up of 43 months. The 'non-dangerous' group had a serious recidivism rate of 8.1% which was slightly higher than that of the treated men (6.1%). Both rates were significantly lower than that of the men released against advice (35%). Kozol *et al* assert that dangerousness can be reliably diagnosed and treated in such an individualised programme. However, they had no measure of psychological changes in their study and their naturalistic design made it impossible to used matched study samples.

Summary

Reports of out-patient psychotherapy are mostly of enforced or imposed treatment (Reckless, 1970; Carney, 1977) and have shown some limited success. Sadoff *et al* (1971) have demonstrated how offender patients who declared enforced group psychotherapy to be most useful had a worse outcome than those offenders who had more negative attitudes towards therapy. Although Lion & Bach-y-Rita (1970) suggested that a good outcome could come from voluntary treatment, this was an uncontrolled clinical study. Woody *et al* (1983, 1985) have shown, in a randomised controlled trial, that both supportive–expressive psychotherapy and cognitive–behavioural therapy can effect changes in drug use, depression and anxiety in opiate addicts. However, those whose addiction was associated with antisocial personality disorder had a worse outcome than other diagnostic groups.

In-patient trials have shown some success in randomised controlled studies of male and female adolescents producing initial improvements in attitudes and behaviour (Truax *et al*, 1966; Persons, 1966; Taylor, 1967; Redfering, 1973). Although adult studies have produced some promising results in terms of recidivism (Jew *et al*, 1972), all are limited by methodological shortcomings. Most studies are limited by very short follow-up periods; although significant effects of treatment are found at six months or a year after therapy or release, those studies which have gone on to follow their subjects for longer periods find the effect diminishes over time.

It may not be surprising that findings are so limited, given the short-term therapy applied in these studies. In the reports reviewed above the out-patient treatment was given for 6–22 months, and in-patient therapies were administered for between 10 weeks and 18 months. Only Kozol *et al* (1972) studied a period of prolonged therapy (43 months) in their prison sample. Sellars *et al* (1992) have noted that psychodynamic psychotherapy with personality-disordered patients will have to be long term. They state that "it is intuitively logical that if an individual has experienced many years of disorganisation, trauma and distress, that it will take a significant amount of time to deal with this effectively".

It is well established in other areas of psychotherapy that some continuation of support or contact after treatment can prevent relapse (Lacey, 1983; Garfield & Bergin, 1986). The importance of after-care to patients is demonstrated in a report by Taylor (1963). He described how released prison inmates, who had experienced group therapy during their time in prison, requested that a similar group be formed which they attended voluntarily after release. Anecdotally he reports how these men had relapsed less often after release. However, no empirical studies have considered the after-care needed to maintain any improvements following psychotherapeutic treatment.

7 Cognitive and behavioural approaches

It is most often a particular antisocial feature of behaviour that brings the psychopath to the attention of the forensic or health care services. It is not surprising, therefore, that a number of interventions have been developed which specifically address the behavioural components of psychopathy. Blackburn (1992) notes that the development of behavioural interventions for mentally disordered offenders has paralleled the development of behavioural treatments throughout mental health services. Certainly, several interventions that focus upon specific features of behaviour have been developed in custodial and health service settings, and 'milieu approaches' may incorporate cognitive and behavioural techniques into their programmes (e.g. Grounds *et al*, 1987).

In line with their underlying philosophy, behavioural and cognitive–behavioural programmes usually focus upon a specific deficit, such as social skills, or a particular behavioural feature or offence category, such as assaultive actions or sex offending. It is rare to find a cognitive–behavioural programme developed for psychopaths as a diagnostic group. However, the features focus upon in cognitive–behavioural therapy may be those commonly exhibited by 'psychopaths'.

Howells (1976) describes a skills training programme for aggressive offenders in a Special Hospital and programmes for sex offenders have been developed in secure settings (e.g. Perkins, 1991). Howells (1986) has also reviewed the sparse literature available on the use of social skills training with violent offenders: although some results are encouraging, he states that conclusions must be tentative, given the preliminary nature of many studies.

Similarly, in his review of relaxation and desensitisation training, Howells (1988) concludes that the sparse literature suggests that some modification of anger and violence is possible.

Turkat & Maisto (1985) used a single-case experimental design to investigate cognitive–behavioural treatment of personality disorders. They found that although individualised programmes were successful for some personality disorder categories (avoidant, dependent, narcissistic, paranoid), patients with antisocial and borderline personality disorders either were not interested in beginning treatment or terminated therapy prematurely. However, Davis & Booster (1988) have described a successful multifaceted cognitive–behavioural treatment approach with an extremely violent patient with a history of arson and substance abuse in an American maximum-security forensic hospital. Although other individual clinical reports exist, very few long-term follow-up studies are available. In addition, it is difficult to know which other aspects of the treatment milieu, in in-patient settings, may be contributing to long-term improvements. Dell & Robertson (1988) noted that, of 106 legal psychopaths detained in Broadmooor Hospital for an average of eight years, 22% had attended a social skills group, 6% had been in relaxation therapy, 4% in sex behaviour modification programmes and 6% in anger control sessions. This indicates that no 'standard package' of cognitive–behavioural therapy is prescribed for psychopaths in at least one Special Hospital. (See Chapter 9, on in-patient milieu therapies, for further discussion of this point.) Some reports which have investigated behavioural and cognitive approaches, employed as the sole or primary means of therapy, are discussed below.

Behavioural programmes

Behaviour modification as a generic term refers to the theory and techniques in the tradition of Pavlov, Wolpe and Skinner. The central axiom is that behaviour is controlled by environmental rewards and punishments, and that if one can identify and change these rewards and punishments then the behaviour related to them will also change. Clinical theory thus focuses upon specific problem features of behaviour, rather than psychological states; the objective is to change these behavioural features through identifying and modifying the circumstances which provoke and maintain them; outcome is then measured with clear behavioural referents. In contrast to psychotherapeutic approaches, the emphasis of behaviour therapy is on the current environmental antecedents and consequences of behaviour.

The majority of reported behavioural programmes have been used in treating adolescent delinquents (for a review see Gross & Brigham (1980)). Although some of the behavioural features targeted are similar to the antisocial behaviour seen in psychopaths, generalisation from delinquent adolescents to personality-disordered or psychopathic adults must be tentative.

Cohen & Filipczak (1971) used a token-economy method which emphasised academic, social and self-help skills in an American institution for 13–19-year-old offenders. They report follow-up of 41 boys after an average of eight months. The treated boys showed academic improvements which were maintained over three-year follow-up. However, although the treated group had less reoffending in the first two years, after three years their recidivism rate was similar to that of a group of non-treated boys.

Scott-Johnson (1975) describes a programme for young offenders at the Kennedy Youth Center, West Virginia, USA. The centre's philosophy was based upon a 'decentralisation of authority'. In particular, custody/treatment lines of authority were blurred by incorporation of custody and therapeutic work under a single administration. Custody staff were assigned counselling rather than custodial responsibilities. The centre is described as a minimum-security institution, like 'a college campus'; each living unit had a 'treatment team' assigned and there were no cell blocks, fences or guns. Male and female offenders were separated in different treatment units. The male offenders were further divided into four subgroups, the individuals within a subgroup being deemed to have common characteristics which required a certain therapeutic approach. This division was based upon groupings (called behavioural categories) devised by Quay (1964*a*) from factor analysis of behavioural observations and case-note data. Members of the four groups are broadly described as:

(a) impulsive and immature, with interpersonal relationship difficulties
(b) neurotic
(c) unsocialised aggressives – manipulative people with no capacity for guilt or relationship formation
(d) 'normal' delinquents – who had incorporated social norms and could form relationships, but these norms and relationships were those of a deviant subculture.

Subjects in the different behavioural categories were exposed to different models of treatment designed to meet the needs of the behaviour and personality types involved; these were respectively:

(a) transactional analysis emphasising a Therapeutic Community model
(b) group and individual counselling
(c) behaviour modification and behavioural contracts
(d) 'reality therapy' using confrontation groups, exposure to 'pro-social' organisations, and other group tasks aimed at developing group identity and responsibility.

However, a token-economy system was employed in each unit whereby the offenders gained points for good behaviour which could be swapped for various privileges.

Scott-Johnson (1975) quotes an unpublished conference paper by Minor & Wotkiewicz (1970) which evaluated the outcome of the behaviour modification for the 'unsocialised aggressive' behavioural category. The group improved academically during their stay, with 57% passing high-school equivalency in a year. Ingram *et al* (1970) also note a decrease in assaultive of this group during the programme. However, despite this claimed success, the behavioural programme was discontinued to allow space for an increasing population of female juvenile offenders in the centre, and in 1972 the behavioural category classification and differential treatment system was discontinued.

Cavior & Schmidt (1978) report outcome for 402 young offenders discharged from the Kennedy Youth Center. The sample was 74% white, with an average age of 17.8 years. Subjects had been arrested on average 4.2 times (s.d. 3.3) and had served on average 10.4 (s.d. 5.2) months in detention. Three release groups were identified by classification of the type of release from the institution – parole, mandatory release, and escape or disciplinary transfer. Overall, 63.2% of offenders were paroled (which is taken as an indicator of a good outcome), 12.2% had mandatory release at expiry of their sentence, and 24.6% escaped or were transferred to another unit. There was no significant difference between the proportions in the three treatment groups who obtained parole.

Outcome after release for 281 subjects was measured in terms of whether or not they returned to prison for at least 60 days in the subsequent 36-month period. Overall, 165 offenders (58.7%) were not returned to prison in the subsequent 36 months. The 'success' rates for the four behavioural categories were: (a) 66.2%; (b) 57%; (c) 64.5%; and (d) 51.6%. The differences between the proportions of 'successes' in the four groups were not statistically significant ($X^2 = 4.28$; d.f. = 3; $P = 0.23$).

Cavior & Schmidt (1978) then compared these findings with those from a group of 488 young offenders detained in another US medium-security unit. These subjects were also classified by the behavioural categories of Quay (1964*a*) but they were not offered any specific treatment programme. Overall, 284 offenders (58%) from the medium security unit gained parole; this proportion was not significantly different from that in the Kennedy Youth Center ($X^2 = 2.2$; d.f. = 1; $P = 0.12$). At three-year follow-up, 57.8% of those released from the medium-security unit had not been returned to detention; again this was not significantly different from the Kennedy Youth Center results. Analysis of outcome by behavioural categories also showed no difference between the two institutions.

The results are disappointing in that they fail to show a positive effect of the treatment programmes on reincarceration. However, the inmate populations of the two institutions are not directly comparable and the study takes a very crude measure of success. No data on recidivism which did not result in reincarceration are presented, and it is impossible to judge the effect of the programme on other aspects of offending behaviour, psychological factors and interpersonal relationships.

Hendrix & Heckel (1982) attempted to modify the social behaviour of 15 male adolescents held in an American maximum-security unit with a two-week training programme for 'positive attention behaviour' (PABs). They postulated that if the adolescents' social behaviour to others was more positive, they would receive similar reinforcement in return. External raters judged that, after two weeks, the number of PABs emitted and received by the experimental group in social interactions did significantly increase. The increase was significantly more than for a randomly selected untrained control group of 15 subjects. However, the effect was not sustained over time, and no attempt was made to relate changes in PABs to amelioration of other features of antisocial behaviour.

A behavioural programme for disruptive adolescents in England was reported by Moyes *et al* (1985). A group of 78 male and female adolescents with "behaviour and/or personality disorders of an antisocial type" (including aggressiveness, self-mutilation, theft, absconding and disruptive behaviour) followed a programme using token economy, social skills training and individualised contingency management. There was a comparison group of 63 adolescents accepted for treatment but not admitted. However, there were some differences between the treated and untreated groups. Significantly more of the comparison group had previously been in a borstal and more of the treatment group had previously been in psychiatric hospitals, had out-patient therapy, abused drugs and had sexually related offending or behaviour problems. At two-year follow-up, the treatment group showed significantly less physical aggression, fewer temper outbursts and less self-mutilation, and significantly more of the treated adolescents were living independently outside institutions. However, the improvements did not relate to future offending behaviour. Although there was no difference in the number of police involvements with the groups after two years, significantly more of the treated group were subsequently involved in court cases.

Colman & Baker (1969) describe in detail a ward programme for delinquent US military recruits which employed an operant-conditioning model. The subjects were 48 soldiers (average age 20 years) who were "diagnosed as having character and behavior disorders by the ward psychiatrist .... Homosexuals, addicts and alcoholics were excluded from the sample." Among the subjects, 23 had made suicidal threats or gestures, four had displayed "homicidal behavior", four had psychotic-like states, and the remainder were admitted for "a range of behavioral problems, often admittedly manipulative in nature". Subjects were randomly assigned to the operant-conditioning ward or to "traditional hospital treatment", which is not described. The average stay on the operant-conditioning ward was 16 weeks, during which courses on military strategy and protocol were taught, formal and informal education and social-skills groups were held, and work tasks were carried out. Participation in tasks and groups was voluntary, but would gain 'points' which could be converted into 'privileges' such as TV, pool, food or authorised absences. Points were deducted, or extra tasks given, following rule violations.

Participation in the programme was voluntary, and all but two of the 48 men completed their admission. The 46 who completed therapy were followed up three months or more after discharge: seven had completed their service and 25 were functioning in their unit (total 70%) whereas 14 (30%) were either administratively discharged, under military arrest or had gone absent without leave and were considered to be failures. Of the 46 men in the comparison group, one had completed duty and 12 were still with their unit (total 28%), while 33 (72%) were discharged or under arrest. Although these initial results indicate the superiority of the operant-conditioning model, no long-term outcome is reported.

Another study of US military personnel is reported by Jones *et al* (1977) who treated soldiers who had diagnoses of "character or behavior disorders", in a token-economy ward. The men were randomly assigned to the treatment group, which received (16 weeks' experimental treatment (51 subjects), or to a comparison group, which was discharged back to duty (27 subjects). Individual agreements were contracted with the men in the treatment group, and reinforcement was with points awarded for such things as appearance, work and educational achievement. The points could then be used to buy food, free time or access to recreational facilities. Comparison with untreated controls 14 months after completion of treatment showed that significantly more of the treated group returned to active duty (80% v. 52%; $P < 0.05$).

Levey & Howells (1990) review studies of behavioural and cognitive programmes for reducing anger and aggression in forensic patients. Very few of these studies focus upon psychopaths as a diagnostic group; however, the authors do cite examples of successful applications of relaxation and social skills training for modifying anger. They report one unpublished British study by McGurk (1980), who found a significant decrease in aggression at six-month follow-up of a group of violent prisoners following desensitisation training. However, there was no demonstrated effect upon subsequent reconviction rates for violent offences.

Cognitive–behavioural approaches

Cognitive–behavioural therapy involves the questioning of an individual's maladaptive or irrational thoughts and providing new cognitions to replace them. It is inferred that thoughts, feelings and behaviour are inherently interlinked, and that through changing a maladaptive cognition the maladaptive behaviour will also be extinguished.

Stermac (1986) reports a study of a cognitive–behavioural anger-management training programme with 40 American male offenders undergoing residential assessment for the courts. Most of the patients (70%) had diagnoses of personality disorder and all had a history of aggressive behaviour; none were psychotic. The modal diagnosis was antisocial personality disorder, although no details are given of how this diagnosis was made. Subjects were randomly assigned to treatment or a control group. The two groups did not differ on measures of age, IQ, educational level, marital status, diagnosis, previous psychiatric or criminal history, or index offence.

The control group attended psychoeducational sessions in a didactic model while the 'treatment' group followed an anger-management programme based upon Novaco's model (Novaco,

1975). After six training sessions the patients showed a significantly reduced score on the Novaco Provocation Inventory ($P < 0.001$) and showed modification of cognitive coping strategies ($P < 0.01$). Both groups showed reduced impulsivity; the degree of reduction did not differ between the groups. However, the long-term effects upon behaviour were not measured, thus the long-term durability of changes is unknown.

Valliant & Antonowicz (1991) employed a cognitive–behavioural group programme with 53 Canadian male offenders in a maximum security jail. A battery of psychological tests was given, which included the Minnesota Multiphasic Personality Inventory, IQ tests, Coopersmith Self-Esteem Inventory, Speilberger State–Trait Anxiety Test and a hostility inventory. After a five-week programme the inmates demonstrated higher self-esteem and lower state anxiety. However, there were no other significant effects. No comparison groups were studied, but assaultive inmates did show less change than those with no assault histories. The authors suggest that this is because aggressive behaviour is admired in prison settings and therefore it is more difficult to alter the faulty cognitions relating to aggression.

Cognitive therapy

It is important to distinguish cognitive–behavioural approaches, which are typically focus upon specific response tendencies and would not claim to treat the entire personality disorder, from cognitive therapy approaches, which are by contrast more comprehensive psychotherapeutic strategies (e.g. Beck, 1976; Beck *et al*, 1979). Cognitive therapists work at the dual level of symptom structure (e.g. manifest behavioural problems) and underlying schema (inferred psychological structures). Beck & Freeman (1990) have described cognitive therapy theorists as sharing with psychoanalytic theorists the view that it is most productive to identify 'core' problems and structures in treating personality disorders. However, in contrast to psychoanalysts, cognitive therapists see the 'core' structures maintaining the dysfunctional behaviours and feelings as being in the realm of awareness and accessible to consciousness.

Beck & Freeman (1990) describe what they see as the pertinent issues in the development of antisocial personality disorder and 'sociopathy' and outline a clinical application of cognitive therapy to antisocial personality disorder. They discuss the view of the 'sociopath' as having a developmental delay in moral maturity and cognitive functioning; in particular, they note Kagan's description of the sociopath's concrete thinking and inability to hold another person's point of view alongside their own (Kagan, 1986). On this basis they suggest that treatment of sociopathy might best be guided by encouraging greater awareness of the rights and feelings of others while aiding the patient towards independence and maturity. They summarise the approach as attempting to improve moral and social behaviour through enhancing cognitive functioning rather than by inducing shame and anxiety.

Beck & Freeman (1990) present three detailed case examples of successful cognitive therapy with a female and two male clients suffering from antisocial personality disorder. However, these are presented in a clinical context and no experimental research findings have been reported by these authors. Blackburn (1992) also describes in detail a single case history of an extremely successful cognitive therapy programme for a psychopathic man in an English Special Hospital. Individual cognitive therapy, social skills training, sex education groups and covert sensitisation were used, viewing his deviant behaviour as part of long-standing cognitive, affective and social dysfunctions. Thomas-Peter (1993) reports on another single case history – that of a sadistic offender treated successfully in a high-security hospital with a programme including cognitive techniques. This man continued with out-patient cognitive therapy in the community after release.

Summary

The short length of this chapter reflects the dearth of studies which have examined the efficacy of cognitive–behavioural approaches for psychopathic disorders. Blackburn (1992) suggests that this may reflect the antipathy of some behaviour therapists to personality constructs. However, the studies reviewed above do present some evidence that cognitive–behavioural approaches can ameliorate certain aspects of behaviour which are relevant to the personality-disordered offender in the short term.

Some initial reduction in recidivism has been noted in young offenders; however, in some studies the effects are not maintained in the long term (Cohen & Filipczak, 1971), and more often studies have not even attempted to evaluate any long-term outcome (Stermac, 1986; Valliant & Antonowicz, 1991).

In-patient behavioural programmes have shown behavioural improvements, which were maintained on follow-up, for 'character disordered' soldiers (Colman & Baker, 1969; Jones *et al*, 1977).

However, it is not clear how these findings would generalise to adults with psychopathic disorder.

Several of the cognitive programmes described above are very short-term (Stermac, 1986; Valliant & Antonowicz, 1991). Thomas-Peter (1989) points out how short-term cognitive–behavioural interventions may not be sufficient to effect changes in personality-disordered patients and that five- or ten-week programmes will probably not work in the long term. Although it has been noted how patients with antisocial personality disorder are difficult to engage in cognitive therapy (Turkat & Maisto, 1985), when longer-term cognitive–therapy is conducted individual case reports are promising (Beck & Freeman 1990; Blackburn, 1992; Thomas-Peter, 1993). Thomas-Peter (1989) emphasises that although there has not, to date, been any conclusive evidence for the treatment of 'psychopaths' with cognitive therapy, there is also little evidence to the contrary. No controlled trials of cognitive therapy have been applied to psychopaths, although other work suggests that cognitive therapy may be effective with offender rehabilitation (Garrett, 1984; Ross & Fabiano, 1985).

Most cognitive–behavioural approaches attend to a specific aspect of behaviour or attitude (such as aggression, or social skills) and do not claim to treat the entire personality disorder of the patient. Therefore, it may be unfair to judge these interventions in this light. Cognitive–behavioural approaches which lead to some reduction of maladaptive and disruptive behaviour may have greatest value for the short-term management rather than long-term treatment of psychopaths. Levey & Howells (1990) note that other, more traditional, hospital methods of controlling aggression and violence (such as seclusion, restraint and sedation) also have a limited short-term effect, with no more evidence for efficacy in reducing long-term violence.

8 Therapeutic Community approaches

The Therapeutic Community (TC) has its origins in the changes occurring after World War II in psychiatric hospitals, which emphasised a move away from an authoritarian doctor–patient model to a more democratic style of staff and patient interaction, including, importantly, more active participation of the patients in their own treatment. Thus, responsibility for the day-to-day running of a Therapeutic Community is shared among patients and staff. This collaborative and democratic style, whereby the community itself is invested with an important decision-making function, forms a cornerstone of therapy (Jones, 1953). Main (1983) suggests that it is not, however, "the structure, but the culture which is decisive for the human relations on offer" and that the TC is a "culture of enquiry ... into personal and interpersonal and inter-system problems" including "the study of impulses, defences and relations, expressed and arranged socially" (Norton, 1992*a*).

Through a relaxing of the staff–staff and staff–patient hierarchy and the collaboration of staff and patients in a wide range of activities, all interactions and relationships in the community can be examined. The aim is that such enquiry will lead to a better understanding of deviant or unhealthy previous behaviour (re-enacted within the treatment setting), which may then result in altered interpersonal behaviour and improved psychosocial functioning. An important aspect of TCs is that membership of the community and engagement in therapy are voluntary. In order for the community to function and social order to be maintained, the members must feel that they have actively chosen to collaborate in the regime. The voluntary nature of TCs does not necessarily preclude their existence within secure settings: although members may not wish to be incarcerated, TCs can be provided as a voluntary option within that incarceration.

Therapeutic Communities have been established to treat psychopathic or personality-disordered offenders, in public health service hospitals, secure hospitals and prisons in Britain and abroad. There are several descriptive accounts of TC treatment in these settings (Kiger, 1967) and there seem to be more writings on TC models for treating psychopaths than on any other treatment modality. However, in common with other treatment options for psychopathic disorder, controlled research studies are rare. The empirical studies addressed below can be broadly divided into two types: those which consider change in behavioural and psychological characteristics of patients during TC treatment and those which consider long-term outcome after leaving TC treatment. Studies of TCs in health service settings, secure hospitals and within the prison system are discussed below.

Health Service Therapeutic Communities

Although the TC model was developed in Britain from the work of two British psychiatrists (Jones and Main) within the British National Health Service, today there is only one TC that specialises in treating patients who are psychopathic or have severe personality disorders. This is Henderson Hospital (see below). Other TCs are found in public health services throughout Europe and North America.

Henderson Hospital, UK

Henderson Hospital was the first British unit to develop a patient-oriented approach to the treatment of psychopathic disorder. It began as a social rehabilitation unit in 1947, using a group-analytic approach with 100 patients. In 1959 the unit was renamed Henderson Hospital (after Professor D. K. Henderson, author of *Psychopathic States*, 1939) and it offered combined psychotherapy and sociotherapy in a TC milieu. The TC programme at Henderson has been described at length in several books and papers (Jones, 1953, 1962; Rapoport, 1960; Whiteley, 1980; Norton, 1992*a*,*b*). Since it opened, Henderson has only accepted voluntary admissions, although initially 10–20% of admissions came directly from the courts or prison. By 1966 the proportion of forensic referrals was 30% (Taylor, 1966). At the present time, about half the patients admitted to Henderson have a history of adult convictions and 20% have served a prison sentence (Norton, 1992*b*). At any one time Henderson treats up to 29 patients (equal numbers of women and men) suffering from severe personality disorder. A study in 1992 showed that, of 168 referrals, 61% met the DSM–III–R criteria for antisocial personality disorder and 87% had borderline personality disorder (Dolan *et al*, 1992*a*). A survey of 24 current residents in 1991 found that on average they each met six DSM–III–R personality disorder diagnoses (Dolan *et al*, 1992*b*).

In an early study of outcome, Rapoport (1960) considered outcome of 64 patients one year after discharge. Patients were personally interviewed and classified according to very basic criteria as 'improved', 'same', or 'worse' than when they entered the unit. On these criteria, 41% of patients discharged were considered improved, 28% unchanged, and 31% worse. The improvement rate increased with length of stay on the unit, with a good outcome reported for 52% of those who stayed more than 200 days. However, the mode of evaluation was far from satisfactory. It was based solely upon clinical judgement, with no objective measurement and no control sample.

Tuxford (1961) studied 86 consecutive male probation and borstal licence cases for up to 22 months after discharge. Sending a postal questionnaire to the probation officer, she obtained a response rate of 84% and found that 61% of patients traced were free of conviction on follow-up. Adjustment was assessed on a scale from 1 (increased sense of responsibility, employment, and no further offending) to 4 (further offending, unemployment, and lack of responsibility). On this rating, 24% fell into the first category and 31% into the second (i.e. 55% showed improvement). However, 28% were in the poor outcome category and a further 17% were considered complete failures.

Taylor (1966) reports a similar good outcome in terms of the employment history of patients discharged between 1959 and 1961. Approximately one-quarter (22%) found their own employment and a further 47% were placed by the Disablement Resettlement Officer (DRO). Those placed by the DRO were followed up nine months later and 60% of those traced were still in work and were given a satisfactory report by their employer.

Whiteley (1970) followed up 112 consecutively admitted male patients. These men are described as suffering from psychopathic or sociopathic disorder, with no psychosis or organic mental illness. In total, 87 (71%) had previously been convicted, 52 (42%) had served a prison sentence and 57 (47%) were on probation at admission; 66 (55%) had had a previous psychiatric admission.

The men were studied two years after discharge; information was obtained on all but 14 men (two of whom had emigrated). Information was gained from the Criminal Records Office and the Ministry of Health Psychiatric Index, and 63 of the men (51%) were followed up by personal interview. In total, 45 patients (40%) had no further psychiatric admission or conviction at two-year follow-up. Of those men with previous convictions, 43.6% remained free of conviction after two years. Of those who had previously been admitted to a psychiatric hospital, 57.5% remained out of hospital over the two-year period.

Whiteley (1970) also examined factors associated with outcome. He found that good prognostic factors were school achievement, holding a job for more than two years, higher social class occupation, ever having been married, and affective disorder. Factors associated with bad prognosis were having previous convictions, having more than two convictions, penal commitment, probation order at referral or admission, current court proceedings, and institutionalisation before age 15 years.

A subsequent study (Copas & Whitely, 1976) followed up two cohorts, of 104 and 87 male patients, to develop prediction equations for successful outcome. As with Whiteley's earlier study, outcome criteria of recidivism and readmission were used. Two-year follow-up established that 42% and 47% of the respective cohorts had no reconviction or readmission. Five-year follow-up information was collected on the cohort of 104 and showed that 33.6% of men were completely free of conviction or admission and that 11% had only one very minor relapse in the first year but had been free of conviction or admission in the following four years; therefore a total of 44.6% could be considered to have good outcome at five-year follow-up. Analysis of those factors predictive of recidivism and readmission found that the effects of age and martial status were negligible, but that previous criminal and psychiatric history were poor prognostic factors.

All of the above outcome studies from Henderson suffer from lack of a control or comparison group and thus it is impossible to judge whether the improvements found can be attributed to the TC treatment. However, Copas *et al* (1984) replicated the above studies in a five-year follow-up study comparing 194 male and female patients treated at Henderson against 51 patients referred to Henderson who were not admitted. According to diagnoses made by their referrers, all subjects were diagnosed as psycho_pathic, sociopathic or personality disordered. Further diagnosis of psychopathy was based upon history factors and extensive psychometric testing (O'Brien, 1976). O'Brien describes a typography of four groups of psychopaths based upon the direction of hostility and level of anxiety shown by subjects, as follows:

(a) neurotic (N), showing high anxiety and intropunitiveness
(b) extrapunitive neurotic (EN), showing high anxiety and extrapunitiveness
(c) intropunitive psychopath (IP), showing intropunitiveness and low anxiety
(d) psychopath (P), showing low anxiety and extrapunitiveness.

Success was considered to be no psychiatric admission or conviction in the follow-up period. At three-year follow-up, 41% of discharged patients were free of both admission and conviction, compared with 23% of the non-admitted group. At five-year follow-up, the proportions were 36% and 19% respectively. Three-year success rates for the N, P and IP groups were similar (48%, 44%, 49%) but there was a lower success rate for the EN group (29%). This pattern was also found in the non-treated sample, success rates for N group (32%), P group (25%) and IP group (25%) being higher than for the EN group (8%). However, as numbers in these groups were small, conclusions must be guarded. The effect of gender was negligible, with overall success rates for men of 36% at three years and 32% at five years, and for women 38% and 34% at the same times.

Further analysis showed that the success rate improved with length of stay: 62% of those admitted for six months and 71% for those who stayed over nine months did not reoffend or get readmitted to hospital in the following three years. Five years after discharge the success rates were still good, at 57% and 65% respectively for six- and nine-month admissions. This compares with a 19% success rate at five years for subjects who were referred but not admitted.

It must be noted that patients not admitted for treatment are not a satisfactory control group: 50% of this comparison group were assessed for admission and rejected; the remainder did not attend the assessment, did not attend for admission, or were imprisoned or admitted to hospital elsewhere. Therefore, differences between the two groups, particularly those factors leading to non-admission (e.g. motivation to change) may have an important influence upon the findings.

A recent questionnaire study (Dolan *et al*, 1990) used the Symptom Check-List (SCL–90–R; Derogatis *et al*, 1975) to investigate psychological factors related to acceptance and rejection at admission assessment for Henderson, and found that the selected clients reported less somatisation, less phobic anxiety, and fewer obsessional symptoms, than the rejected group. The two groups did not differ on scores of anxiety, depression, interpersonal sensitivity, psychotic symptoms, hostility, or paranoid ideation.

All the above outcome studies from Henderson Hospital take employment status, reconviction, or readmission to hospital as their main criteria of success. Although these life events are important indicators of social integration, mental health and offending behaviour, they are, at best, crude measures. The last two are, more accurately, only indicators of future service use, and psychological or psychiatric status cannot be evaluated using only subsequent hospital admission data. Similarly, reconviction data do not inform about psychological state and do not even take account of those people who reoffend but are never charged or convicted.

However, two outcome studies from Henderson Hospital do complement findings from these earlier reports of behaviour change by considering the effect of TC treatment upon psychological factors. Norris (1985) used a repertory grid technique to measure changes in 103 patients during treatment at Henderson Hospital (70 men and 33 women) on five parameters: self-esteem; percept of self; percept of ideal self; aspirations regarding rule-breaking; and independence. After three months, 60% of Henderson patients were judged as less rule-breaking, 75% reported feeling more independent, and 45% had increased self-esteem. In total, 59% of patients were assessed as 'benefiting' from therapy, in that they improved on at least three of the five measures above. Norris then compared Henderson Hospital subjects with clients in two other institutions. The proportion of the Henderson sample who benefited was significantly greater than in a group of subjects in a detention centre and a group in a voluntary trust community. However, the three subject groups were heterogeneous samples and direct comparison is limited.

More recently, Dolan *et al* (1992*c*) reported on 62 subjects with severe personality disorder who were followed up for an average of eight months after discharge (response rate 65%). Results showed a highly significant reduction in symptomatic psychological distress, as measured by the SCL–90–R questionnaire. The reliability and clinical importance of the changes in individual subjects were shown on the global SCL-90-R scale: 55% of subjects had improved reliably, and in 32% the improvement was also clinically significant, whereas only 6.5% of subjects had deteriorated reliably. No control group was included in this study and thus it cannot be

TABLE 8.1
Summary of outcome studies from Henderson Hospital

Study	*No. of subjects*	*Follow-up period*	*Criteria of success*	*Success rate*	*Description of sample*
Rapoport (1960)	64	1 year	Improved clinically since admission	41%	Discharged men
Tuxford (1961)	86	2 years	In employment	55%	Men discharged
			No recidivism	61%	on probation or borstal licence
Taylor (1963)	?	9 months	In employment	60%	Discharged men
Whiteley (1970)	112	2 years	No recidivism	44%	Discharged men
			No readmission	58%	
			Neither of above	40%	
Copas & Whiteley (1976)	104	2 years	No recidivism	42%	Discharged men
	87	2 years	or	47%	Discharged men
	104	5 years	readmission	34%	Same 104 as above
Copas *et al* (1986)	194	3 years	No recidivism	41%	Discharged men and women
		5 years	or readmission	36%	
	51	*3 years*	*No recidivism*	*23%*	*Non-admitted controls*
	(controls)	*5 years*	*or readmission*	*19%*	
Dolan *et al* (1992*d*)	62	8 months	Improved psychological functioning on SCL–90–R	55%	Discharged men and women

ascertained whether the improvement found in this sample could not also be found in less intense treatment or even with no treatment at all. However, the referral process at Henderson Hospital makes it unusual for patients to be admitted in acute crisis and therefore it is unlikely that the above findings are a simple result of regression to the mean. A second study (Dolan *et al*, 1992*d*)looked at factors related to length of stay at Henderson Hospital and found that, although length of stay was not significantly related to outcome, there was a tendency for those who stayed longer to improve more on psychological symptoms. In addition, those patients who showed the greatest changes in SCL--90–R scores during the first three months of admission stayed significantly longer in therapy. Gender was also significantly related to length of stay, with women staying longer in the community.

The outcome studies from Henderson Hospital are summarised in Table 8.1. The three studies which measured recidivism and readmission have remarkably consistent findings in that an overall success rate of around 41% is found at two years and there is a slight drop to around 34% at five years. These rates are much better than those of the untreated controls in one study; also, recidivism is much less than the criminal recidivism rate for general offenders in Britain. The studies using objective measures of recidivism and readmission are complemented by the studies of psychological states and subjective well-being and all show improvements following therapy. However, the patients with severe personality disorder who are treated at Henderson are only those who, at the time, do not need secure containment and who are able to engage in voluntary treatment (although 20% will have been in prison and 10% in secure hospitals previously). The TC treatment offered at Henderson has greatest efficacy for those who stay longer in therapy and this model is not so successful for those with little motivation to engage in treatment, or the one-third of admitted patients who drop out of treatment within the first three months (Dolan *et al*, 1992*d*).

Balderton Hospital, UK

An early investigation of adolescent psychopaths remains one of the few studies to compare the outcome of two alternative approaches to treatment by randomly allocating subjects to each (Craft *et al*, 1964). The Balderton Hospital experiment was begun by Craft and colleagues in 1959. The subjects of the study were 50 male adolescent psychopaths meeting the following criteria: (a) aged 13 years or over; (b) having offended; (c) personality disorder of such an extent such as to induce community officials to request in-patient treatment; (d) IQ over 55; and (e) no psychosis. The age range of the subjects was 13–25 years, and all were on probation with a condition of residence or transferred from approved schools.

Subjects were allocated on an alternate basis to two voluntary treatment wards. The first offered intensive group therapy with self-government in a model described as generally following "the programme offered by Henderson Hospital, but, it soon developed its own code of behaviour". The second ward provided individual treatment of a more authoritarian, hierarchical style with strict rules and a disciplinary programme. Three years after discharge treatment outcome was evaluated on four factors:

(a) recidivism
(b) employment record
(c) clinical recovery
(d) residual neurotic symptoms.

In addition, a Minnesota Multiphasic Personality Inventory (MMPI) assessment was made.

There were no significant demographic or psychological differences between the subjects on the two wards, but those on the group therapy ward had committed significantly fewer property offences and more sexual offences than those on the authoritarian ward. Length of stay varied from less than a month to 18 months, with six patients staying less than three months (four from the group therapy ward).

The boys on the authoritarian ward tended to have a lower mean IQ score on admission, but this improved significantly during treatment and was similar to that of the group therapy boys at discharge. There was little evidence of changes during treatment on other psychological measures. Only one significant difference was found on the MMPI, the group therapy boys showing a decrease in social introversion. The authoritarian group did show a more positive test-taking attitude. Fourteen months after discharge, 24 of the 25 in each group were traced. Overall, 14 (58.3%) of the group therapy subjects and 11 (45.8%) of the authoritarian subjects had reoffended (six boys and two boys respectively had been in custody). Although the difference in proportion of reoffenders was not significant, the group therapy subjects had committed significantly more offences than the subjects from the authoritarian regime (27 v. 14 offences; $P < 0.05$). Three from the authoritarian ward and six from the group therapy ward had needed readmission to hospital. Most of the subjects had held a job since discharge, with the group therapy boys tending to have a better work record, although no statistical difference was shown.

Craft *et al* (1964) conclude that the most important single result from their study is the smaller number of offences on follow-up from the authoritarian ward. However, in evaluating this finding, one should also note that the number of reoffenders in the two groups did not differ significantly, and that twice as many of the group therapy subjects dropped out of treatment before three months. However, on the basis of these findings the Balderton group therapy unit was discontinued and Craft went on to set up another authoritarian treatment programme for psychopaths (see Craft (1968) in Chapter 9, p. 183).

Harperbury Hospital, UK

Miles (1969) studied the effects of a TC on the interpersonal relationship of a group of 40 psychopaths in a hospital for learning-disabled patients. A psychopathic unit was established for male, mostly adolescent, offenders. The study considered changes during stay in hospital and aimed to investigate whether the TC treatment improved one major psychopathic trait – the inability to form satisfactory personal relationships. The 40 patients in the TC were compared with 20 psychopaths treated in the general hospital setting. Although the groups were not matched, after the initial admissions patients were allocated alternately to the two treatment settings. The groups had similar mean age (21.7 in TC v. 19.6) and IQ (86.8 in TC v. 84.1). No information is given on how psychopathy was diagnosed; however, 83% of the sample had criminal convictions, the remainder being "violent and unmanageable".

Aspects of interpersonal relationships were examined using qualitative methods (a sociometric questionnaire) by means of individual interviews with the patients on admission and after one year of treatment. Four aspects examined were:

(a) acceptance and rejection of each other
(b) friendships and reciprocity in the choice of friends
(c) informal friendship groups
(d) leadership.

Miles found that the TC group increased in their ability to accept peers twofold, and were less isolated after one year. In contrast the control group showed some slight increase in acceptance, but also increased their rejection of some fellow patients. The TC sample were found to form friendships and show leadership more than the hospital group.

Ullevål Day Hospital, Norway

Since the early 1960s Ullevål Hospital has pioneered TC therapy in Scandanavia: a day hospital has operated since 1981 catering for both personality-disordered and neurotic patients (Vaglum *et al*, 1982).

Vaglum *et al* (1990) considered 97 patients (28 men, 69 women) admitted to the day hospital from a defined inner-city catchment area. DSM–III–R personality disorders were diagnosed on the basis of a two-week clinical assessment and case-note material. Following Millon & Everly (1985), 52 patients were classed as severely personality disordered (SEVPD) and exhibited multiple personality disorder (PD) morbidity (borderline PD, 44; schizoid PD, 21; paranoid PD, 6; antisocial PD, 7). These were compared with the other patients, of whom 23 had other PDs (OPD) and 22 had no personality disorder (NOPD).

Patients' subjective experience of psychological distress was assessed using the SCL–90 questionnaire at admission and discharge. An independent rater evaluated pathology on the Health and Sickness Rating Scale (HSRS). There was no difference in length of stay of the three groups (mean 5.5 months), although 77% of patients considered to be treatment 'drop-outs' were from the SEVPD group. Overall, there was a significant improvement in subjective symptom level following treatment and the degree of this improvement did not differ between the diagnostic groups. However, the proportion of subjects who scored in the non-patient range on the SCL–90 was significantly higher in the NOPD group (60%) than in the OPD group (22%) or the SEVPD group (40%). The positive change on the HSRS scale was significantly greater for the NOPD than the SEVPD groups, with 73% and 10% respectively scoring in the non-patient range.

One important aspect of the study is that axis I disorders (in the main, anxiety, substance use and phobias) are controlled for, allowing the effect of personality disorder to be assessed. The study then confirms other reports that patients with concurrent personality disorder do less well in treatment than those with no personality disorder. However, it should be remembered that the outcome measures are more related to the outcome of the axis I disorder, and no attempt was made to assess changes in the personality disorder following therapy. It is important to note that researching in the real world, it was impossible for the authors to control for the fact that almost one-third of the 52 patients with SEVPD dropped out or were discharged from treatment prematurely. Therefore we do not know if their outcome would have been better had they remained in treatment. The reader remains keen to know whether these findings at discharge are maintained at follow-up and the second paper addresses this.

In the second paper, Mehlum *et al* (1991) give longer-term follow-up results for 80 of these patients for an average of three years after admission and show that the improvement (in mean SCL–90 and HSRS scores) at discharge was maintained at follow-up for all diagnostic groups. However, those patients with borderline PD and schizotypal PD had a significantly higher rate of readmission to hospital than other groups (57% v. 20%). Social adjustment improved significantly in patients with no personality disorder and those with 'cluster C' personality disorders, but there was no improvement in social adjustment in those with borderline PD or schizotypal PD. Although the results in terms of changes in neurotic symptoms are encouraging, again it is unfortunate that no follow-up measures of personality pathology are reported, as it would be valuable to know the longer-term effect of the treatment upon axis II personality disorders as well as upon the axis I neurotic symptoms.

Karterud *et al* (1992) investigated whether the TC day-hospital model employed represents an adequate level of treatment containment for decompensated patients with personality disorders. They note how in-patient treatment of personality disorders has often been the treatment of choice, as it was thought that only hospital admission could provide the containment of self-destructive acting-out behaviour and flight from treatment. Using the Moos ward atmosphere scale, they showed that the unit was characterised by high levels of autonomy, problem orientation, anger and aggression but low levels of order and organisation. This is a typical profile for an insight-orientated programme. Containment was indicated by the low levels of suicide attempts ($n = 2$), psychotic decompensation ($n = 2$), and transfer to other units ($n = 2$) found during the admission of 97 consecutive patients. Around one-third (32%) of patients stayed less than three months in treatment and 22 patients (23%) were discharged prematurely after breaking rules or left against medical advice. The paper concludes that the containing capacity of a day-hospital TC is substantial and that day-hospital treatment may reduce the need for long-term in-patient treatment.

Therapeutic Community units in British prisons

Research from three British prison institutions which embrace a TC philosophy in dealing with offenders. Grendon Underwood Prison is the one which is most true to the TC model espoused by

Maxwell Jones, and the entire prison is divided into wings, each of which is run as an individual TC. Wormwood Scrubs Annexe (for sex offenders and drug addicts) and Barlinnie Special Unit (for difficult-to-manage prisoners) are both units within the parent prison which have run modified versions of a TC model.

HMP Grendon Underwood, UK

In 1962, Grendon Prison was opened offering "a Therapeutic Community approach to the psychiatric treatment of non-psychotic recidivist offenders with moderate to severe personality disorders" (Gray, 1974). Grendon is unique in the British penal system in that inmates are referred specifically for psychiatric treatment and must be willing to cooperate with the regime. All inmates are 'voluntary', i.e. free to return to an 'ordinary' location on request. Men are received into an assessment unit where those unsuitable for treatment are filtered out. The assessment unit also allows inmates to have a slow induction to the regime and to the alternative ways of relating to staff and other inmates. Following assessment, inmates are randomly allocated to the four treatment wings (for a description of the assessment process, see Woodward, 1991).

Gray (1974) noted that the importance of group values and the social structure at Grendon is reflected in the fact that in its first 11 years of operation there were no major incidents, such as escape or episodes of serious violence. For some years Grendon has had the lowest prison offences rate of any security establishment, and during a 3.5-year period no night sedation or tranquillisers were required on the wing for disturbed young offenders (34 men, aged 18–21).

Changes during treatment at HMP Grendon

Gunn *et al* (1978) considered psychological change in 80 inmates between admission and discharge (or after 15 months, whichever was sooner). Using the MMPI they showed a significant reduction in neurotic features (depression and anxiety) and in social introversion and hostility. There was a significant increase in extraversion and ego strength. The men also completed the General Health Questionnaire (GHQ) on admission and after nine months in Grendon and again a significant decrease in pathology was found. The decrease in GHQ score was significantly greater than the change recorded in a random sample of male prisoners in 'ordinary' prisons over the same period. The change in inmates' attitudes to authority figures (police, prison staff, etc.) was measured using semantic differential scales and again a significant improvement in the positive evaluation of authority figures was found over nine months. In addition the men's self-evaluation improved significantly during their admission.

Sleap (1979) used the Goal Attainment Scale (GAS) to evaluate how inmates changed under the Grendon regime. This technique requires observable treatment goals, stated in concise operational terms to be elicited from the client on beginning therapy. These goals are later re-evaluated with the client, and the level attained is noted to indicate how therapy has progressed (Kiresuk & Sherman, 1968). At assessment, goals were set for all men which related to violent behaviour, educational achievement and reconviction. Additional goals concerning specific problems were set for individual inmates.

Initially, 356 inmates were evaluated. Of these, 209 were still at Grendon and re-evaluated 6 months after admission, and 94 were available for evaluation at 12 months. There was a significant improvement in overall scores at both 6-month and 12-month follow-up ($P = 0.001$). The change between the initial score and the six-month scores was the most dramatic, with a lesser though significant change thereafter. Despite the sample size at follow-up being reduced, there was no difference in initial GAS score between those who were transferred out of Grendon before the follow-ups and those who remained. It did not seem, therefore, that those who remained had dissimilar goals in treatment. Although there was greater variance in follow-up scores than in initial scores, the results indicate the beneficial effect of the therapy process at Grendon and bear out the clinical impression that initial improvement is often rapid.

Two studies have considered changes on the Hostility and Direction of Hostility Questionnaire (HDHQ) during inmates' stay at Grendon. Newton (1973) studied 211 men on intake and release and found lower scores on the total hostility scale and on the intropunitive hostility scale on release. The difference tended to be greatest for the men not reconvicted, but this was not statistically significant. Miller (1982) considered six-month HDHQ retest results of 83 inmates and, similarly, reported a fall in total hostility score. Miller also noted that, on the Eysenck Personality Questionnaire (EPQ), psychoticism and neuroticism scores fell, while extraversion was increased and locus of control became more internal. The men also appeared more able to take responsibility for their own behaviour. Miller summarises his findings concerning the first six months of therapy at Grendon as showing that men become more outgoing and less worried and that some antisocial attitudes are challenged. However, he cautions against these attitudinal changes being taken as evidence of behaviour change without further research into how they relate to outcome.

Follow-up studies of treatment at HMP Grendon

Although psychological changes during treatment have been measured, the difficulty in obtaining self-report from men after release has meant that most follow-up studies from Grendon have focused upon recidivism as the measure of 'success'.

The first follow-up study from Grendon considered the first cohort of men to be treated there, who were released in 1964 (Grendon Psychology Unit, 1966). Sixty-one men were followed up 18 months after release. They had been at Grendon for between one and 23 months on sentences of six months to seven years. Twenty-one had a previous psychiatric history and 18 were transferred back to other prisons. Progress was assessed by personal interview and contact with the probation or parole officer. Overall, 13% were described as 'settled' (had a secure home, had been in work for six months and had no reoffending); 15% were 'improved' (may have reoffended but had not been sentenced to prison, were working or receiving National Assistance); 12% were 'satisfactory' (for at least one year their parole officer had heard of no incidents involving them); 34% were in prison having reoffended; and 23% were untraced.

All men sent to Grendon from 1964 to 1966 were followed up by Newton (1971) one to five years later, and subsequent convictions were noted. When Grendon inmates were compared with samples of men from Wormwood Scrubs Prison, there was no difference in the reconviction rates at one-year follow-up, with approximately 40% of each group reconvicted within a year. Matching for previous convictions still showed no difference between samples.

There was a tendency for those who stayed longer in therapy at Grendon to show better outcome. After two years, 50% of those staying more than a year had been reconvicted, compared with 58% of those staying less than a year. However, the study did not control for differences in the demographic or criminological characteristics of the short- and long-stay groups and it may be that those who stay longer are 'better bets' for reduced recidivism. This point is discussed further below, in connection with responses by Williams (1973) and Hickey (1973) to the study by George (1971).

A five-year follow-up of 111 Grendon men from 1964 considered their criminal history in the five years before Grendon sentence and in the five years after Grendon. On average, the men had 2.72

convictions in the five years before Grendon and 1.89 in the five years after. In this post-Grendon period, as compared with the pre-Grendon period, 70 men (63%) had fewer convictions (or none), 12.5% had the same number and only 24% had more.

An attempt was made to match each Grendon inmate with an inmate from Oxford Prison who had a similar age, index offence, previous number of convictions and length of sentence. It was only possible to match 87 men, but reconviction rates were essentially the same.

Newton (1971) highlights the difficulties of finding adequate control groups for Grendon studies. Although criminological variables may be matched in samples, the psychological and personality variables are difficult to match, and these may be the more important influences on future recidivism.

George (1971) found more encouraging results when he followed up 263 inmates from 1967 to 1968 two years after release. In total, 41.4% of men had not been reconvicted after two years. When the length of stay in Grendon was considered, it was found that the success rate for those staying more than a year was 60.5%, compared with 34% for those staying for one year or less. This difference was statistically significant.

However, Williams (1973) criticised George's study on the grounds that those who stayed over a year in the therapy were not matched to short-stay inmates and may have differed on variables which are linked to reoffending, giving a different prognosis for recidivism regardless of therapy received. Hickey (1973) responded to these comments by reanalysing George's data, matching long-stay inmates with short-stay inmates for age, marital status, index offence, previous convictions, and age at first conviction. It was possible to match 62 of the 72 inmates in the long-stay group. The rates of recidivism found in the matched samples remained significantly different and were essentially the same as those in George's original study, with 65% of the short-stay inmates and 39% of the long-stay inmates reconvicted within two years.

Gunn *et al* (1978) studied a cohort of 61 men admitted to Grendon in 1971–72. On release these men were matched with non-Grendon prisoners from the Parole Index for age, forensic history, marital status, previous occupation and living arrangements. The two groups did not differ on MMPI ratings. However, significantly more of the Grendon sample reported previous psychiatric treatment and histories of drug abuse and alcoholism. In addition, the Grendon sample were more likely to come from a higher social class background and were less financially dependent upon crime. After two years, the overall reconviction rate of the

Grendon sample was 70%, compared with 62% for the comparison group. A longer-term, ten-year follow-up investigation of the same groups showed a 92% reconviction rate in the Grendon group compared with 85% in the comparison sample (Robertson & Gunn, 1987). Offences of serious violence were committed by 20% of the Grendon sample and 17% of the control group. There was no significant difference between groups in these results. For the Grendon sample, the number of further offences was significantly positively correlated with the number of pre-Grendon court appearances, the number of previous alcohol-related offences, lower IQ, poor motivation and negative attitudes to psychiatry.

Although the above study found little difference between recidivism rates of Grendon and non-Grendon prisoners, it has been extensively argued that reconviction data are an inappropriate measure of Grendon's performance[1]. The aim of Grendon is not simply to lower offending rates but to help men with severe mental problems and to make them manageable in the prison system (Smith, 1984). Certainly, Gunn *et al* found that "massive changes" in social attitudes took place while men were at Grendon, there was a decrease in the amount of hostility and antagonism felt by the inmates towards other people (particularly authority figures), and neurotic state and self-esteem were significantly improved. Gunn *et al* (1978) conclude that the experimental variable in their research design (treatment in Grendon) represents such a small proportion of the total variance affecting reconviction that it could not be expected to produce measurable effects. Given the unsatisfactory matching of the two groups on several variables which may be related to recidivism, it is difficult to interpret their findings. Robertson & Gunn (1987) assert that Grendon is a paradigm for good prison management. The ordinary system often represents wasted time for prisoners whereas Grendon provides inmates with an opportunity to examine past behaviour and current problems, which for some will produce an alteration in lifestyle. It is clear from Gunn *et al*'s (1978) study that changes are effected in the neurotic state and attitudes of inmates at Grendon and that the prison still fulfils its custodial role. The authors argue that if the reconviction rate is no worse than for other prisons, Grendon is demonstrating an effective therapeutic function and can claim success. In Gunn *et al*'s studies, it was noted that the men had reported finding the therapy more useful as time went on, and the proportion who felt they had "learned a considerable

1. The issues pertinent to measures of 'treatment success' in offender patients are adressed at length in Chapter 11.

amount about themselves" increased from 66% at three months to 85% at nine months.

Genders & Player (1994), in detailed qualitative study, evaluated the therapeutic process at Grendon. They were particularly interested in which changes were achieved at which time, and whether there was a staged therapeutic process. Qualitative data regarding perceived benefits from therapy and attitudes to the inmate culture were collected from three cross-sections of men ($n = 102$): those who had been at Grendon for less than six months, for six months to a year, for over a year. Using interviews and observational data they found that over time the men dropped the 'them and us' mentality of prison culture. Feelings of isolation and alienation seemed to be reduced soon after admission to Grendon. However, over time, the men became significantly more likely to talk with prison officers about personal matters and to approve of uniformed officers being present in therapy groups. The longer a man had been at Grendon, the less likely he was to think his problems emanated from an external factor such as drugs or alcohol, and the more likely he was to attribute his problems to difficulties in establishing and maintaining personal relationships. Inmates also exercised more social responsibility over time and would control illicit activities. For example, the majority of those who had been at Grendon more than a year said they would intervene if they suspected the presence of heroin on the unit.

Genders & Player (1994) refer to the stated aim of Grendon:

> "to create an atmosphere in which an individual can explore and acknowledge his pattern of behaviour, understand the motives

TABLE 8.2
The 'therapeutic career model' of HMP Grendon

Stage 1	*Recognition*	Definition of problem
Stage 2	*Motivation*	Expression of desire to change
Stage 3	*Understanding*	Recognition of interconnected and related aspects of life
Stage 4	*Insight*	Identification of solutions to problems
Stage 5	*Testing*	Putting new ways of coping into practice

From Genders & Player (1994).

> behind it, and modify his behaviour both during sentence and in the longer term when he is released into the community at large" (Home Office, 1987)

They argue that the evaluation of therapeutic success should be based upon criteria which relate to this stated aim, and that reconviction rates *per se* are not the only, nor even the most appropriate, measure of success of Grendon. It is imperative to assess how far the establishment succeeds in facilitating the therapeutic process prior to considering recidivism rates. From their data, Genders & Player (1994) constructed a five stage "therapeutic career model" against which an individual's progress in Grendon can be evaluated. This provides a means of assessing whether the establishment is achieving its stated objective (see Table 8.2).

They found that the progression through these stages was highly correlated with the length of time spent in therapy, and that although individuals progressed at different speeds, there was a critical period, at or after 18 months, when the majority of men leaving Grendon (88%) had progressed to the final stage. They contend that, although some indication of success could be gained from studying reconviction rates, this should be focused upon those men who have successfully completed their 'therapeutic career', rather than on a random population of admissions which includes some men who will have failed to embark upon the therapeutic process.

In the most recent outcome study from Grendon, Cullen (1992) followed up a sample of 244 fixed-sentence men released or transferred from Grendon, who had been at liberty for at least two years. Overall, 33.2% had been reconvicted. This is a lower rate than found in previous studies. Additionally, when the 18-month cut-off point suggested by Genders & Player (above) was considered and groups were matched for offence type, sentence length and previous convictions, only 20% of those who completed at least 18 months in therapy at Grendon were reconvicted within two years, compared with 40% of those staying less than 18 months. This difference in proportions reconvicted is highly statistically significant. Furthermore, if only those 43 men released from Grendon direct to the community (rather than transferred back to the main prison system) are considered, the two-year reconviction rate for the longer-stay group is even lower, at 16%, compared with 45% for the short-stay group.

A summary of recidivism rates found in follow-up studies from HMP Grendon is shown in Table 8.3. The results of all released men in Cullen's study show a much lower two-year recidivism rate

TABLE 8.3
Summary of studies of recidivism after release from HMP Grendon

Study	*No. of subjects*	*Follow-up period*	*Description of sample*	*Recidivism rate*
George (1971)	263	2 years	All releases	59%
			Stayed less than one year	56%
			Stayed more than one year	40%
Newton (1971)	377	2 years	Stayed less than one year	58%
			Stayed more than one year	50%
Gunn *et al* (1978)	61	2 years	All releases	70%
Robertson & Gunn(1987)	61	10 years	All releases	92%
Cullen (1992)	214	2 years	All releases	33%
			Stayed less than 18 months	40%
			Stayed more than 18 months	20%

than the two earlier reports. However, Cullen (1992) and Genders & Player (1994) note that, in the intervening years between the studies, the inmate population of Grendon changed considerably. Gunn's subjects were younger, they were on shorter sentences and more were sentenced for acquisitive offences, whereas Cullen's subjects had more often committed crimes related to violence and sexual victimisation. In both Cullen's and George's studies recidivism rates are significantly lower for those men who had been longer in therapy than for those who stayed a shorter time in treatment, indicating that those who are most likely to have progressed further through their 'therapeutic career' benefit most from therapy. This finding highlights the fact that TC treatment is not a short-term measure and a considerable length of stay in therapy may be needed to effect change. It is unsurprising that results are worse when outcome results are presented which include subjects who did not stay in therapy.

Barlinnie Special Unit, Scotland

Barlinnie Special Unit was opened in 1973, as an experimental unit to contain prisoners who had been seriously violent, subversive or disruptive in the main prison system. The unit operates upon principles derived from a TC model with a loosening of the staff/inmate boundaries: the prisoners take an active part in decision-making on the unit and, to an extent, are held responsible for their own behaviour and that of their peers. Inmates are encouraged to express their aggressive feelings verbally and to learn to deal with their emotions in more constructive ways. Prisoners at Barlinnie enjoy privileges such as frequent visits, single cells which they may decorate themselves, and self-catering facilities, although any of these can be withheld by a community decision if the social 'rules' of the unit are infringed. The 'cost' to the inmate is living with fewer facilities than in the ordinary system, a lack of privacy, and most particularly the emotional cost of facing and changing their own aggressive behaviour.

Cooke (1989) described the changes in behaviour of the first 25 inmates during and after their stay at Barlinnie. These men were in the unit for an average of 41 months. All had convictions for violent offences (64% for murder) and only three (12%) had a sentence of less than ten years. All had been deemed uncontainable in the normal system, as evidenced by the fact that 68% had received additional sentences while in prison, and prior to transfer the men had been responsible for 195 episodes of disruptive behaviour in prison. Ratings on the Hare psychopathy scale showed that 5 (20%) were classified as psychopaths (score over 32) and a further 14 (56%) showed significant psychopathic traits (score 25–32).

Changes during and after admission to the unit were assessed by considering the inmates' yearly rate of 'serious incidents' against prison discipline before admission (such incidents included assault, violence, disruption, demonstration, firesetting, self-mutilation, and absconding). Extrapolating from previous behaviour the expected frequency of incidents at Barlinnie was 154, whereas the actual frequency was 9. After transfer back to the ordinary system, the expected frequency of such incidents was 99. Again the actual rate was much lower, at 17. It seems from these findings that a substantial change in disruptive behaviour had been effected by admission to Barlinnie, although Cooke acknowledges that the research is a "one group–pretest–post-test" design without any control sample.

Twelve of the men were subsequently released from prison, and after two years only four of them (33%) had been reconvicted. Although these were all serious offences, the recidivism rate was significantly lower than that predicted using a parole prediction equation. The expected frequency of reoffending was 8.3 (Cooke, 1989).

HMP Wormwood Scrubs Annexe, England

The Annexe was established as a therapeutic unit at Wormwood Scrubs in 1973. Originally, it catered for inmates with addiction problems, but later extended its regime to include sex-offenders and patients with personality problems, including persistently violent offenders. The Annexe accommodates up to 40 patients, who are referred from the local inmate population and other prisons and stay for an average of six months to a year. The Annexe is drug free, so no tranquillisers or psychotropic drugs are prescribed. The regime follows the TC model in that all treatment is in group therapy: small groups, large groups and community meetings. The general ethos is that therapy extends beyond these groups to all interactions and social situations within the Annexe. Annexe staff also have regular meetings for information exchange and a staff-support group is established (Clark & Glatt, 1985).

Jones (1990) considered the changes in inmates during their stay in the Annexe, using a repertory grid, in a cross-sectional design with inmates still in treatment. He showed that treatment did have a positive effect upon self-esteem. There was a significant reduction in the discrepancy between the inmates' view of themselves and their 'ideal self' with time spent on the Annexe. Inmates also saw themselves as becoming less aggressive over time.

A first outcome study compared 127 Annexe inmates (received 1977–79) with 46 men who were referred but not admitted to the Annexe (Sewell & Clark, 1982). A second comparison group of 100 men from C Wing of the main prison was collected. Comparison of the Annexe and C Wing groups showed that, although mean age did not differ, the Annexe inmates had significantly more previous convictions and included more men with previous drug offences and more men with a previous psychiatric history. There were no such differences between the Annexe inmates and the non-admitted group.

Reconviction data two years after release showed that 55% of the Annexe group had been reconvicted, compared with 63% of the non-treated referrals. Only 50% of the C Wing group had been reconvicted in the same period. However, the initial differences in forensic and psychiatric history between the Annexe and C Wing groups render comparison on simple reconviction rates inadequate, in that a number of studies would suggest that the Annexe group was in fact more criminal and more psychopathological than the C Wing group and therefore more likely to be reconvicted.

Subsequently, Jones (1988) followed up all Annexe inmates discharged from prison between 1983 and 1984 – 122 men, comprising 87 'addicts' and 35 'personality disorders' (mainly sex offenders). By the time of this second study the admission procedure to the Annexe had changed: under the new arrangements all referrals were now admitted for an assessment period in the Annexe. Therefore it is important to note that this second study included a group who would have been non-admissions in the Sewell & Clark (1982) study discussed above. The reconviction rate after two years was 67% (82 men). This is higher than that found by Sewell & Clark. In 25% of cases the reconviction was for a less serious offence and in only 17% was a more serious offence committed.

Regression analysis was performed to account for the inmates' length of stay and reason for leaving the Annexe (i.e. whether the treatment was discontinued because of the inmate's lack of motivation and/or 'misbehaviour' in the Annexe or because the inmate had completed his treatment or sentence). It was found that both variables were related to reconviction and that there was an interaction between them. The 'treatment discontinued' group and the 'time served' group differed significantly from one another in terms of whether they went on to reoffend. This difference was greater the longer they had spent in the Annexe. The reconviction rate of the 'treatment discontinued' group was 82%, compared with 57% for the 'time served' group. Regression analysis also showed that, in keeping with other studies, reconviction rate was significantly related to the number of previous convictions. Although no untreated comparison group was used in this study, the reconviction rate for the 'time served' group was very similar to the 55% reported by Sewell & Clark above.

Unfortunately, neither of the above studies assessed their samples in terms of personality disorder or psychopathy. The groups are defined merely by their criminal conviction, and although it is likely that a substantial number of the men admitted to the Annexe could be classified as 'psychopaths' there is no information presented on which this can be assessed.

Therapeutic Communities in non-British prisons

Fink *et al* (1969) described outcome of a TC regime, based upon Maxwell Jones's (1953) model, in a Californian prison. Men with 6–18 months left to serve, before going before the parole board, were admitted. Inmates were mostly aged over 25 years and had a persistent record of offences and imprisonments. Men with histories of mental disorder, addiction or chronic alcoholism were not accepted. Although the programme was originally designed for voluntary treatment, in order to conduct research with matched control groups, the procedure was changed. Fifty-four men were randomly selected on a non-voluntary basis for the first six weeks and thereafter could request transfer back to the main system. A control group of prisoners meeting the same criteria who continued in the main prison system were also studied.

Outcome was to be measured with self-report personality tests. However, over half of the control sample refused to complete the six-month pretesting follow-up and therefore the data are not reported. The treated group are, anecdotally, reported as showing an improvement in ego strength, social relations, trusting of others and self-concept, and had a reduction of tension, frustration and depression. More objective follow-up data are the recidivism and parole revocation of the inmates, which did not differ between groups. Of 41 programme inmates and 37 controls followed up six months after release, 19% (8) and 16% (6) respectively had been returned to prison or reoffended. One of the untreated group had been murdered. It is difficult to draw conclusions on the efficacy of this TC approach, given that the normal procedure of voluntary admission was changed for research purposes, as this may have substantially affected the culture of the community being studied.

Ogloff *et al* (1990) evaluated changes in Canadian male prison inmates during voluntary treatment in a TC programme at a regional forensic hospital designed for men broadly described as personality disordered. All inmates were serving sentences of two years or more and voluntarily participated in the TC treatment programme which was based upon Maxwell Jones' original model. Eighty inmates were assessed using the Psychopathy Check-List (PCL) (Hare, 1985): 21 (26%) scored over 27 and were classed as psychopathic (P), 12 (15%) scored less than 17 and were classed as non-psychopathic (NP), and the remainder were described as "mixed" (M). Treatment variables reported are the objective measure of length of stay and subjective ratings of degree of motivation and improvement during treatment.

The psychopathic group had a significantly shorter length of stay in treatment (103 days v. 207 days M; 241 days NP). Inmates were discharged from treatment early for security reasons, at self-request, or for lack of motivation. Not surprisingly, given their shorter treatment time, the psychopathic group as a whole showed significantly less improvement and motivation than the NP and M groups. The results indicate that psychopathic subjects are more difficult to engage in voluntary TC treatment than non-psychopathic subjects. However, the authors' claim that their study demonstrates "the predictive validity of the PCL to the prediction of treatment outcome in a TC in a correctional setting" seems difficult to substantiate, given that no post-discharge follow-up data are reported.

Sandhu (1970) reports an experiment in dealing with "violent psychopaths" in an Indian prison in Hissar, Harayana. Psychopaths are described as men who had committed either murder or robbery with violence and who had "a pattern of violent megalomanic behaviour which had become accentuated or identified in prison". A Therapeutic Community consisting of 30 "well-behaved" prisoners (on both long and short sentences) was set up which accepted six psychopaths at any one time. Within the TC the prisoners worked in maintenance, cooking and gardening and were given full responsibility to plan their own work. Creativity was encouraged and good behaviour would result in reduction of sentence. Prisoners in the TC were allowed more visits by their families and could return home to help with harvesting or a family emergency for four weeks per year.

In a two-year period, 18 psychopaths were admitted for an average of nine months. Behavioural change was assessed by staff observation, and a staff/group consensus of improvement was used. On this basis, 13 (72%) were assessed as improved and five (28%) as demonstrating no change. During the course of the experiment there were no serious assaults, riots, suicide attempts or attempted escapes in the TC. Although a qualitative assessment of change was the only measure used, Sandhu considered the experiment successful in containing violent prisoners.

The findings of this Indian prison TC study are similar to those found at Barlinnie, Scotland, by Cooke (1989), who also reports behaviour changes in disruptive and violent prisoners. However, the Hissar Prison model contrasts with that of Barlinnie, where the most violent prisoners were separated from the other inmates.

Maximum-security hospital Therapeutic Communities

Dr Henri van der Hoeven Clinic, The Netherlands

The van der Hoeven Clinic is one of several Dutch institutions where, until 1988, mentally disordered offenders were treated under an order for detention at the government's pleasure (*Terbeschikkingstelling van der Regering* – TBR). A TBR order was semi-indeterminate, being initially for two years but subsequently renewable on a court order. TBR could be imposed only if the offender constituted a danger to society. Offenders could also be considered either to be not responsible for their offence due to impairment of mind, or to have diminished responsibility (in which case TBR could be in addition to a prison sentence). Also, offenders deemed unfit for prison confinement owing to impairment of mind might be given TBR disposal (Emmerik, 1987; Ministrie van Justice, 1992). Since 1988 a change in Dutch law has removed the words 'at the government's pleasure' and the order is now described as TBS (*Terbeschikkingstelling*).

The van der Hoeven Clinic is a 75-bedded residential unit. Around 80% of the hospital's population are aged 20–35 years, and 10% are women. The average length of stay is four years. The hospital has treated psychopaths since 1955, and they make up 80% of the clinical population (Feldbrugge, 1992). The thrust of treatment is a TC model in which the inmate group accepts responsibility for decision-making. Living tasks are shared by staff and patients and a considerable amount of freedom is given to patients. For example, patients are often left unsupervised and, at night, one patient's room is left unlocked and this person will respond, alongside the staff, to any major incident.

Jessen & Roosenberg (1971) considered the outcome of 338 male patients admitted to the van der Hoeven Clinic between 1955 and 1968. No psychiatric diagnosis or description is given for these men. By 1970, 116 (34%) had returned to the community on 'probationary leave' or conditional discharge (PL group), 2 had died, 21 had had treatment terminated, 94 had been transferred to other institutions (this occurred soon after admission), and the others were missing or still in treatment.

For outcome data, the 116 patients in the PL group were taken as the 'treated' group as they had been considered well enough to leave the hospital. Of this group, ten (8.6%) had been recalled from leave and 26 (22.4%) had reoffended. Only six patients (5.2%) had committed sexual or aggressive offences since discharge, and 20 had committed economic offences. The average time to the first offence was 31 months after discharge. Nineteen reoffenders (16.4%) had received another sentence, five (4.3%) had suspended sentences and two (1.7%) had their cases dropped. The duration of treatment for the recidivist group was 58 months, compared with 49 months for the non-recidivist group. The non-recidivist group had been at liberty for an average of 5.75 years at the time of the study.

These reoffending rates, of 22% after five years at liberty, are extremely low and only six patients (5%) were considered as having committed serious new offences. However, the group studied represent only a third of those originally taken on for treatment at the van der Hoeven Clinic. Those 80 subjects who were discharged to the community, and remained free of conviction, represent only 23.7% of the 338 patients actually assessed. If the 94 patients who were admitted and then transferred untreated to other institutions are excluded, the 80 released non-recidivist represent 33% of those taken on for treatment.

In a more extensive study, van Emmerik (1987) followed up all 517 patients released from the van der Hoeven Clinic between 1955 and 1980, 368 of whom had been released for more than five years. Data were collected from case-notes, court records, and personal interviews with 71% of released ex-patients.

Recidivism after discharge was defined as at least one reconviction for a serious offence (minor offences were not considered). The overall recidivism rate for those discharged for over five years was 52%. The recidivism rate was highest in patients transferred to other institutions: these had 70% recidivism compared with only 31% recidivism in those conditionally discharged from the van der Hoeven Clinic. During their stay at the van der Hoeven Clinic, a third of patients had reoffended while on authorised or unauthorised leave. Considering social outcome, on follow-up 29% of ex-patients were unemployed or unfit to work (cf. 7% of Dutch general population), and 63% of conditionally discharged patients were employed, compared with 30% of those transferred.

The low recidivism rate and high employment rate, of the conditionally discharged group are much better than the rates for those transferred. However, the transferred patients obtained less therapy at the van der Hoeven Clinic and differed from the conditional discharge group on a number of pretreatment criminal and social history factors which made them more likely to have a worse treatment outcome.

Penetanguishene, USA

Harris *et al* (1989) and Rice *et al* (1992) report a ten-year follow-up study of criminal and violent recidivism in psychopathic offenders who were treated in a "TC model" in a maximum-security hospital, Penetanguishene in USA. The programme evaluated differed from a 'true' TC in several ways. Firstly, and most importantly, entry into and participation in treatment was not voluntary, and stated willingness to participate was not a selection criterion. Any individual convicted of violent crime or found not guilty by reason of insanity could be assigned to the programme. Any patients who refused to engage in the programme were "sent to a sub programme ... until they complied with programme requirements. Patients could leave the programme by convincing an independent review board that they had made clinical progress, they could not simply get out by misbehaving" (Rice *et al*, 1992, p. 402). Secondly, the 'treatment' programme was almost entirely patient-run: "patients had very little contact with professional staff". This is in contrast to traditional TC, where patients and staff share responsibility and are jointly involved in therapeutic aspects. Thirdly, the treatment programme incorporated several radical and unusual techniques. Although the basic programme involved up to 80 hours of intensive insight-oriented group therapy, a variety of "innovative defence disrupting techniques" were used, including administration of drugs (scopolamine, sodium pentathol, alcohol and LSD) and using nude encounter groups and marathon therapy groups (Harris *et al*, 1989, p.8.)

The subjects were 176 men who had spent at least two years in the community from 1968–78. They were matched for age, index offence, and criminal history with 146 forensic assessment cases (30 subjects could not be adequately matched). Overall, 57% of treated and 68% of untreated subjects reoffended within ten years. PCL scores were calculated for the treated group retrospectively from case-notes, using 25 as the cut-off point. (The usual cut-off point is 30 (Hart *et al*, 1988).) There were 52 inmates (31%) classified as psychopaths. When 'treated' psychopaths were compared with their matched comparison subjects, 89% of the former and 81% of the latter had reoffended at ten-year follow-up. However, despite matching for age and forensic history most psychopaths were matched with a comparison subject who did not himself meet the criterion for psychopathy. Overall, 78% of treated psychopaths had committed a violent offence, compared with 55% of comparison subjects and 21% of non-psychopaths.

The authors claim that the study shows that the TC had no effect in reducing recidivism and that psychopaths do worse in treatment than non-psychopathic subjects. However, the findings can only be accepted with caution, given that the treatment programme applied and evaluated differs from the more usual TC model and philosophy in fundamental ways. The authors do concede that "an inappropriate institutional environment can actually increase criminal behaviour . . . the kind of TC described in this article is the wrong programme for serious psychopathic offenders" (Rice *et al*, 1992, p. 408). Certainly, one of the major goals in TC approaches to treatment of psychopathy is to increase the patients' sense of self-responsibility and self-worth through their voluntary participation in the community. This aspect is completely lost in an enforced treatment regime.

Hierarchical Therapeutic Community model

The treatment model employed in a hierarchical Therapeutic Community combines different treatment settings, often in-patient and out-patient, through which the patient progresses in therapy. These communities, also called concept-based TCs, originate in the self-help model, and staff are often ex-sufferers with TC experience. On admission, clients are given menial jobs and have little status, but with time, through commitment to the programme, they progress to more responsible positions and have increased status. Although hierarchical TCs differ from the democratic–analytic TC model (of Jones and Main), the principal assumptions are similar. Responsibility is delegated to community members, and the social environment and the 'living and learning' experience remain fundamental to effecting personality and behaviour changes. Confrontational techniques are frequently used and there is a high degree of structure in these TCs.

Many hierarchical TCs have been developed for dealing with specific problems such as substance abuse. However, it is recognised that a high proportion of these patients will have concurrent personality disorders (Gerstley *et al*, 1990; Bukstein *et al*, 1989; Woody *et al*, 1985)

Skolnick & Zuckerman (1979) compared the outcomes of TC treatment and a prison sentence upon drug abusers. The subjects were 59 male drug abusers treated in a drug rehabilitation centre TC, and 37 men, who had at least a one-year history of drug abuse and were newly sentenced to prison. There was no random allocation to the groups and the ages of the men are not given. In addition, forensic history, degree of drug usage and racial composition of the groups were not equated. The prison group had no prior treatment for their drug abuse and the groups did not differ on IQ.

Both groups of subjects showed abnormal pretest scores on the MMPI, and the Sensation Seeking Scale (SSS). The modal MMPI pattern was similar to that found in psychopathic subjects, with peaks for the psychopathic deviate and hypomania scales. At 6–8-month follow-up, the TC group had decreased significantly more than the prison group on MMPI scores of depression, psychasthenia, schizophrenia and social introversion, but there was no difference in changes on the psychopathy scale. The TC group had decreased significantly more than the prison group on the experience-seeking score of the SSS and also scored higher on extraversion at follow-up. However, the authors do not compare intake scores of the groups, and initial mean scores may have differed. Although the study indicates greater improvement in TC treatment than in prison on some psychological variables, there seems to be no effect on psychopathic traits. The study period of 6–8 months is very short and does not represent 'completed' treatment for either group. Additionally, the methodology of the study is poor, the groups are inadequately matched, and conclusions must only be very tentative.

Wexler *et al* (1990) evaluated a voluntary concept-based TC in a New York prison which had operated for over 12 years. A quasi-experimental design with over 1500 subjects compared all clients completing the TC programme between 1977 and 1984 (the TC treated group) with inmates who volunteered for the programme and were placed on a waiting-list, but never participated because of time limitations (untreated group) and those who participated in drug programmes in other prisons (counselling and milieu therapy). Around 50% of subjects were black, although no further analysis of ethnicity is reported. Both male and female inmates were studied separately using outcome measures of arrest, time to first arrest and parole outcome. Positive parole outcome was take as completion of parole with no rule violations, arrests or parole revocation. The average time on parole was three years and the findings are summarised in Table 8.4.

The percentage of arrests was significantly lower for the male TC group (27%), than for the combined comparison groups although the rate of positive parole discharges (58%) was not significantly different from any of the other groups. For the women, the TC groups also had the lowest rate of arrest (18%) and highest rate of parole success (77%), although in this smaller sample neither rate differed significantly from that of the other comparison groups. However, a X^2 analysis did show that the arrest rate of the TC women was significantly lower than that of the women who received counselling ($X^2 = 6.0$; $P < 0.05$).

Analysis of time spent in therapy indicated that, for the TC group, positive outcomes increased with length of stay up to one year, and thereafter fewer positive outcomes were found. Wexter *et al* suggest this represents a 'dosage' model, where more exposure to treatment produces a positive effect but there is a plateau beyond which additional therapy may no longer improve outcome. This may also be because the model employed is based upon inmates staying one year and then having parole and release to the community or less secure environment. Those who do not obtain their parole at 12 months as expected may become disillusioned or frustrated with the programme and therefore not gain further benefit.

TABLE 8.4
Outcome of a prison concept-based TC programme for drug addicts: a summary of findings from Wexler et al (1990)

Group	*No. of subjects*	*% arrested*	*Mean no. of months to arrest*	*% positive parole outcome*
Male groups				
TC programme	435	26.9%	13.1	58.1%
Milieu therapy	573	34.6%	11.4	52.6%
Counselling	261	39.8%	12.0	52.7%
Untreated controls	159	40.9%	15.0	60.6%
All comparison groups	993	37.0%	–	54.2%
Significance of group differences	–	$P < 0.001$	NS ($P = 0.07$)	NS
Female groups				
TC programme	247	17.8%	12.4	77.2%
Counselling	113	29.2%	14.6	68.2%
Untreated controls	38	23.7%	8.6	52.9%
Both comparison groups	151	27.8%	–	65.7%
Significance of group differences	–	NS ($P = 0.07$)	NS ($P = 0.07$)	NS

This study confirms the assertion that TC treatment within prison settings can be effective in reducing recidivism in both male and female drug addicts and that it is more effective than other treatment modalities. Wexler *et al* emphasise how their programme contains elements that all successful treatment programmes have in common: social learning model; authority structures; rules and sanctions; using community resources; prosocial modelling; and open communication, trust and empathic relationships. However, the subjects of their study are all drug addicts and, although many may have coexisting personality disorders, the generalisation to psychopathic offenders must be tentative.

Ravndal & Vaglum (1991) note how many studies have shown changes in neurotic psychological symptoms following hierarchical TC treatment, but few studies have shown any impact upon character disorder (Kennard & Wilson, 1979; Leon & Ziegenbuss, 1986). Ravndal & Vaglum (1991) examined changes in antisocial aggressiveness during treatment in their hierarchical TC for substance abusers in Norway. Thirty-six substance abusers were assessed for personality disorder using the Millon Clinical Multiaxial Inventory at admission and on completing their in-patient phase of treatment one year later. On admission the group scored highest on passive–aggressive and borderline personality. After a year in therapy these scores had significantly decreased; however, there was a significant increase in mean score on the antisocial aggressiveness, narcissism and histrionic scales.

Ravndal & Vaglum suggest that in a hierarchical confrontational TC model the level of tolerance for aggressive feelings may be high, and therefore clients with a high level of antisocial aggressiveness may complete the in-patient treatment although their aggressiveness has not changed. They divided their subjects into those who began with low scores and increased in aggression during treatment and those who began with high scores and did not change. They found that the drop-out rate from the out-patient stage of therapy was lower in the increased aggression group than in the non-increase group (5/25 (20%) v. 5/11 (45%)). They suggest that the non-increase group consisted of clients with strong antisocial personality traits which did not change in treatment and although they may have adapted superficially to the in-patient TC programme their attachment was not sufficiently strong to prevent drop-out as out-patients.

Summary

The length of this chapter, in comparison with chapters considering other treatment modalities, is indicative of the existence of several TC units treating psychopaths, in range of different countries and settings, from which a considerable amount of treatment outcome research has originated. However, despite the quantity of research into TC treatment, the studies are bedevilled by methodological problems similar to those which have occurred in other studies throughout this review.

In summarising the findings of TC outcome studies, it should be noted that these studies cover an extensive and heterogeneous range of settings and patient groups. Therefore any direct comparison between different TCs or generalisation of findings from one setting to another would be meaningless. However, there are some general criticisms which relate to all TC studies and some common findings which may be inferred from existing research. These are summarised below.

Diagnostic criteria. Few studies use rigorous diagnostic criteria of psychopathy. Cooke (1989), Ogloff *et al* (1990) and Rice *et al* (1992) used Hare's PCL–R for diagnosis. However, these studies used three different cut-off points for psychopathy, of 32, 27, and 25 respectively; the recommended cut-off point is 30 (Hart *et al*, 1988). Vaglum *et al* (1990) and Mehlum *et al* (1991) applied DSM–III–R criteria for all personality disorders. Copas *et al* (1984) used a four-way classification of psychopathy developed in an early doctoral study by O'Brien (1976).

Improvement on psychological measures. Uncontrolled studies of changes during TC treatment have generally demonstrated an improvement on psychological measures. Norris (1985) at Henderson Hospital found that both women and men improved on repertory grid measures of rule-breaking, independence, self-perception and self-esteem. Newton (1973) and Miller (1982) both showed significant decreases in hostility measures during treatment at HMP Grendon. Miller also found decreases in EPQ psychoticism and neuroticism scores. Similarly, Gunn *et al* (1978) found significant decreases in MMPI scales of depression, anxiety, hostility, and social introversion during treatment.

However, Craft *et al* (1964) found very few changes in psychological measures from admission to discharge in their comparative study of adolescents in TC and in authoritarian treatment wards. The TC group did show a significant decrease in social introversion and the authoritarian sample increased their IQ score.

Fewer serious incidents. Those studies which consider the management of violent offenders within prison TCs report fewer serious incidents than in the normal prison system (suicide, violence, riot, etc.) (Sandhu, 1970; Gray, 1974; Cooke, 1989). This supports Robertson & Gunn's (1987) assertion that regardless of outcome the TC model is a paradigm for good prison management.

Maintenance of psychological changes. Studies which have considered the maintenance of psychological changes after discharge from TC treatment are generally limited by a short follow-up period. Gunn *et al* (1978) report a decrease in pathological scores on the GHQ nine months after treatment at Grendon. Two uncontrolled studies have shown significant changes in distress due to psychological symptoms as measured by the SCL–90–R questionnaire (Vaglum *et al*, 1990; Dolan *et al*, 1992*c*). Dolan's study, from Henderson Hospital, showed that 55% of subjects improved reliably and only 6% deteriorated after treatment; however, results are limited by short follow-up, of eight months. The significant group mean changes in the Vaglum study were maintained after three years (Mehlum *et al*, 1991).

Cooke (1989) notes that the reduction in "serious incidents" of violent or disruptive behaviour in Barlinnie is maintained after transfer of offenders back to the main prison system. The actual occurrence of such events represent an 83% reduction in the predicted incidence based on pre-treatment behaviour.

Measure of long-term success. In most outcome studies, recidivism is most often used as the measure of long-term success. Length of follow-up in the reviewed studies varies widely, from six months to ten years.

Only two studies had a ten-year follow-up, and both showed no difference or more recidivism in treated male offenders than in matched controls (Robertson & Gunn, 1987: 98% v. 85%; Rice *et al*, 1992: 78% v. 55%). However, in both cases the control samples were matched on criminological and historical data but were not matched on psychological factors or for diagnosis of psychopathy.

Five-year follow-up studies of recidivism have been reported from only two other institutions: Henderson Hospital (Copas & Whiteley, 1976; Copas *et al*, 1984) and the van der Hoeven Clinic (Jessen & Roosenberg, 1971; Emmerik, 1987). Copas *et al* (1984) at Henderson Hospital considered recidivism and readmission for psychiatric treatment as a relapse and found that, after five years, the relapse rate was significantly lower in a treated group than among untreated referrals (64% v. 81%).

Voluntary participation. Three studies which suggest a less favourable outcome for psychopaths after treatment did not allow voluntary participation in the TC treatment (Craft *et al*, 1964; Fink *et al*, 1969; Rice *et al*, 1992). Non-voluntary treatment is in conflict with the TC model, which depends upon the patients' cooperation in the community; therefore such findings are perhaps unsurprising.

Patient drop-out. The voluntary nature of TC treatment does mean that some patients drop out of therapy. Dolan *et al* (1992*b*) note that around a third of patients leave Henderson Hospital in the first three months. Ogloff *et al* (1990) found that psychopaths had a shorter length of stay than non-psychopathic inmates in a prison TC. The numbers who drop out or who are discharged from treatment early are of importance when the wider utility and applicability of TC programmes are considered.

Allocation of subjects. Only one study compared subjects after random allocation to a treatment or no-treatment condition (Fink *et al*, 1969). However, the follow-up was only six months and treatment was not voluntary. Greater changes in psychological state of the treated group were not reflected in group differences on parole revocation or recidivism.

Only one study randomly allocated subjects to two different treatment modalities (Craft *et al*, 1964). It found no conclusive differences between a TC and an authoritarian regime for adolescent delinquent boys. Although the recidivism rates of the two groups were the same, those in the authoritarian group who did reoffend committed fewer crimes. However, treatment was not voluntary and these findings with adolescents may not be generalisable to adult psychopaths. Despite the preference for an authoritarian approach suggested by Craft *et al* (1964), another study comparing an authoritarian and a more humanitarian 'milieu therapy' regime for adolescent psychopaths found that the authoritarian regime was unsuccessful in reducing recidivism (McCord & Sanchez, 1982 - see Chapter 9).

Length of stay and outcome. Length of stay in TC therapy has been shown to be positively related to improved outcome. Copas *et al* (1984) found that the success rate after three years, in terms of not reoffending or needing readmission, improved from 33% for those staying three months at Henderson Hospital to 71% for staying over nine months.

Studies at HMP Grendon support the finding that length of stay is positively related to outcome (Newton, 1971; George, 1971). Cullen (1992) found a significant difference in success rate (no recidivism) after two years between those staying less than 18 months (55% success) and those staying over 19 months (84% success).

Jones (1988) at Wormwood Scrubs Annexe also found significantly less recidivism after two years in those inmates who stayed in treatment (43% success rate) than in those who dropped out or had treatment discontinued (18% success rate).

Obviously, the length of time spent in voluntary therapy may be linked to factors such as motivation to change, and if these results on length of stay and outcome are taken with the point above on voluntary participation, it seems that TC treatment is most successful for those who want to be treated.

Conclusion. Many workers have commented that TC approaches offer the most hope for treatment of psychopathic or personality-disordered patients (McCord, 1982*b*). However, despite the large number of treatment outcome studies reviewed here, the support for such a statement is equivocal.

9 Hospital admission and 'milieu' therapy

A striking feature of reports of outcome after long-term in-patient treatment in hospitals is that, with few exceptions, the actual treatment received by the patients is not described. Treatment is often described as 'milieu' therapy, which Blackburn (1992) points out is usually a euphemism for an orderly regime within the hospital. 'Milieu' therapy offered within secure and non-secure hospitals includes pharmacotherapy, psychotherapy, occupational therapy, cognitive therapy, group therapy, behavioural therapy, social skills training, and the effect of admission to the hospital. These elements of therapy are delivered by a range of staff from differing professional backgrounds who are often operating within different conceptual frameworks and applying different models of treatment to one aspect, behavioural feature or symptom of the patient.

Different patients will receive different 'treatment packages' within the 'milieu', which may be tailored to the individual. It is often impossible to judge the 'dose' of each element of the milieu which each patient has received. Some patients may have experienced all, and others only a few, of the various elements of the 'milieu'. This is illustrated by Dell & Robertson (1988), who found that, of 106 male psychopaths who had been in Broadmoor Special Hospital for an average of 8.2 years, 43% had been given individual therapy, 71% had been in group therapy and 42% had received other psychological treatment (such as social skills training and behavioural therapy). However, 16% of men had received none of these types of treatment during their admission and 14% were on psychotropic medication at the time of the study. These findings are concordant with the fact that the form or purpose of treatment had not been described in the medical treatment recommendations for over three-quarters (76%) of these patients. Treatment in a 'structured milieu' had been recommended for only 10% of patients, and psychotherapy for 8%. Similarly, Collins (1991), studying legal psychopaths admitted to Rampton Special Hospital, found that for 57% of the patients the purpose of admission had not been stated, and for 55%, who were deemed 'treatable', no statement had been made about the form of treatment that might be appropriate. In cases where treatment was recommended, this was various combinations of structure, counselling, education, occupation, rehabilitation, socialisation and psychotherapy, in unspecified amounts. Brett (1992) has noted that "patients with personality disorder, and treatments for them, tend to be scattered haphazardly through the Special Hospitals" (p. 152).

It is not surprising, therefore, that in many research reports of long-term hospitalisation in secure institutions, the only description of treatment given is length of stay. It will become apparent, from the review below, that many of the published outcome studies are not assessing the actual treatment given but are evaluating the appropriateness of the decision to release a patient after a long-term, non-voluntary, admission. Such studies could perhaps be described as investigations of 'the outcome of the discharge decision' rather than investigations of the outcome of any specific treatment approach.

In-patient treatment in non-secure hospitals

Despite pessimism regarding treatability of psychopaths, even some early studies of in-patient hospitalisation produced some favourable results. Heaver (1943) studied 40 male psychopaths treated in a New York mental hospital in the period 1935–40. Diagnostic criteria applied were those of Cheney (1934), which include emotional immaturity, defect of judgement, not learning from experience, impulsive reactions, and emotional instability. The average age of the patients was 28.7 years, they were described as mostly middle class and of average intelligence, and all had shown "gross antisocial behaviour prior to adult life". The number with forensic histories is not given, although previous offences include forgery, assault, theft, misuse of funds, drug abuse, exhibitionism, and impairing the morals of a minor. The men entered hospital voluntarily and stayed for an average of four months (range nine days to one year). Therapy consisted of individual "interviews" with a doctor, occupational therapy, gymnasium activities and social activities. The men's visits and freedom within the hospital were restricted.

No psychological or behavioural measures of change are presented, only a clinical opinion is given. However, on discharge 36 (90%) were considered "improved" by the clinical staff. At follow-up between two and seven years after discharge, 31 patients were traced, of whom 23 (57% of initial sample) were described as having "become more acceptable to society, including 16 (40% of initial sample) who can be regarded as essentially recovered". The follow-up was during World War II, and 11 men had tried to enlist for service. Six men were turned down on their hospital record; however, two applied to officers training school and were ultimately commissioned! In addition, three men were working in the American Field Service, three in defence plants, one as an air-raid warden and one in an "important diplomatic post". Heaver (1943) concludes that "for the less vicious and moderately unbridled psychopathic personality, the traditional adherence to therapeutic nihilism is unjustified".

Craft (1958) followed up 43 men and women "convicted of offences with gross personality disorder", who had been treated in a British hospital for an average of five years. No diagnostic criteria for psychopathy are given, but ten patients had previously been in a Special Hospital, and all had an IQ of over 60. After three years out of hospital, living in the community, 88% were free of conviction and 78% were employed. Craft suggests that most appeared to have lost their psychopathic traits on follow-up, but no psychological or behavioural measures were made to support this subjective clinical judgement.

Following from his randomised comparative study of adolescents treated in therapeutic-community and authoritarian wards at Balderton (Craft *et al*, 1964; see Chapter 8 of this review), Craft (1968) developed a treatment unit in Wales based upon a "paternalistic work-training programme similar to that of enlightened approved schools". The unit admitted 100 male psychopaths. The criteria of psychopathy were

(a) age 13 years or over
(b) having offended
(c) personality disorder of such an extent to induce community officials to request in-patient treatment
(d) IQ over 55
(e) no psychosis.

Reasons for conviction included acquisitive offences (61 patients), sex offences (16 patients) and offences of violence (18 patients, including 5 convicted for attempted murder and two for arson). The mean number of convictions was 2.8. There were 33 patients under psychopathic and subnormality provisions of the Mental Health Act. The age range was 12–51, with an average age of 19.2 (69 patients were between 12 and 19 years). Treatment was "less intensive" than that at Balderton, with two sessions of weekly group therapy. Hospitalisation was longer (average 11.1 months) and there was "more emphasis on training and discipline to ensure good manners and good working habits".

During treatment, 21 absconded and there were six court appearances as a result. Follow-up was made at 14.5 months after discharge. One patient had died through suicide and 6 were currently described as schizophrenic. Of the remainder, 35 had been convicted, 52 were in living institutions (prison, hospital or hostel) and 36 were employed. No psychological measures of outcome are reported.

Comparison was made with the follow-up data for the 100 subjects in the Balderton series, but it is noted that the Welsh series were: a more disturbed group, with more impulsive psychopathic traits, and more severe criminal history; on average had two months more treatment; were older; and came from a more rural community background, by different referral routes. Additionally, the Balderton series included patients treated within two different types of therapy ward. The Welsh series had significantly fewer convictions than the Balderton group (37.6% v. 57%), and more were in prison (7.5% v. 21%). Other variables showed little difference, and Craft concludes that "the overall treatment success of each system is remarkably similar". However, given the fundamental differences between the two groups, and the fact that the Balderton group had two different types of treatment, such a statement based upon this comparison should only be tentative.

McCord & Sanchez (1982) report a long-term follow-up study of adolescents treated in two different milieu treatment programmes for a minimum of 18 months. A supportive psychoeducational programme was used at one centre, Wiltwyck, while at the other, Lynam, an authoritarian regime was employed. Boys from each regime who had originally been described as psychopaths were followed up for 25 years through official records. Between the ages of 15 and 19, Wiltwyck 'graduates' ($n = 42$) had a significantly lower recidivism rate than Lynam graduates ($n = 37$) (11% v. 79%). However, over time the rates of criminal offending levelled out and more Wiltwyck than Lynam graduates were still offending between the ages of 35 and 40 (33% v. 19%). The boys were not randomly assigned to the different treatment programmes and no account was taken of life factors in the intervening years. In particular, the Lynam boys who reoffended in early adulthood may have been subject to subsequent periods of incarceration which in turn affected future offending behaviour.

Although there seems to be a common view that psychopathically disordered patients should not be treated on open hospital wards, Gabbard & Coyne (1987) note that patients with antisocial traits are regularly treated in general psychiatric units. In a retrospective study they attempted to identify positive and negative predictors of response to therapy of 33 antisocial patients admitted to their own general psychiatric ward. Over a four-year period, 16 patients with DSM–III–R antisocial personality disorder and 17 patients with antisocial traits were admitted. Disruptive behaviour caused 23 (70%) to be discharged from hospital prematurely and staff ratings for 19 of these (57% of patients) indicated that they had made no progress in treatment. Only five patients (15%) were rated as attaining the treatment goals. Predictors of positive response to treatment were the presence of anxiety, and an axis I diagnosis of depression. Negative response was related to a history of felony arrests, repeated lying, and an unresolved legal situation on admission. On the basis of these findings, Gabbard & Coyne suggest that patients with antisocial traits should be referred to specialist treatment settings rather than to general psychiatric units with heterogeneous patient populations.

Hospital careers of legal psychopaths

Walker & Macabe (1973), in their in-depth study of the implementation of the Mental Health Act 1959 (MHA), surveyed 1031 offender patients who were made the subject of hospital orders in a one-year period 1963–64. In their sample, 6% of mentally ill and subnormal patients were sent to Special Hospitals, compared with 34% of the psychopathic patients. When tracing the hospital careers of the patients, Walker & McCabe had "to be content with paper follow-up based upon information supplied by the hospitals themselves" or government statistics. Although they would "have liked to organise a more personal follow-up of offender patients who left hospital [they] were dissuaded by psychiatric advisers who felt strongly it would be regarded by psychiatrists and patients as an improper intrusion" (p. 157).

From the whole sample, 47 psychopaths were discharged from hospital within 12 months and it was possible to match these 'first-year leavers' for age, sex, previous convictions and after-care with 45 schizophrenic and 32 mentally subnormal first-year leavers. At two-year follow-up, the psychopathic group had been convicted significantly more often than their schizophrenic controls (55.6% v. 35.6%; $P < 0.01$) and were significantly less likely to be rehospitalised (35.6% v. 62.2%; $P < 0.01$). There was no difference between the reconviction and rehospitalisation rates of the matched pairs of psychopathic and subnormal subjects. There were 12 matched pairs in which both subjects were reconvicted. In every case the mentally ill or subnormal patient was rehospitalised as a result, whereas only 50% of the psychopaths were rehospitalised following conviction.

Quinsey & Maguire (1983) considered the disposal of psychiatrically disordered offenders in Canada who were remanded for reports by the courts. Of the 58 offenders with a psychotic disorder, 97% were recommended for treatment by a multidisciplinary assessment team, while only 37% of the 118 personality-disordered offenders were recommended for treatment. There was little difference in the index offences committed by the two groups; however, the court's order was that 74% of the psychotic and 36% of the personality-disordered offenders should receive treatment, while 21% and 66% of each group respectively were given a correctional sentence.

In-patient treatment in medium-secure units

Woodside *et al* (1976) describe an integrated ward, treating both men and women with 'sociopathic behaviour disorders', run as a medium-secure unit within a Scottish general hospital. The unit was set up to cater for disturbed and aggressive patients, to enable observation and treatment while decisions were made about long-term needs. A multidisciplinary team provided a broadly based programme including twice-daily community meetings, social skills education, resocialisation, sociodrama and active recreation. Of the first 100 patients, 49% had a diagnosis of psychopathic personality disorder. The majority of patients stayed on the ward for under two months; 65% of the patients became sufficiently settled to return to other hospital wards, 23% were discharged to hostels or home, and only 7% were sent to maximum-secure environments (6% to prison and 1% to Carstairs State Hospital). After five years of functioning, Basson & Woodside (1981) reassessed the ward and the first 400 patients admitted. The main primary diagnoses catered for were 33% schizophrenic, 21% personality disordered and 17% affective psychosis. As before, 64% of patients were transferred to open wards and 21% to home or hostels. Although no other follow-up data were presented, the authors conclude that their experiment of placing disturbed men and women of all ages, social backgrounds and psychiatric conditions together in a secure unit was successful.

In-patient treatment in British Special Hospitals

The treatment of psychopaths in Special Hospital settings has been described by a number of authors. Black (1984) has given a general description of treatment in maximum-security settings; Cox (1976, 1986) has described both group psychotherapy and the importance of dynamic psychotherapy in secure settings; and Grounds *et al* (1987) and Brett (1992) have described in detail the philosophy and organisation of a special unit for treating psychopathic disorders within Broadmoor Hospital which integrates concepts of psychoanalytic and cognitive–behavioural therapy. Yet, although these are valuable descriptions, as noted above the treatment provided within Special Hospitals is rarely described in the context of treatment outcome or follow-up studies.

Tong & MacKay (1959) reported on 587 male patients from Rampton Hospital who were discharged on licence or transferred to another hospital between 1945 and 1956. No diagnosis is made beyond a description of patients as "mental defectives of dangerous or violent propensity" with "behaviour of a sort proscribed by the criminal law" and "not infrequently called psychopathic". However, given the population of Rampton, it is likely that this heterogeneous group contains learning-disabled patients.

Follow-up was for between 1 and 12 years (no mean reported), and relapse was defined as "return to the state hospital or conviction involving other means of disposal". Of the 423 patients traced, 40.4% (171, i.e. 29% of total sample) relapsed, 20% (85) were returned to hospital and 20.3% (86) were convicted. However, the crimes committed after discharge were generally less serious than the earlier offences, and only 50% (43) of the convicted sample were given custodial sentences. Relapse tended to occur soon after discharge and the mean length of stay at Rampton for the relapsed group was significantly shorter than for the non-relapsed group (8.7 years v. 10.9 years).

The authors do not report how many of the 423 patients were transferred from Rampton to other hospitals, and it is possible that those transferred to another hospital may have been still in a secure environment and therefore less likely to reoffend than those discharged to the community. Of the 206 patients aged 15–29 years who were known definitely not to have relapsed, 192 (93%) had been transferred to another hospital or "mental deficiency" unit.

Tong & MacKay (1959) claim "it is apparent that the state hospital system is therapeutically effective in that serious relapses are relatively uncommon" (p. 284). However, it seems difficult to substantiate this claim when outcome is only reported in terms of whether ex-patients reoffend or return to the hospital. This is arguably a study of success of discharge and may inform the reader more about the adequacy of the discharge or transfer decision than the adequacy of treatment.

Other workers have looked at the rate of return to Special Hospitals of discharged patients. McGrath (1966) reported that, overall, 3% of discharges were returned to Broadmoor, but "seldom because they are dangerous or violent" (p. 143), while Craft (1965) reported that of 75 discharges from Moss Side between 1951 and 1962, nine (12%) were returned and five (6.7%) were admitted to other Special Hospitals, giving a total of 18.7%.

Gathercole *et al* (1968) attempted a postal follow-up of 100 discharged patients from Moss Side Hospital from 1961. They obtained data on 72 patients who had an average stay of 6.5 years; 33 had psychopathic disorder and 26 of these were also subnormal. Both men and women were included in the study (patients were treated on segregated wards). Results of follow-up at 4–6 years are given; however, the psychopathic patients are not distinguished from others in the follow-up report. Sixteen patients (22%) were readmitted to a Special Hospital (5.5% following reconviction) and a further 15 (21%) were convicted and given other disposals; 25 (35%) were still being treated in the local hospital system and four (5.5%) had died. If relapse is taken as readmission or reconviction, a total of 31 (43%) had relapsed. This relapse rate is similar to the 40.4% reported by Tong & MacKay (1959) at Rampton.

The Aarvold Committee (1973) reported a four-year follow-up of 273 patients on restriction orders released into the community in 1966/1967. They found that reconviction was related to the type of release. The majority (70%) of those given unconditional discharges were reconvicted, whereas only 16% of those on conditional discharges reoffended. Over three-quarters of the conditionally discharged group were not recalled or reconvicted after four years, and 40% of these patients had originally been admitted to Special Hospital following a homicidal assault.

Acres (1975) considered the two-year outcome of the 17 women and 75 men who were released from all Special Hospitals in 1971 (the patients were treated in segregated wards). At follow-up, a third were in institutions: 13% were in prison; 17% had been returned to a Special Hospital; 2% were in a National Health Service (NHS) hospital; and 4% were dead. The 17% reconviction rate for the 28 patients with mental illness was substantially lower than the rates for those diagnosed as psychopaths (53% of 43 reconvicted) and subnormal (67% of 21 reconvicted). There was compulsory supervision by a probation officer or social worker for 39% of the group, and an additional 50% had voluntary supervision. Acres showed that those who had supervision had significantly lower rates of reconviction (44% v. 66%), and that those who were supervised but nevertheless reoffended had significantly fewer supervision contacts than those supervisees who did not reoffend (18.9 v. 27.1%).

Dell (1980, 1982) followed up 105 Special Hospital patients who were transferred to NHS units. She was interested in discovering factors relating to ease of transfer, and which patients ran into difficulties following transfer. Of 2200 Special Hospital patients in 1976, 8% were approved for transfer. Of the 161 patients transferred, 39 were women (24%), 100 were offenders (62%) and 17 had diagnoses of psychopathy (10.6%). Dell found that, after two years, 7 (6.6%) patients were recalled to Special Hospitals and 3 (2.8%) were convicted of serious offences. Unfortunately, no details are given of how relapse related to diagnosis of psychopathy.

Black (1982) studied male discharges from Broadmoor in order to "discover, if possible, the degree of success or failure of our discharging process and whether any features could be identified which might increase the efficiency of the process" (p. 308). As with other Special Hospital studies, it is noticeable that it is the discharging process rather the treatment outcome itself which is presented as the main focus of the study. The five-year study covered only those 125 males discharged direct to the community during 1960–65 (and still in England). This was 20% of the discharges in that period. (The majority of patients who leave Broadmoor are transferred to other psychiatric hospitals.) The men had been detained for an average of 7.5 years and 54 (42%) had a diagnosis of psychopathy. Information on readmission and recidivism was collected with the 'no news is good news' criterion of success being applied. The findings are shown in Table 9.1.

TABLE 9.1
Five-year outcome of 125 men from Broadmoor discharged directly into the community

Criterion	*Number*	*%*
Readmitted to any psychiatric hospital	36	29%
Any court appearance	50	40%
Reimprisoned	29	23%
Lived in the community for the whole five years	64	51%

From Black (1982).

Black does not present separate outcome figures for psychopaths. He states that the best predictors of success were having fewer previous psychiatric admissions and fewer previous criminal convictions. Being classed as having psychopathic disorder was also related to a poorer outcome. He suggests that this is probably because previous convictions are often related to the diagnosis of psychopathic disorder. The choice of sample makes generalisation to the rest of the Special Hospital population impossible, as the study sample was not representative of Broadmoor patients. The general hospital population at that time included 25% psychopathic disorder patients (42% of the study sample) and 6% affective illness patients (32% of the study sample). Psychotic patients were under-represented in the discharged sample.

In a further analysis of Black's data, Black & Spinks (1985) noted that only 13 (10.4%) of ex-patients committed dangerous assaults in the five-year follow-up. However, they were aware of four further assaultive offences, in subsequent years, committed by the study group, including two homicides. They do add the caveat that one of these homicides was of a fellow prisoner by an imprisoned ex-patient and therefore the public could still have considered themselves adequately protected.

Norris (1984) carried out an extensive study of the integration of male Special Hospital patients into the community. All 588 men leaving Broadmoor between 1974 and 1981 were examined to see which events or characteristics were associated with successful resettlement in the community. There were 330 men (56%) in the sample who had lived in the community at some time in the follow-up period and these were considered the "active core sample". (Others had been transferred to another Special or NHS hospital, had died, or had left the country.) A third of the core sample (104) had diagnoses of psychopathy or personality disorder.

Follow-up was for a minimum of three years after release. Some "police contact" was noted for 69% of the psychopaths and 47% of the schizophrenics from the core sample. New offences were committed by 48 psychopaths (46%) and 43 schizophrenics (19%). Overall, 64 core sample patients (20%) returned to an institution during the follow-up period, 14 patients (4.2%) were sentenced to prison, 28 (8.4%) were recalled to Special Hospital, and 22 (6.7%) were admitted to NHS hospitals.

Pre-admission psychiatric history and criminal history were significantly related to relapse for all patients, although it should be noted that pre-admission history was also the most important factor in determining diagnosis. There was also evidence that a longer length of stay was related to a better outcome for the psychopathic group, but not for mentally ill patients.

Tennent & Way (1984) considered men admitted to three British Special Hospitals between 1961 and 1965. By 1978 there were 617 (62%) who had been discharged and for whom follow-up information was available. Of these, 340 (55%) had reoffended (21% with violent offences). The mean length of time spent outside hospital was six years for the non-offenders and 7.5 years for the offenders. Predictors of violent reoffending were pre-admission multiple violence and juvenile institutionalisation. However, the recidivism of the 202 men held under the Mental Health Act category of psychopathic disorder was significantly higher than that of men having other classifications: 68% of these had reoffended, 28% (57) violently, and only 32% were free of offending on follow-up. Overall, 304 of the discharged men had been given a medical diagnosis of personality disorder. The recidivism rate for this group was 66% with 25% (78 men) reoffending violently. Considering only those of the original sample who reoffended, Tennent & Way established that 40% of the 340 reoffenders were classed as psychopaths and 60% had a personality disorder (although no diagnostic details are given).

Dell *et al* (1987) report on factors related to the length of detention in Broadmoor. In a sample of 76 psychopathic disordered male patients, they found that 53% spent more than eight years in hospital while 25% were released in less than four years. The length of stay was directly related to the severity of the index offence, with those committing violent or sexual offences and those with offences reported as "apparently motiveless" or related to jealousy or revenge being detained for the longest periods. This association was not found for 111 men with mental illness, except that sexual offences resulted in longer stays.

Robertson (1989) reports a 5–10-year follow-up of 121 men released from Broadmoor to non-secure facilities. The sample included 31 men (25%) admitted under the MHA category of psychopathic disorder: all these had been discharged within four years of admission and so they represent a specific 'short-stay' population of psychopaths. On follow-up, 12 (39%) of the psychopaths had reoffended, but serious reoffending was rare: four had committed actual bodily harm and there were six cases of criminal damage. Of the 90 mentally ill men, 24 (27%) had reoffended, but serious convictions in this group too were rare. This proportion of reoffenders in the mentally ill group did not differ significantly from the proportion in the psychopathic group.

Bailey & MacCulloch (1992*a*) considered 112 discharges from Park Lane Hospital direct to the community between 1974 and 1989. This represented 16% of admissions. Average length of stay was 42 months. (Some had already been in other Special Hospitals and transferred when Park Lane was opened.) In the whole sample of 112, 44% were classified as having psychopathic disorder and 46% were diagnosed personality disordered. After between six months and 14 years at liberty (mean six years), 55% of the psychopathic disorder group and 53% of the personality-disordered men had reoffended. Serious offences (i.e. homicide, rape, indecent assaults, arson and robbery) were committed by around 25% of each group. The reconviction rate was lower in the mental illness group, with 13 (21%) being reconvicted.

Bailey & MacCulloch (1992*b*) went on to examine the after-care given to the subjects of their initial study and reported that those who were conditionally discharged were reconvicted significantly less often than those given absolute discharges. However, detailed analysis of their results shows that this finding does not hold true for the psychopathic disorder group if their reconviction rates are analysed separately from those of the mentally ill group (see Chapter 10 for further discussion of this issue).

One important finding of this study was that almost all the reconvictions in the mentally ill sample occurred within three years of discharge, whereas reconvictions in the psychopathic group accumulated over the six-year mean follow-up period. This suggests that studies with a shorter follow-up period will tend to underestimate reconviction rates of discharged psychopaths.

MacCulloch *et al* (1993) report on the 19 patients from their original sample who seriously reoffended (i.e. committed homicide, serious assault, rape, robbery or arson). Of these, 13 were classified as having psychopathic disorder. MacCulloch *et al* consider these cases to represent "failures of the system which admitted, treated and discharged patients" and report on all the patients' pre-admission careers, diagnoses and outcomes. However, it is noteworthy that even in a detailed audit of these cases, which concludes by calling for "the provision of *appropriate* treatments" (their italics) the actual treatment received in the hospital is not reported.

Dolan *et al* (1993) note that although there is a substantial body of literature concerning characteristics of those who fail in the community after discharge from Special Hospitals, there is a dearth of studies reviewing the management of cases which fail and the processes involved in recall. In an audit of 'failed' (i.e. recalled) discharges from Ashworth Hospital between 1981 and 1991, Dolan *et al* found that, of 233 patients, 30 (12.8%) were recalled. However, they do not report separately on those patients who had mental illness and those who had psychopathic disorder. On the basis of a detailed audit of eight patients (including four having psychopathic disorder), they suggest that recall is a "seemingly chaotic system" and that once a patient relapsed or reoffended, recall appeared automatic regardless of the appropriateness of the decision. This study highlights how recall after discharge is an unsuitable measure of treatment outcome from Special Hospitals. However, recall has been used as a treatment outcome indicator in previous studies (Tong & MacKay, 1959; Gathercole *et al*, 1968).

Summary of Special Hospital studies

Although psychopaths in Special Hospitals are often considered as a homogeneous group, it should be noted that the studies reviewed above are of heterogeneous patient populations arising from hospitals with differing clinical management policies. The studies have used different methods of selecting their cohorts of patients, and the patients are discharged to different facilities after different lengths of treatment and follow-up. Additionally, the studies span three decades, during which both legal statutes and psychiatric treatment have changed. To aid an overview, the outcome data from the studies reviewed are summarised in Table 9.2, but direct comparison of studies is only tentative.

Despite these caveats, there are some constant features of these studies.

TABLE 9.2

Summary of studies of outcome of discharge from Special Hospitals (patients in some samples are of heterogeneous classifications, including psychopathy)

Study	*No. of subjects*	*Follow-up period*	*Criterion of failure*	*Rate*	*Description of sample*
Tong & MacKay (1959)	423	8.7 years	Readmitted to Special Hospital Reconvicted	20.1% 20.3%	Males discharged, tranferred or on licence; all diagnoses
Craft (1965)	75	–	Readmitted to Special Hospital	18.7%	Males discharged from 1951–62; all diagnoses
Gathercole *et al* (1968)	72	6.5 years	Readmitted to Special Hospital Reconvicted	22% 21%	All patients discharged, transferred or on licence; all diagnoses
Acres (1975)	92	2 years	Readmitted to Special Hospital Imprisoned	17% 13%	All patients released in 1971
	(28) (21) (43)	2 years	Reconvicted	17% 67% 53%	Mental illness Mentally subnormal MHA psychopaths
Black (1982)	125	5 years	Readmitted any hospital Imprisoned	29% 23%	Males discharged direct to the community; includes only 54 pyschopaths
Norris (1984)	330	3 years	Readmitted to Special Hospital Reamitted to NHS hospital	8.4% 6.7%	All males discharged to the community

Norris (1984)	330	≥ 3 years	Any new offence Police contact	46% 69%	MHA psychopaths discharged to the community
			Any new offence Police contact	19% 17%	Schizophrenic men discharged to the community
Tennent & Way (1984)	617	6 years	Any new offence Violent new offence	68% 28%	Discharged men held as MHA psychopaths
			Any new offence Violent new offence	66% 25%	Discharged men with personality disorder
			Any new offence Violent new offence	55% 21%	All males discharged; all diagnoses
Robertson (1989)	121	5-10 years	Reconvicted	30%	All men discharged to non-secure facilities
	(31) (90)	5–10 years	Reconvicted	39% 27%	MHA psychopaths Mental illness
Bailey & MacCulloch (1992*a*)	125	0.5–14 years	Any new offence Serious new offence	55% 25.5%	Discharged men held as MHA psychopaths
			Any new offence Serious new offence	53% 26%	Discharged men with personality disorder
			Any new offence Serious new offence	37% 17%	All males discharged; all diagnoses

Treatment

No study has reported upon the actual treatment given to the patients in hospital. Apart from reports on length of stay, the actual treatment received is not considered as a possible outcome variable. The one study which has considered length of treatment received by recidivists and non-recidivists (Norris, 1984) showed that longer time in therapy produced better outcome. However, none of the available studies allow outcome of psychopathy to be related to the type of treatment received.

Subjects

The majority of studies do not include women in their samples, and even those two which do (Gathercole *et al*, 1968; Acres, 1975) fail to report outcome for female psychopaths, or even distinguish follow-up findings of female from male patients in general.

Patients' psychological state

None of the reviewed studies has considered changes in patients' psychological state while in hospital or on follow-up. Mainly, data presented have been confined to subsequent life history events, recall from conditional discharge, recidivism and readmission to hospital.

Patients' disorder

Outcome for patients with psychopathic disorder is often not reported separately from that of other diagnostic groups (Tong & MacKay, 1959; Craft, 1965; Gathercole *et al*, 1968; Dell, 1980; Black, 1982).

Worse outcome for patients with psychopathic disorder

When studies do discriminate on the basis of diagnostic categories, a worse outcome in terms of recidivism and/or rehospitalisation for psychopathic disorder patients compared with mentally ill patients is often reported (Acres, 1975; Tennent & Way, 1984; Norris, 1984; Bailey & MacCulloch, 1992*a*). However, Robertson (1989) found no significant difference between the post-discharge reoffending rates of psychopathic and mentally ill patients who were admitted to Broadmoor for less than four years.

Reoffending

Approximately half of discharged psychopathic or personality-disordered patients reoffend within three years (Tennent & Way, 1984; Norris, 1984; Bailey & MacCulloch, 1992*a*). Serious or violent offences are committed by around a quarter of psychopaths (Tennent & Way, 1984; Bailey & MacCulloch, 1992*a*).

Life history factors

Life history factors associated with a good outcome after release for psychopathic patients are:

(a) fewer previous hospital admissions (Black, 1982; Norris, 1984; Dell & Robertson, 1988)
(b) fewer previous criminal convictions (Black, 1982; Norris, 1984)
(c) a previous conviction for homicide (Aarvold Committee, 1973)
(d) not having been in an institution as a juvenile (Tennent & Way, 1984)
(e) fewer previous convictions for violent offences (Tennent & Way, 1984)
(f) longer stay in hospital (Norris, 1984)
(g) supervision and after-care (Acres, 1975; Norris, 1984)
(h) being on conditional discharge (Aarvold Committee, 1973).

Approach of studies

Dell *et al* (1987) point out how psychopathic disorder is very different from mental illness, and note that patients often are not thought to need psychiatric detention unless they have committed offences. It is difficult for doctors to monitor the course of psychopathic disorder in the same way they may do schizophrenia, where the psychiatric illness rather than the nature of offence is the dominant consideration. For the psychopathic disordered offender the choice of treatment is seldom clear and it is felt difficult to establish when relevant change has occurred. It is not surprising that the patient's offending assumes inappropriate importance and reoffending becomes a primary focus of outcome. Therefore, throughout the Special Hospital research, much of focus is upon prediction of recidivism and features of the client which can aid this prediction.

Researchers seem to be swayed by this view and minimise the importance of changes in psychiatric or psychological features of the patient. In addition, research which continues to ignore psychological change merely serves to reinforce the prevailing attitude that the outcome of treatment has more to do with the features of the incoming client than anything which happens during his/her stay in hospital. Although there is good evidence that "as is the case for penal offenders it is the preadmission criminal profile that is the best predictor of reoffending" (Grounds, 1987, p. 476), nevertheless it should be noted that no Special Hospital study has addressed the issue of how the actual psychiatric treatment received relates to reoffending.

Special Hospital studies in general take a criminological rather than a psychological or psychiatric approach and are primarily concerned with the appropriateness of the decision to discharge the patient (Black, 1982). This view may not be surprising given the responsibility held by the discharging responsible medical officer and the potential repercussions of discharging a patient who then reoffends seriously (Coid, 1992). However, evaluation of discharge decisions seems to have become the main concern, at the expense of any true evaluation of treatment or comparison of different types of treatment offered within a single Special Hospital.

It is telling that the Special Hospital Case Register, set up in 1972 to record the particulars of patients in Special Hospitals, collects information about criminal background, psychiatric history, social background and diagnosis, but that data about the patient's progress or treatment in hospital are not collected (Dell *et al*, 1987).

Although long-term in-patient 'milieu therapy' in hospital (which attends to various aspects of the patient's behaviour, character and symptoms) may be a valuable approach, no treatment studies have been able to consider which treatment, or aspect of the 'milieu' is the most effective. Without this information one cannot judge the appropriate balance of the elements of therapy. Such information would be potentially useful as it may lead to refinement and increased efficacy of in-patient programmes and, in turn, a shorter period of compulsory admission for the patient.

In-patient 'milieu treatment' in non-British maximum-security units

Follow-up studies are reviewed below from three maximum-security units, in Canada, Denmark and Austria. These units are very roughly equivalent to British Special Hospitals in that they detain 'psychopathic' patients for indeterminate treatment under the relevant mental health legislation of the country or state. However, they are all seen as part of the prison service rather than the health service.

Patuxent Institution, USA

Patuxent was opened in 1955 as a maximum-security treatment institution for 500 inmates held under the Maryland Defective Delinquent Statute. A defective delinquent was defined as:

> "an individual who, by the demonstration of persistent aggravated antisocial or criminal behavior, evidences a propensity toward criminal activity, and who is found to have either such intellectual deficiency or emotional imbalance, or both, as to clearly demonstrate an actual danger to society." Article 31B, Maryland Legislature (1951)

The original method of operation was that individuals held at Patuxent were on indeterminate sentences, incarcerated until, as a result of treatment, they no longer presented a threat to society. A progressive tier system classified inmates in four tiers of improvement, the highest tier leading to parole or release. The treatment at Patuxent consists of milieu therapy, with therapists involved in the day-to-day lives of inmates. Treatment methods include individual depth therapy, group therapy, and psychotropic drugs. Patuxent has its own paroling authority and after-care is an important part of treatment.

Patuxent is usually described an as 'experimental' unit, yet, despite 20 years of existence in its original form, all systematic evaluations of outcome have used only recidivism as their criterion (Lejins, 1977). In an initial study of the first eight years of Patuxent, Boslow & Kohlmeyer (1963) found that, of 81 men paroled, 41 (51%) violated their parole, although only 28 (35%) committed new offences. For the remaining parolees, it was thought that their adjustment was too tenuous for them to remain in the community without treatment. Ten men had been given unconditional discharge after their parole and none of these had reoffended by the time of the study. Of the 71 men who went on weekend leave or holiday leave or worked outside the institution, 26 (36.6%) had their leave rescinded, but reoffending accounted for only 9 (12.6%) of these instances.

In the first 11 years of Patuxent's existence, 740 men were admitted and a further 156 were judged to be 'defective delinquents' by Patuxent staff but were not committed by the courts.

Hodges (1971) compared recidivism rates in three groups of these Patuxent subjects (using first admissions only): 156 men "treated" and released on parole; 112 "partially treated" men who were released by the court during their stay; and 129 men accepted by Patuxent but adjudicated not defective by the court and therefore committed to conventional custody and "untreated" (360 other admitted men were still in confinement). After three years, post-release conviction rates were: 37% in the treated group; 71% in the partially treated group; and 81% in the untreated group. However, a further 31 (20%) of the treated group returned to Patuxent for further treatment during the follow-up period; therefore a 'failure' rate of 57% is probably a fairer estimate for the treated group. Hodges claims that his findings support the use of the indeterminate sentence for these offenders, as "without the statute 807 men diagnosed as defective delinquents would have served fixed sentences and an 81% recidivism rate in this group would have produced 654 recidivists" (p. 74). However, later studies of Patuxent consider both arrests and convictions of men paroled and question the earlier success rates.

Steadman (1977) studied recidivism by Patuxent inmates using five comparison groups:

(1) all inmates on parole status in 1971–72 ($n = 106$)
(2) all inmates released by redetermination hearings or legal technicalities in 1971–72 ($n = 105$)
(3) all inmates referred for evaluation and accepted by Patuxent staff but not certified by the courts 1964–72 ($n = 46$)
(4) inmates referred in 1967 but not accepted by Patuxent staff ($n = 39$)
(5) inmates paroled from other Maryland correctional facilities in 1971–72 ($n = 74$).

Pre-incarceration history showed that men in group 1, who can be considered as having completed treatment, had been arrested, convicted and incarcerated more often than those in any other group. This finding would be expected given the 'defective delinquent' criterion (above) for admission to Patuxent. Group 1 entered Patuxent with longer sentences and were detained longer than other groups, although their average detention of seven years was only 57% of the average maximum sentence. Group 2, who terminated treatment before completion, had been detained for an average of five years but had actually completed 86% of their maximum sentence at release.

TABLE 9.3
Criminal activity three years after release of Patuxent parolees and comparison groups

Group	*Arrested:* %	*Convicted:* %	*Mean no. of arrests*	*Violent arrests:* %	*Violent convictions:* %
1	60.4	23.6	0.9	31.2	8.5
2	74.3	54.3	1.8	33.3	25.7
3	67.4	32.6	1.7	41.3	17.4
4	66.7	43.6	1.8	33.3	17.9
5	63.5	35.1	1.2	24.3	16.2

Data from Steadman (1977).

All subjects had been at liberty for at least three years on follow-up and comprehensive FBI records provided re-arrest and reconviction data for the subjects in this period. The results found are shown in Table 9.3.

Little difference was found in the proportion of men ever re-arrested in the five groups, although the Patuxent parolees had slightly lower re-arrest rates and the mean number of arrests was noticeably lower than for other groups. Fewer of the Patuxent parolees were subsequently reconvicted, but it is possible that for the Patuxent parolees re-arrest led to their parole being revoked and their return to Patuxent without conviction occurring.

Steadman (1977) summarises his findings as follows: "inmates certified as defective delinquents (DD) come into Patuxent with worse prior records and are subsequently re-arrested and reconvicted at rates similar to or lower than those persons found DD by Patuxent staff but not committed, those evaluated DD by Patuxent staff but returned to correctional facilities and those who spend their whole time in correctional facilities and for whom the question of DD is never raised" (p. 206).

A summary of the studies of outcome from Patuxent is given in Table 9.4.

A cost-effectiveness analysis of Patuxent (Singer & Bloom, 1977) compared 102 inmates with 46 offenders in other Maryland high-security establishments who had been considered 'defective delinquents' by Patuxent staff but who had not been so adjudged by the courts at their commitment hearings. Again, the groups

TABLE 9.4
Summary of studies of outcome from Patuxent institution

Study	*No. of subjects*	*Follow-up period*	*Criterion*	*Rate*	*Total*
Boslow (1963)	81	1–8 years	Reoffended	35%	51%
			Returned from parole	18%	
Hodges (1971	156	3 years	Reoffended	37%	57%
			Returned from parole	20%	
Steadman (1977)	106	5 years	Reconvicted	24%	60%
			Re-arrested (no conviction)	36%	

differed in that the Patuxent groups had more previous convictions and incarceration episodes; they had committed more violent crime and were older than the inmates from conventional prisons.

The cost analysis considered the monetary cost to the state of incarceration and estimated inmates' loss of earnings during incarceration. The 'effectiveness' measure used was post-release FBI arrest records. The minimum post-release follow-up time for any subject was three years.

Incarceration at Patuxent cost 57% more per inmate than at conventional prisons, at that time ($5300 v. $3370 per annum). However, while Patuxent ran at design capacity, the conventional high-security prisons were running at 133–200% of design capacity. Such overcrowding significantly reduces capital costs per head. However, even if capital costs were similar, Patuxent would still be more expensive per inmate once the costs of assessment, treatment, education, redetermination hearings, parole, the pre-release centre, provision of a halfway house and the longer stay at Patuxent were added to the equation. Overall cost per inmate incarceration episode was estimated at $101 910 for Patuxent compared with $46 640 in a conventional prison.

Rather than take a basic recidivism measure, the researchers tried to account for the differences in previous criminal histories of the two groups by measuring effectiveness in terms of the number of re-arrests which were likely to result in reincarceration, given the offenders' previous arrest and incarceration histories. Using this method, they estimated that, after three years, the average ex-Patuxent inmate would commit 0.69 crimes leading to reincarceration, compared with a rate of 0.72 for normal system inmates. Singer & Bloom (1977) concluded that Patuxent was not a cost-efficient use of resources, given that it cost twice as much as the conventional system to incarcerate an inmate and its effectiveness in reducing crime was not substantially different.

The findings of the studies cited above from Singer & Bloom (1977) and Steadman (1977) were used to support the abolition of indeterminate sentencing for psychopathic offenders in Maryland. In 1977, the indeterminate sentence legislature was repealed and Patuxent now operates an intensive treatment programme to which convicted criminals can be transferred while under sentence (Lejins, 1977). Carney (1981) considers that the new legislation did not essentially affect the treatment programme. However, he notes that with short determinate sentences some psychopaths may now be considered untreatable who with a longer sentence might be seen as an acceptable treatment candidates.

Herstedvester, Denmark

Herstedvester treats recidivist criminals, described as antisocial with a persistent pattern of social and interpersonal difficulty (Stürup & Reid, 1981). Inmates may have an indefinite sentence and are received from all Danish penal institutions and courts. The therapy programme is based upon "humanitarian responses to incarcerated men and aims to strengthen self-respect and responsibility". The regime at Herstedvester has been termed "integrated individualised group-therapy", but Stürup (1959) points out how all aspects of the milieu contribute to change in patients. Physical treatment (medical and surgical) is used alongside psychological methods.

Many anecdotal clinical reports of improvement have been written (Stürup 1974), with claims that over 50% of patients can resume normal life in the community after treatment. Stürup (1953) reported outcome of 199 sex offenders admitted under the Danish 'psychopathy' law: 159 men (80%) had been discharged and after 4–17 years were successfully holding employment in the community. However, of these 159 men, 51 (32%) had reoffended (27 sexual and 24 non-sexual offences). The 99 men had been castrated and had a lower reoffending rate for sexual offences than those 60 men not castrated (5% v. 36%), but had a similar reoffending rate for non-sexual offences (14% v. 17%).

One study following treatment was developed from the suggestion that recidivism may be related to social and economic factors. Offenders were offered the same social security help as those with disability and given a 'pension' rather than having to live on welfare payments as an ex-convict. Littauer & Kjærgård (1971) followed up 91 detainees released from Herstedvester for 2–5 years after the commencement of their 'pension'. Around 70% of these men had originally been convicted for property offences, 20% for sexual offences and 10% for violence and arson. The frequency of new sentences ("relapse") was 20%, 10% and 10% respectively. Although these results seem good, no comparison was made with non-pensioned offenders.

Justizanstalt Mittersteig, Austria

Justizanstalt Mittersteig, in Vienna, is a treatment facility within the Austrian prison system. 'Psychopathic' offenders are committed to Mittersteig for treatment following the court proceedings and make up 16% of the institution's population. Berner & Karlick-Bolten (1986) studied the five-year outcome of men discharged from prison after their first sex offence. They compared recidivism of 52 men having diagnoses of ICD–9 sociopathic personality disorder (PD) with 13 men having ICD–9 diagnoses of schizophrenia (S) and 15 having neurotic disorders only (N). When all offences were considered, the recidivism rate five years after release was highest for the personality-disordered men and lowest for those who had schizophrenia (76% for PD v. 16.7% for S v. 54% for N); sexual offences were also committed by significantly more personality-disordered men (48% for PD v. 16.7% for S v. for 17% N).

Summary

Reports on follow-up of treatment of psychopaths in 'milieu' therapy settings are limited by the almost total reliance upon recidivism and readmission as outcome criteria. However, that aside, two early studies of treatment in non-secure hospitals (Heaver, 1943; Craft, 1958) do suggest that a good outcome can be obtained for psychopathic patients who do not need high levels of security. These are both uncontrolled studies and outcome for both was, in the main, based upon clinical judgement, so conclusions are only tentative.

Follow-up studies in the more secure environments of Special Hospitals suggest that, for some patients, detained under the MHA psychopathy category, hospital admission results in a reduction in offending. Although the 'success' rate is poorer than that found for mentally ill patients, around 50% of psychopaths do not reoffend within three years, and serious violent offences are committed by a quarter of those released. However, the lack of importance or attention given to the actual treatment received by patients makes commentating about efficacy of specific treatment methods impossible. No controlled studies of treatment versus non-treatment or comparing two different treatment approaches are available, so it cannot be assumed that it is the therapy rather than passage of time that is effecting change.

Milieu therapy in non-British maximum-security settings has also shown some improvement in inmates' recidivism following incarceration. Two studies at Patuxent have shown that those men who complete treatment have a significantly lower reconviction rate than men 'partially' treated or referred but 'untreated' because of legal decisions. However, the factors contributing to some men not having a full course of treatment before release from Patuxent may also be correlated with reoffending. In Denmark, Herstedvester has also suggested good outcome results, but again no controlled trials are available. The patients at Special Hospitals, Patuxent and Herstedvester may represent the most difficult psychopathically disordered offenders to control within a conventional system, and the most likely to reoffend; however, without appropriate descriptions of treatment and randomised controlled trials, conclusions about the efficacy of the institutions must remain guarded.

10 Community supervision

It is perhaps more suitable to classify community supervision as a form of patient management than a treatment modality. Nevertheless, analyses of research into the effects of community surveillance of offenders as a condition of their release from prison (Palmer, 1992) and conditions of supervision of patients discharged from maximum-security hospitals (MacCulloch & Bailey, 1993) suggest that community supervision could act as an essential adjunct to treatment programmes for psychopaths. But, when evaluating any programme of community supervision, it must be determined at the outset exactly what the supervision entailed and what the ultimate goals of the programme were. For example, did the programme primarily involve surveillance as an alternative to institutionalisation, but still involving significant punitive or restrictive elements, or was it primarily designed to be rehabilitative? Community supervision of psychopaths cannot be fully evaluated unless this dichotomy is understood. Furthermore, the official pressures on professionals involved in supervision may be in one direction, while their personal goals of clinical management may be quite different.

The most important evidence in support of community supervision in reducing recidivism comes from research into studies of the effects of parole on previously sentenced prisoners. Hann *et al* (1991) reviewed a number of research studies from Canada, the USA, and the UK which suggested that offenders granted parole are reconvicted less often than those for whom parole is not granted. (Parole involves the supervised release on licence of prisoners before expiry of their sentence.) These research studies had included a measure of risk of reconviction in the form of a statistical predictor. Previous research had shown that predictor scales could be devised which were powerful instruments and were robust across time and between prisoner groups. Outcome studies indicated that paroled groups of prisoners tended to be reconvicted less often than expected using such instruments. More importantly, when prisoners granted parole and prisoners refused parole, were followed up after release, it was found that parole prisoners were reconvicted less often, except for those in the highest risk groups in one UK study. Hann and colleagues rejected the conventional position that this reflected the skill of parole boards in identifying variables which predict reconviction, but which were not incorporated into the statistical predictors used in these studies, arguing that studies have shown that parole boards have not managed to out-perform statistical predictors. Their hypothesis was that something about the granting or the process of parole itself seems to work to reduce reconviction. But they also conceded that current research has not yet identified what factors are important within these processes.

When considering the community supervision of psychopaths, however, there are several more difficult questions to consider. The first is whether supervision conveys any clear benefit. The second is how this should be measured: for example, should it be primarily in terms of reconviction or in other forms of social readjustment? The third question is whether community supervision should employ a primarily rehabilitative model or programmes designed to protect the public by increasing control and surveillance; at the same time, which elements of any programme (which is likely to contain both approaches to some degree) are the most effective? The fourth question is whether any specific resources or new programmes are necessary to implement a more effective programme of community supervision in the future.

Evaluating community surveillance of psychopaths

No study has specifically set out to evaluate whether psychopaths released into the community and allocated to community supervision or a controlled form of management (or simply no supervision at all) have a better outcome at follow-up. In Britain, legislative powers under the Mental Health Act 1983 allow for compulsory supervision of psychopaths under the terms of section 41, which can be imposed by a Crown Court in addition to a hospital order when an individual is considered a potential danger to the public. Such patients can only be discharged from hospital by the Home Secretary or by a Mental Health Review Tribunal. Discharge can then be 'absolute' or 'conditional,' the latter usually involving conditions of residence, treatment, and attendance at a specified place to see one or more supervisors on a regular basis. As it is usual for supervisors to consist of a named psychiatrist and a social worker or probation officer, it is often assumed that the supervision involves supervision in a rehabilitative sense. Closer examination of the procedures involved, including regular updates on progress expected in the form of a report to C3 Division of the Home Office, will indicate that surveillance, involving a component of public protection, is implicit in this form of community supervision.

Chapter 9 documents how several studies have demonstrated that patients who have been detained under the legal category 'mental illness' rather than 'psychopathic disorder' have a better prognosis in terms of reoffending after subsequent release into the community (see also Home Office, 1993). Furthermore, follow-up studies of Special Hospital patients seem to suggest a better prognosis, using the same measure of outcome, for patients who are given a conditional rather than an absolute discharge, although these advantages are not as marked when serious reoffending is examined. Unfortunately, it is possible to compare the effects of receiving a conditional or absolute discharge on reoffending by psychopaths using data from only two follow-up studies. Either the comparisons where not carried out by other researchers, or else the categories of mental disorder were combined to obscure the effect on the subjects of interest in this volume. This method has several major limitations, however, which are described below.

Park Lane Hospital Follow-Up Study

Bailey & MacCulloch (1992*a*,*b*) followed up the first 106 male patients discharged from Park Lane (subsequently known as Ashworth North) Special Hospital from 1974 to 1989. Subjects had been detained under the Mental Health Act legal category 'mental illness' ($n = 61$) or 'psychopathic disorder' ($n = 50$). The majority of the former category had diagnoses of paranoid schizophrenia. No details are given of ICD or DSM diagnostic categories of the psychopathic group, other than that they had received a diagnosis of personality disorder. Follow-up ranged from 5 months to 14 years, with a mean of 6 years for the entire sample. Overall, 41 subjects (37%) were reconvicted after discharge. However, 28 (55%) of the psychopathic-disorder group were reconvicted compared with 13 (21%) of the mental illness group, a statistically significant finding ($X^2 = 14.19$, d.f. $= 1$, $P = 0.0004$).

TABLE 10.1

Comparison of reconvictions of absolutely and conditionally discharged psychopaths (n=50) (average follow-up 6 years, range 6 months to 14 years)

	Conditional discharge (n=36)	*Absolute discharge (n=14)*	X^2 *(with Yates' correction)*
All offences			
Not offended	19 (53%)	3 (21%)	X^2=2.85, P = 0.09
Offended	17 (47%)	11 (79%)	CI = -0.58 to -0.04
Serious offences			
No serious offences	28 (78%)	9 (64%)	X^2 = 0.38, P = 0.53
Serious offence	8 (22%)	5 (36%)	CI = -0.15 to +0.42

CI, 95% confidence interval.
Data from: Bailey & MacCulloch (1992*b*, Tables 2, 3).

Subjects were divided into those who received an absolute discharge and those who received a conditional discharge. A conditional discharge involved at least one supervising officer (usually a probation officer or social worker), usually in conjunction with a supervising psychiatrist, and required the patient to report at regular intervals for a review, along with other conditions such as continuation of medication and residence at a specified location. The patient was liable to recall to hospital if these conditions were not complied with or if there was a deterioration in mental state or in the patient's behaviour. In this series, conditional discharges were most commonly applied to those subjects who had committed the most serious offences, such as homicides and rapes. None of the subjects who had originally been convicted of property offences received a conditional discharge. Table 10.1 shows the reconvictions of the psychopathic subjects according to whether they received an absolute or conditional discharge. Data from the original paper have been reanalysed for this table (Bailey & MacCulloch, 1992*b*).

Table 10.1 shows that, although there is a tendency for psychopathic disorder subjects who received an absolute discharge to be reconvicted more often than those who received a conditional discharge (79% v. 47%), the difference between the groups is not statistically significant when Yates' correction is applied to the X^2 test to account for the small sample sizes. Also, for serious reoffending there is no significant difference between the groups.

Bailey & MacCulloch had originally demonstrated overall superiority at follow-up for the conditional discharge group in comparison with the discharge group, but it seems that this finding arises from combining the mental illness and psychopathic disorder subjects. Bailey & MacCulloch argued that this reduction in recidivism may lie in the process of compulsory supervision in the community of those who receive a conditional discharge. Furthermore, those selected for conditional discharge are perceived as a greater risk to the public, particularly in relation to serious reoffending. But the reanalysis would suggest that the authors' positive findings for conditional discharge were contributed to mainly by the mental illness group. Furthermore, for the mental illness and psychopathic disorder groups combined, the overall rate of serious reoffending did not differ between the absolute discharge and conditional discharge groups. The authors were not impressed by the argument that a high level of previous convictions for property offences was likely to predispose one subgroup or another to similar convictions, and that such a group (in the absence of serious offences) may have been the most likely to receive an absolute discharge, as well as being the most likely to have been reconvicted, albeit of a minor offence. But despite the authors' arguments to the contrary, and without more information on the previous patterns of offending in the absolute and conditional discharge groups, it still cannot be assumed that the reduction in recidivism in the conditionally discharged group was entirely due to the process of community supervision. It would appear that some index of risk of reoffending must be taken into account in any future studies with such subjects, where random allocation to one group or another cannot be officially sanctioned.

The Oxford Survey

Walker & McCabe (1973) carried out a survey of all patients made subject to hospital orders by courts in Oxfordshire, England, from April 1963 to March 1964. In a subsequent part of their study, they followed up the subjects leaving hospital and examined the reconvictions for 105 females and 351 males one to two years later. Subjects had been detained under the Mental Health Act 1959, and by re-examining their data it is possible to partially estimate the effect of community supervision on subsequent reconviction in those detained as legal 'psychopaths' and 'subnormals'. Subjects detained under the legal category 'subnormality' can be considered an overlapping group with the 'psychopaths', differentiated primarily by their level of intelligence, the definition otherwise remaining the same for the two categories. This study is of major importance as the authors constructed an index of risk, giving a score for each subject according to

(a) any previous convictions
(b) a history of previous custodial sentences
(c) a category of psychopathic disorder or subnormality, and, in male subjects, whether they had been unemployed at the time of the offence.

A slightly different scoring system was adopted for the two sexes, which are therefore examined separately below. The majority of the cohort had middle-range scores, but 37% were considered "high" risk or "low" risk individuals. Although the study included a majority of patients suffering from mental illness, data were analysed according to whether particular subjects who fell into any group according to risk scores were likely to receive a further conviction, according to whether they later received after-care or not. The most serious limitation in the re-examination of these data is that the exact number of psychopaths and subnormals within each risk category is not actually available. Walker & McCabe described those in the highest category (groups 3 and 4, Table 10.2) as comprising "mainly psychopaths and subnormals with substantial experience of penal institutions". For the purpose of their study, "after-care" was defined as follow-up supervision by health-care professionals which was "more than casual, unplanned contacts, or single visits to out-patient departments. Trial leave was treated as after-care."

Data from their original study have been re-examined and are presented in Table 10.2, which compares all male subjects according to whether they received after-care or not and according to their risk scores. Surprisingly, subjects who had the highest risk scores were significantly more likely to be discharged, or otherwise leave hospital, without after-care having been arranged for them. This finding may be of considerable concern in the light of the final overall outcome, where only 39 (28%) of those receiving after-care were later reconvicted, compared with 109 (51%) who received no after-care, a highly significant difference ($X^2 = 17.1$, d.f. = 1, $P < 0.0001$). Table 10.3 redistributes male subjects from Walker & McCabe's original table into risk score groups and compares the rates of reoffending of those who received after-care and those who did not. The table shows the results of X^2 tests in the different score categories, as to whether or not receiving after-care was followed by reconviction. After-care in the lower risk

TABLE 10.2
Male subjects receiving after-care according to risk score (n=351)

Risk score	*After-care (n=138)*	*No after-care (n=213)*	X^2 *test*
0	24 (17%)	25 (12%)	$X^2 = 9.8$, d.f. = 3, $P = 0.02$
1	58 (42%)	73 (34%)	
2	37 (27%)	58 (27%)	
3 + 4	19 (14%)	57 (28%)	

Data from Walker & McCabe (1973, Table 23).

categories conveyed no significant advantage in terms of reconviction. But in the higher risk categories (which, according to the authors, contained a majority of psychopaths with the greatest likelihood of reoffending) the risk of reconviction was significantly increased when subjects did not receive after-care.

Table 10.4 shows a similar analysis carried out for the female subjects. The table suggests a trend for the groups with a higher risk score to be reconvicted if not receiving after-care, but none of these comparisons are statistically significant. Among the entire sample, 10 (20%) of the women who received after-care were reconvicted, compared with 22 (39%) of those who received no after-care; this difference in proportions was not statistically significant. However, caution should be exercised when interpreting results from such a small sample of women with a low overall reconviction rate.

As with the follow-up study of Bailey & MacCulloch (1992*a,b*), these findings cannot prove conclusively that community supervision reduced reconviction rates. An alternative explanation could be that those offender patients for whom it is easier to arrange after-care (for other reasons) are also less likely to be reconvicted. For example, they may have been more cooperative or less likely to drift out of touch than those whom health care professionals realistically did not recommend for after-care. But if this had been the case, then the association should have also been absent from the high-risk groups. Since after-care is intended to reduce the likelihood of relapse, the results of the reanalysis are consistent with the hypothesis that it does. If these results were confirmed in future studies, however, it would indicate that for the high-risk psychopaths, after-care is especially warranted.

TABLE 10.3

Comparison of reconviction of men according to risk score and after-care (n=351)

Risk score	*After-care (n=138)* Reconviction	*After-care (n=138)* No reconviction	*No after-care (n=213)* Reconviction	*No after-care (n=213)* No reconviction	χ^2 (*with Yates' correction*)
0	2	22	8	17	2.89 ($P = 0.09$)
1	20	38	23	50	0.03 ($P = 0.8$)
2	8	29	33	25	6.2 ($P = 0.01$)
3 + 4	9	10	45	12	5.5 ($P = 0.02$)
All men	39	99	109	104	17.1 ($P < 0.001$)

Data from Walker & McCabe (1973, p. 192, Table 23).

TABLE 10.4

Comparison of reconviction of women according to risk score and after-care (n=105)

Risk score	*After-care (n=49)* Reconviction	*After-care (n=49)* No reconviction	*No after-care (n=56)* Reconviction	*No after-care (n=56)* No reconviction	χ^2 (*with Yates' correction*)
0	1	17	1	17	0.53 ($P = 0.6$)
1	3	14	5	9	0.54 ($P = 0.5$)
2	2	6	9	8	0.78 ($P = 0.41$)
3 + 4	4	2	7	0	0.79 ($P = 0.39$)
All women	10	39	22	34	3.5 ($P = 0.06$)

Data from Walker & McCabe (1973, p. 192, Table 23).

Problems of community supervision

The dichotomy between risk reduction, in terms of reoffending, versus rehabilitation has been explored in several reviews of community casework, parole, and probation supervision (see Clear &

O'Leary, 1983; Rodger, 1988; Rumgay, 1990). This conflict of approach will apply equally to the supervision of mentally disordered offenders by health care professionals. For example, the probation service has voiced its concern that it could be forced to abandon the rehabilitative goals of its profession for an alternative 'punishment' model of close surveillance and the restriction of offenders' movements in the community, as an alternative to imprisonment for political reasons and to reduce prison overcrowding. It has been argued that such alternatives to incarceration are not really alternatives at all and that they can do more harm than good.

An important US study does give partial support to this ethical argument, and serves as an important lesson for any programme which is designed to rehabilitate psychopaths, but where the main aim is to protect the public from their reoffending. In a Texan study of two cities (Dallas and Houston), researchers randomised parolees to intensive supervision parole (ISP) or routine parole, with the intention of observing whether, by intensifying the level of surveillance of released offenders in the community the level of criminal recidivism would be reduced (Turner & Petersilia, 1992). ISP subjects received more counselling and participated in more work training, and had more face-to-face contacts with their supervising officers, telephone checks, and checks for substance abuse. High-risk subjects were deliberately selected for this study with the highest probability of returning to prison, as measured by previous parole performance and serious previous criminal recidivism. It could be argued that the subjects chosen may have been in the higher range of scores on the Hare psychopathy scale (see Chapter 2). Unfortunately, at the end of the first year of study, ISP was not associated with a reduction of re-arrests, despite the raised level of surveillance. Instead, it was associated with increased levels of technical violations of parole; particularly in Houston, where the ISP model was implemented more fully. Thus, by the end of the year, 30% of all ISP parolees were returned to prison compared with 18% of subjects on routine parole. It was concluded that the ISP group could have been committing fewer crimes (self-reported crime was not measured), but in terms of all arrests, seriousness of arrests, and the total number of arrests while on parole, there were no differences between the ISP and routine parole groups at the end of a one-year period. Violations of parole conditions which had been detected by the ISP model, rather than criminal arrests, had accounted for the higher level of incarceration of the ISP group by the end of the study period. Furthermore, a cost analysis of the study found that instead of saving the State of Texas money, the cost of ISP supervision was 1.7 times that of routine parole.

It was concluded that the ISP programme had constituted an appropriate intermediate punishment, which had been one part of the Texas Board of Pardons and Paroles' original objectives. Thus, if it was the aim to provide flexibility in terms of sentencing by providing an option of an intermediate punishment to fit the crimes of these offenders more closely, then ISP had been highly successful. Similarly, there was some suggestion that the increased level of surveillance could fit better with the concept of protection of the public from known recidivists showing worrying signs of a tendency or predisposition to further offending. However, there was ultimately no improvement found on recidivism as a result of intensive supervision of high-risk parolees, so this argument is not sustained, and the final costs of the programme were higher.

The implications of this study for the community supervision of psychopaths by health care professionals are clear. Any hope of simultaneously reducing prison or hospital overcrowding, enhancing the public's safety, and rehabilitating psychopaths (all at a cost saving) is totally unrealistic. It is therefore essential for future studies to be specific as to what the goals of the treatment programme actually are from the outset, what model of supervision will be used, and the degree to which the programme will involve surveillance and/or rehabilitation, along with a realistic appraisal of what the programme can be expected to accomplish.

Unfortunately, community supervision of psychopaths released from UK Special Hospitals does not always appear to proceed along these recommended guidelines. This may potentially disadvantage supervisors who take on high-risk groups of patients and where reconviction rates are significantly higher than those of patients detained under the legal category 'mental illness'. In a follow-up study of released patients, Norris (1984) revealed that many medical and social supervisors do not understand their role in supervision, especially those who supervise psychopaths. Some supervisors voiced their opinion that the patient did not benefit from supervision and that they themselves or the patient resented the process, particularly in the case of patients subject to restriction orders under section 41 of the Mental Health Act 1983. It appeared from Norris's study that the better socially integrated patients were significantly more likely to resent their supervision. In some cases, reoffending (rather than relapse of mental illness) by the patient came as a form of relief for the supervisor. It meant that the 'patient' could be dealt with by the criminal justice system and the wearisome and unsatisfactory supervision of the patient could cease. Often, behaviour which previously had been regarded as symptomatic of a mental disorder, and for which the patient's responsibility had been considered to be altered as a result, could be redefined as 'criminal'. The patient now became responsible for behaviour which had previously justified compulsory hospitalisation for years of treatment.

The burden imposed by high-risk patients cannot be underestimated. It has been argued that the responsibility for psychopaths in the community should not be undertaken without adequate facilities, and that there is a genuine risk to professional and institutional reputations when these patients reoffend (Coid & Cordess, 1992). Accepting clinical responsibility for community supervision may in itself lead to personal blame and accusations of unsatisfactory professional performance, within a wider background of official reluctance to take personal responsibility for the release of high-risk offenders, with the possibility of a political and public outcry if such individuals reoffend seriously. In one medium-secure unit which accepted 20 psychopaths transferred from maximum-security hospitals over a ten-year period, two reoffended seriously (one homicide, one rape) following conditional discharges to the community from the unit (Cope & Ward, 1993). Official enquiries in each case failed to fault the quality of clinical assessment or community supervision by the responsible clinical team. Nevertheless, if health care professionals risk a public enquiry into their clinical practice for 1 out of every 10 of their psychopathic patients, then few will be willing to accept such an onerous responsibility in the future.

Case management for psychopaths

Within the rehabilitative model of community supervision, further evaluation is required of the suitability of the system of 'case management' (Renshaw, 1988; Kanter, 1989; Thornicroft, 1990) for patients with severe personality disorders. British government policy has now identified case management as a key coordinating mechanism across a range of community care client groups (Her Majesty's Stationery Office, 1989). The aims of case management systems are to enhance the continuity of care and accessibility, accountability, and efficiency. Shepherd (1990) has outlined the major components which are focused on the individual patient as:

(a) assessment of need
(b) development of a comprehensive service plan
(c) arrangement of delivery

(d) monitoring and assessment of services.

Case management systems are intended to overcome the fragmentation of services and to offer long-term flexible support. In theory they place emphasis on tailoring services to the individual needs of clients, rather than fitting the client into existing services. Two contrasting models have been identified. In the first, paraprofessional case managers act as 'service brokers', and are responsible for, but do not necessarily provide, the assessment and implementation of a package of care. In the second, 'clinical case management', a highly skilled psychiatric professional is directly concerned with all aspects of the patient's physical and social environment. The latter is now considered superior to the service broker model (Franklin *et al*, 1987). A clinical case manager not only arranges access to appropriate services but also provides a range of interventions, including intermittent psychotherapy, training in community living skills, psychoeducation of family and patient, and support during crisis. Ideally, clinical case managers should anticipate impending crises and take appropriate action. Success in dealing effectively with relapses and other difficulties can then give both client and carers a sense of confidence and control over events.

Unfortunately, there have been no empirical trials to assess the suitability or applicability of the case management model to patients with severe personality disorder, despite government policy. This is possibly due to an overemphasis on criminal recidivism and further behavioural disorder as the main criteria of success when following up these patients, along with a subsequent expectation that a model of surveillance is more appropriate. But it could also result from anxiety and apprehension in health care professionals about responsibilities for a subgroup of patients in the community who are, by definition, expected to be uncooperative, ungrateful or even at risk of directing their antisocial behaviour towards the carers themselves. It remains unclear to what extent such anxieties are justified in the absence of adequate data on a sufficient number of personality-disordered patients. Anecdotal evidence from clinicians who have taken a rehabilitative approach to the community supervision of psychopaths suggests that many of the principals of case management are already being applied, if not in a systematic fashion. But at the same time, many of these patients are especially time-consuming, have specific needs which do not apply to the mentally ill, and have frequent crises, suggesting that if the case management approach is to be applied on a routine basis it may require specific modifications.

Stein & Test (1980) articulated a pragmatic needs model which has influenced several case management services. They identified several factors which they felt to be important in maintaining people with long-term disabling mental illnesses in the community and which apply equally to patients with severe personality disorder. These include adequate material resources, the skills to cope with daily life, motivation to persevere in the face of day-to-day problems, appropriately supportive relationships, a supportive local community, and an assertive service system. The model also explicitly acknowledges the importance of the control of symptoms in mentally ill patients and the role of in-patient psychiatric care, factors which can in certain cases equally apply to the personality-disordered, but where crisis, respite, or day care may sometimes be a more appropriate consideration.

In any future developments of community support services for patients with severe personality disorders, consideration will have to be given to whether or not a very different model of service delivery is required, and what specialist training is needed for care managers. It has been argued that good quality community psychiatric care requires teamwork (Test, 1979; Intaglia, 1982; Wooff & Goldberg, 1988), and this may require a very high level of management skills when dealing with a client group which is particularly demanding and where some individuals are adept at splitting staff teams. Whether the typical case-load ratio of 1:10 for mental illness (Taube *et al*,1990) is appropriate when adopting assertive community treatment for these patients also remains unclear. However, pilot schemes could begin to examine many of these important issues.

Conclusions

It has not been possible to answer any of the original four questions posed at the beginning at this chapter with regard to evaluating the community supervision of psychopaths. There is some evidence that patients who have been detained under the legal categories 'psychopathic disorder' and 'subnormality' (mental impairment in the Mental Health Act 1983) are less likely to reoffend in the first two years after discharge if they are receiving community supervision rather than no supervision at all. However, the evidence is not conclusive. One study suggested that reduction of recidivism was more substantial for the higher-risk subjects; the other suggested no effect on this particular subgroup. However, in neither study was it possible to observe directly the effects on the psychopaths within what was a mixed group of subjects. Future research might examine more closely the post-discharge histories of subjects with severe personality disorders who are, or have been, released from maximum-security hospitals. But it would be necessary to control for some measure of risk upon their release, based on their previous behaviour, including offending. Studies of parolees and those refused parole may yield larger numbers of subjects on a prospective basis than patients released from Special Hospitals. If subjects were interviewed with standardised research instruments, in addition to measures of an index of risk, then it might be possible to carry out a more specific evaluation of the factors involved in any final outcome.

More reliable diagnostic measures might also help in evaluating whether a primarily rehabilitative or surveillance model is more suitable for the community supervision of these subjects. But it is still essential to be clear from the outset to what extent any programme involves the quite different goals of rehabilitation, surveillance, testing alternative measures to institutionalisation, and whether any punitive elements such as social control are included. In addition, the extent to which the protection of the public is included in the programme will have to be decided. It is only by formulating these goals at the outset that any decision can be made on the most suitable means of measuring outcome, including measures such as criminal recidivism and social readjustment.

The dichotomy within community supervision is in itself highly illustrative of the many difficulties in evaluating other treatment modalities for psychopaths. The question is frequently posed of whether evaluation of the standards of care provided by health care professionals should or should not outweigh the effectiveness of their control of these patients in terms of protecting the public from their further offending. The case management model could be highly relevant to the community supervision of psychopaths, but few health care professionals who have previously been involved in such programmes for the mentally ill would see this model fitting easily with the notion of community surveillance. Future research will ultimately need to parcel out the effects of care and control in any programmes which are evaluated.

11 Methodological issues

Our earlier contention, that there is little research on the treatment of psychopathy, may seem unwarranted after more than 200 pages reviewing studies of treatment. Certainly, over 80 studies have been reviewed here which could claim to have investigated at least some aspect of the outcome of treatment of psychopathy. However, what is clear from reviewing this literature is that the quality of these studies is generally poor.

There are two major questions to be answered in a critical review of treatment studies. First:

(1) *Can psychopaths be treated?*

If the answer to this first question is *yes,*

(2) *Which treatment methods are the most effective for psychopaths?*

Working within the traditional experimental model, question 1 should be answered before the researcher can go ahead to design a study to test question 2. The way to answer question 1 may seem simple enough:

> A group of *psychopaths* are *measured* and then *randomly* allocated to *treatment* or *non-treatment.* Outcome and long-term follow-up are evaluated by considering the *differences* between the two groups *statistically.*

However, each italicised point raises a separate issue which the careful researcher should address:

(a) Who is a *psychopath*?

(b) What is the most appropriate *measure(s)* of psychopathy?
(c) Is *random* allocation possible or ethical?
(d) What constitutes *treatment*?
(e) What constitutes *non-treatment*?
(f) What constitutes an acceptable measure of *outcome*?
(g) How *long-term* is follow-up?
(h) What is an adequate number of subjects to be sure of a *difference*? That is, what is an acceptable power for *statistical* tests?

TABLE 11.1
Key to methodological summary tables

Diagnostic criteria	Have diagnostic criteria for psychopathy been applied? If so, which are they?
Sample characteristics	Who were the sample studied (gender, offenders etc.) and how were they described?
Age	Mean age and/or range, if given.
No. of subjects	Number of 'psychopaths' in the study.
Setting of treatment	For example in-patient or out-patient; individual or group; voluntary or compulsory; security of setting; average duration of treatment.
Treatment description	This considers whether the treatment applied in the study is described well enough for the independent reader to replicate the study exactly. The treatment description provided by the authors is graded on three levels. *Good* A detailed description of the treatment applied is either in the reviewed paper or available from other referenced sources. *Some* The treatment applied in the study is outlined, but is not described well enough for replication by an independent researcher. *None* The actual treatment applied is not described at all.
Follow-up period	This is the length of the follow-up period *after the end* of treatment. If the study only considers changes between admission and discharge from treatment, this is shown by '0'.
Outcome criteria	Which outcome criteria were used and/or which psychological tests were administered?
Control sample	Was a control sample or comparison group reported? If so, how were they selected and what are their features?

The studies reviewed here may be evaluated by considering how well each study has dealt with these eight questions. In order to facilitate such an overview of studies, headings relevant to these questions (as described in Table 11.1) have been used in Tables 11.2 and 11.3, which summarise the studies discussed in Chapter 3 and Chapters 5–9 respectively.

Investigation of these summary tables reveals that, although many studies have been considered in this review, it is the 'holes' in the existing research, rather than the 'substance' of research findings, that are most noticeable.

Definition and measurement of psychopathic disorder

(a) Who is a psychopath?
(b) What is the most appropriate measure(s) of psychopathy?

Although most of the studies purport to be of 'psychopaths', the definition and diagnosis of such is addressed by very few authors. This is a matter of concern, since the confusion over terminology in this area is well known. If we had included only those studies which used specific psychiatric criteria for the diagnosis of psychopathy, only 15 studies would have been reviewed.

Recognised diagnostic criteria are used as follows: Cheney's (1934) criteria are used in two studies (Heaver, 1943; MacKay, 1948); Henderson's (1939) criteria are used in one study (Gibbens *et al*, 1955, 1959); Gough's (1961) socialisation scale is used in one study (Maas, 1966); Hare's PCL–R (1985, 1990) is used in three studies (Cooke, 1989; Ogloff *et al*, 1990; Rice *et al*, 1992); and DSM–III (or DSM–III–R) is referred to in five studies, although subjects are assessed by different methods (Woody *et al*, 1985; Gabbard & Coyne, 1987; Vaglum *et al*, 1990; Mehlum *et al*, 1991; Murch & Dolan, 1992). Craft (Craft *et al*, 1964; Craft, 1965) developed his own criteria for psychopathy (age over 13; has offended; personality disorder to the extent of needing treatment; IQ over 55 and no psychosis), while Maddocks (1970) used clinicians' diagnoses supplemented by his own criteria for impulsiveness. Copas *et al* (1984) used a four-way classification of psychopathy developed in an early doctoral study by O'Brien (1980).

All outcome studies arising from Special Hospital populations, with the exception of Mackay's (1948) study of lobotomy, have side-stepped the issue of psychiatric diagnosis by relying upon the legal (Mental Health Act) categorisation of psychopathic disorder. Bailey & MacCulloch (1992*a*) report that their 'legal psychopaths'

Table 11.2

Methodology of studies of the natural history of untreated psychopaths

Study	*Diagnostic criteria*	*Sample characteristics*	*Age: years*	*No. of subjects*	*Setting of treatment*	*Follow-up period*	*Outcome criteria*	*Control sample*
Gibbens *et al* (1955, 1959)	Henderson (1939) (by prison doctor)	Convicted male psychopathic persistent offenders	18–58	69	No intervention in prison	2–5 years + 5–8 years	Offending	Non-psychopaths matched for age and current offence
Maddocks (1970)	Labelled by psychiatrists, plus impulsive behaviour	33 men, 19 women; assessed but not treated	–	52	No treatment after NHS referral	5.5 years	Hospital and probation reports of progress; convictions	None
Murch & Dolan (1992)	DSM–III–R by PDOR[1] self-report measure	103 men, 43 women; referred for specialist personality disorder treatment but not admitted	–	146	No treatment after NHS referral to Henderson Hospital	1 year	Referrer's and GP's reports of offending and psychiatric service usage	None

1. Personality Diagnostic Questionnaire.

TABLE 11.3

Methodology of studies

Study	*Diagnostic criteria*	*Sample characteristics*	*Age: years*	*No. of subjects*	*Setting of treatment*	*Treatment description*	*Follow-up period*	*Outcome criteria*	*Control sample*
Physical treatment									
Green *et al* (1944)	None	Male prisoners 'criminal psychopathic' trends in personality	22	24	Petit-mal electro-shock therapy	Good	6 months	Subjective clinical assessment	None
Darling & Sandal (1952)	None	Antisocial psychopaths; hospital inmates	–	18	Lobotomy	None	0	Subjective clinical assessment	None
Poblete *et al* (1970)	None	Aggressive hospitalised patients; no gender given	–	25	Thalamotomy (lamella mediolic)	Good	1–3 years	Subjective clinical judgement (at home, working, non-aggressive)	None
Balasubramanian & Rammamurthi (1970)	None	Aggressive 'behaviour disorder' patients, hyperkenetic; 82 men, 18 women	15 (0–50)	100	Amygdalotomy (85% bilateral)	Good	Not given	Subjective clinical assessment	None
Andy (1975)	None	'Psychopathic' patients with brain damage	10–35	6	Thalamotomy	Good	1–11 years	IQ; behavioural changes	None
MacKay (1948)	Cheney's (1934)	"Feeble minded psychopaths" at Rampton hospital; 14 women, 6 men; 13 no organic condition	–	20	Leucotomy	None	6 months	Subjective clinical assessment	None

Out-patient psychotherapy									
Reckless (1970)	None	"Sociopathic" or "pseudo-sociopathic" women presenting with antisocial problems	17–23	21	Individual and group; 13 under conditions of probation	None	0	Sujective clinical impression	None
Carney (1977)	None	Male; aggressive personality-disordered offenders	–	16	Group therapy (13 months) under conditions of probation order	Some	9 months	MMPI	None
Woody *et al* (1985)	DSM–III ASPD	Male opiate addicts with depression and/or ASPD	18–55	62	Individual psychotheraphy or cognitive–behavioural treatment	Good	1 month	Offending; SCL-90, BDI, MPI; employment	Addicts with no ASPD
Cook *et al* (1991)	None	Male, non-violent recidivist sex offenders on probation	38	55	Group therapy under condition of probation order (22 months)	Some	4 years	Recidivism	Compared with 22 drop-outs
Sadoff *et al* (1971)	None	Male sex offenders on probation	–	43	Group therapy under condition of probation order (40 weeks)	None	2 years	Recidivism	None

TABLE 11.3 *(continued)*
Methodology of studies

Study	*Diagnostic criteria*	*Sample characteristics*	*Age: years*	*No. of subjects*	*Setting of treatment*	*Treatment description*	*Follow-up period*	*Outcome criteria*	*Control sample*
In-patient psychotherapy									
Persons (1966)	None	Male adolescent offenders in institution	15–19	41	Individual and group (20 weeks)	None	0	MMPI, PDS, TMAS; disciplinary reports	Random allocation of matched pairs
Traux *et al* (1967)	None	Female adolescent delinquents in institution	14–16	35	Group therapy (3 months)	Some	1 year	MCI; leaving institution	35 randomly to no treatment
Taylor (1967)	None	Female adolescent delinquents	16–18	11	Group therapy with psychoanalytic orientation	Some	26 weeks	Self-rating; staff rating; recall, reconviciton	11 randomly allocated; 11 having counselling
Persons (1965)	None	Male adolescent offenders; case-note diagnosis of sociopathy	22	12	Individual eclectic (10 weeks)	None	0	PEAQ, PDS, TMAS	40 untreated random controls
Maas (1966)	Gough's socialisation scale	Women prison inmates, 'sociopaths'	25	23	Prison actional group therapy (3 months)	Some	0	Block Ego-Indentity Scale	23 untreated, randomly selected

Jew *et al* (1972)	None	Male personality-disordered offenders on parole	–	257	Prison psychoanalytic group therapy (18 months)	None	4 years	Recidivism	Matched group of 257 in prison
Kozol *et al* (1972)	None	Dangerous male psychopathic offenders	–	226	Prison group and individual therapy (43 months)	Some	3.5 years	Recidivism	49 untreated men released by court order
Cognitive–behavioural therapy for adolescents									
Cohen & Filipczak (1971)	None	Adolescent offenders	13–19	41	Token-economy ward (8 months)	Good	3 years	Academic improvement; recidivism	Untreated adolescents
Cavior & Schmidt (1978)	None	Young male offenders	18	56	Minimum-security institution	} Some	3 years	Gaining parole; recidivism	None
		"Unsocialised psychopaths"	–	158	Medium-security institution; behaviour modification				
Hendrix & Heckel (1982)	None	Male adolescents (12 black)	14–18	15	Maximum-security institution; social behaviour training (2 weeks)	None	0	Emission of positive attention behaviour	15 untreated randomly allocated controls
Moyes *et al* (1985)	None	40 male and 38 female adolescents; behaviour or personality disorders, of an antisocial or aggressive type	18 (14–25)	78	In-patient behavioural programme	Good	2 years	Aggression, temper outbursts, independent living; police involvement	63 not admitted

Table 11.3 *(continued)*
Methodology of studies

Study	*Diagnostic criteria*	*Sample characteristics*	*Age: years*	*No. of subjects*	*Setting of treatment*	*Treatment description*	*Follow-up period*	*Outcome criteria*	*Control sample*
Cognitive–behavioural therapy									
Colman & Baker (1969)	None	Clinical diagnosis; delinquent US military recruits; "character or behaviour disorder" (no alcoholics, addicts or homosexuals)	20	48	Operant-conditioning model ward (10 weeks)	None	3 months record	Military service record; arrest traditional treatment ward	48 randomly allocated to a
Jones *et al* (1977)	None	Clinical disgnosis; military personnel; "character or behaviour disorders"	–	51	Token-economy ward (16 weeks)	None	14 months	Return to active duty	27 randomly assigned no treatment
Stermac (1986)	No details	Male offenders; 70% personality disorder	29	20	Anger-management training; court-ordered residential assessment unit (6 sessions)	Good	0	Novaco provocation inventory; coping strategies	20 randomly assigned no treatment
Valiant & Antomowicz (1991)	None	Male offenders	–	53	Cognitive–behavioural group programme; maximum-security jail (5 weeks)	None	0	MMPI; self-esteem; Speiberger state-trait anxiety test	None

Therapeutic Community (TC) treatment (Henderson Hospital)

Rapoport (1960)	None	Males with personality disorder	–	64	In-patient TC, Henderson Hospital	Good	1 year	Clinical impression	None
Tuxford (1961)	None	Male probation borstal licence cases	–	86	In-patient TC, Henderson Hospital	Good	22 months	Questionnaire to probation officers on current state and employment	None
Taylor (1966)	None	Discharged men placed in employment	–	–	In-patient TC, Henderson Hospital	Good	9 months	Employment status	None
Whiteley (1970)	None	Male psychopaths; no psychosis and no organic mental illness	18–43	112	In-patient TC, Henderson Hospital	Good	2 years	Reconviction; readmission to hospital	None
Copas & Whiteley (1976)	None	Male psychopaths; no psychosis and no organic mental illness	–	104 87	In-patient TC, Henderson Hospital	Good	5 years 2 years	Reconviction; readmission to hospital	None
Copas *et al* (1984)	O'Brien's (1976)	"Psychopathic or sociopathic" 174 men, 60 women	26.5 (17–39)	194	In-patient TC, Henderson Hospital	Good	5 years	Recidivism; readmission to hospital	51 referred "psychopaths" not admitted
Norris (1983)	None	70 men, 33 women; current patients	24	103	In-patient TC, Henderson Hospital	Good	0	Repertory grid measure	None; compared with other residential settings
Dolan *et al* (1992*c*)	None	Consecutive 29 men, 33 women	25 (17–44)	62	In-patient TC, Henderson Hospital	Good	8 months	SCL-90-R	None

TABLE 11.3 *(continued)*
Methodology of studies

Study	*Diagnostic criteria*	*Sample characteristics*	*Age: years*	*No. of subjects*	*Setting of treatment*	*Treatment description*	*Follow-up period*	*Outcome criteria*	*Control sample*
TC treatment, other hospitals									
Craft *et al* (1964)	None	Male adolescent psychopaths	13–	50	TC in-patient	None	3 years	Recidivism; employment; clinical recovery; MMPI; IQ	50 randomly allocated to authoritarian treatment
Mehlum *et al* (1991)	Million & Everly (1985); DSM–III–R	Personality-disordered adults; 28 men, 69 women	36	97	TC day unit (5.5 months)	None	3 years	SCL-90R; HSRS; hospitalisation	Comparison with 19 patients not personality disordered
TC treatment, HMP Grendon: changes during stay									
Gray (1974)	None	Young male offenders	18–21	34	Voluntary TC within prison	Good	3.5 years since admission	Psychotropic drug usage; prison incidents	None
Gunn *et al* (1978)	None	Adult male offenders	27 (21–48)	80	Voluntary TC within prison	Good	15 months since discharge	MMPI; CHQ; attitude scales semantic differential scales	None

Sleap (1979)	None	Adult male offenders	–	209	Voluntary TC within prison	Good	6 and 12 months since admission	Goal-attainment scale	None
Newton (1979)	None	Adult male offenders	–	211	Voluntary TC within prison	Good	0	HDHQ	None
Miller (1982)	None	Adult male offenders	–	83	Voluntary TC within prison	Good	0	HDHQ; EPQ	None
TC treatment HMP Grendon: treatment outcome									
Newton (1971)	None	Adult inmates	–	111	Voluntary TC within prison	Good	5 years	Reconviction	87 matched inmates at other prisons
George (1971)	None	Adult inmates	–	263	Voluntary TC within prison	Good	2 years	Reconviction	None
Gunne *et al* (1978)	None	Adult inmates	27 (21–48)	61	Voluntary TC within prison	Good	2 years	Reconviction	61 matched inmates from parole index
Robertson & Gunn (1987)	None	Adult inmates	27 (21–48)	61	Voluntary TC within prison	Good	10 years	Reconviction	61 matched inmates from parole index
Cullen (1992)	None	Adult inmates	–	214	Voluntary TC within prison	Good	2 years	Reconviction	None

TABLE 11.3 *(continued)*
Methodology of studies

Study	*Diagnostic criteria*	*Sample characteristics*	*Age: years*	*No. of subjects*	*Setting of treatment*	*Treatment description*	*Follow-up period*	*Outcome criteria*	*Control sample*
TC treatment, other prisons and secure settings									
Cooke (1989)	Hare psychopathy Check-List (PCL), cut-off 32	Disruptive male – violent offenders, 20% having score over 32, 50% show psychopathic traits		25	Prison TC, Barlinnie (41 months)	Some	0	Prison "incident"; reconviction	None
Jones (1990)	None	Male inmates	20–50	31	TC, Wormwood Scrubs Annexe	Good	0	Repertory grid measures	None
Sewell & Clarke (1982)	None	Male inmates	29.5	127	TC, Wormwood Scrubs Annexe	Good	2 years	Reconviction	100 comparison main prison inmates; 46 not admitted to annexe
Jones (1988)	None	All male referrals; 57 addicts, 35 with personality disorders	30.6 (20–69)	122	TC, Wormwood Scrubs Annexe	Good	2 years	Reconviction	Comparison with untreated inmates in annexe
Fink *et al* (1969)	None	Male inmates; pre-parole board board review; no addiction or alcoholism	25	54	Non-voluntary treatment in prison	Some	6 months	Parole revocation; reoffending	54 randomly selected, stayed in prison
Ogloff *et al* (1990)	Hare's Psychopathy Check-List (PCL-R), cut-off 27	Male prison inmates	27	21	Voluntary TC (average 3.4 months)	Some	0	Subjective staff ratings of improvement and motivation	12 non-psychotic, 17 mixed on PCL ratings

Sandhu (1970)	None	Male offenders; "violent psychopaths"	–	18	TC with 30 "well behaved men" (9 months)	Some	0	Staff observation; consensus staff opinion on improvement	None
Jessen & Roosenberg (1971)	None	All male patients admitted	–	338	In-patients TBR; voluntary TC (50 months)	Good	5.75	Getting discharge; recall from leave; reoffending	None
Emmerik (1987)	None	Male discharges released for 5 years	–	517	In-patients TBR; voluntary TC	Good	5 years	Reconviction for serious offence; employment	None
Harris *et al* (1989) Rice *et al* (1992)	Hare's Psychopathy Check List (PCL–R), cut-off 25	Male psychopathic offenders, 51% PCL psychopaths	23	52	Non-voluntary TC "patient run"; used alcohol, scopolamine, LSD, nude encounter groups	Good	10 years	Reoffending	146 men matched forensic assessment
Hierarchical, TC treatment									
Skolnick & Zuckerman (1979)	MMPI psychopathic deviate pattern	59 male drug abusers	–	59	Hierarchical TC treatment	Some	6–8 months	MMPI; SSS	37 drug abusers sent to prison
Wexler *et al* (1990)	None	Drug abusers; 435 male, 247 female; 50% black	29	682	Prison hierarchical TC volunteer-run	Good	3 years	Arrest record; parole outcome	197 waiting-list volunteer controls, 247 other treated prisoners

Table 11.3 *(continued)*
Methodology of studies

Study	*Diagnostic criteria*	*Sample characteristics*	*Age: years*	*No. of subjects*	*Setting of treatment*	*Treatment description*	*Follow-up period*	*Outcome criteria*	*Control sample*
In-patient milieu treatment									
Heaver (1943)	Cheney's (1934) criteria	Middle-class man	28.7	40	Voluntary hospital admission (4 months)	None	2–7 years	Clinical opinion	None
Craft (1958)	None	Men and women with gross personality disorders, 10 from Special Hospitals; average IQ 60	14+	43	Hospital (5 years average)	None	3 years	Conviction; employment; clinical opinion	None
McCord & Sanchez (1987)	None	Male adolescents; behaviour and personality disorder; lower-class, urban areas; IQ over 80	9–13	42 37	2 milieu settings; 1 psychoeducation, 1 authoritarian	Some	25 years	Offending; offending rate; imprisonment; hospital admission	None
Gabbard & Coyne (1987)	DSM–III–R	Antisocial personality disorder or antisocial traits	23.6 (16–49)	33	General psychiatric admission	None	0	Staff ratings	None
Woodside *et al* (1987)	Clinical diagnosis	76 men, 24 women; 49% personality disordered; all showed aggressive, suicidal or disturbed behaviour	11–74	100	Secure intensive-care forensic ward for sociopathic behaviour	Some	0	Discharges	None
Basson & Woodside (1981)	Clinical diagnosis	285 men, 115 women, 21% personality disordered	20–40	400	Secure intensive-care forensic ward for sociopathic behaviour	Some	0	Discharges	None

Treatment in Special Hospitals

Tong & MacKay (1959)	None	Male discharges; "mental defective of dangerous or violent propensity"	32.5	423	Rampton Hospital	None	1–12	Disposal; conviction re-admission	None
Craft (1965)	None	Male discharges, all diagnoses	–	75	Moss Side Hospital	None	–	Readmission to Special Hospital	None
Cathercole *et al* (1968)	Mental Health Act (MHA) category	All discharged patients, 33 psychopathic disorder (on admission)	30.6	72	Moss Side; 6.5-year admission	None	4–6 years	Conviction; readmission	None
Acres (1975)	None	17 women, 75 men	–	92	All Special Hospitals	None	2 years	Institutionalis-ation; reconviction	None
Aarvold Committee (1973)	None	All patients on restriction orders, 40% homicides	–	–	All Special Hospitals	None	3 years	Convicition; recall	None
Dell (1980, 1982)	MHA category	Transfers to NHS units, including 39 females; 19 psychopaths not reported separately	–	105	All Special Hospitals	Some	2 years	Recall; conviction	None

Table 11.3 *(continued)*
Methodology of studies

Study	*Diagnostic criteria*	*Sample characteristics*	*Age: years*	*No. of subjects*	*Setting of treatment*	*Treatment description*	*Follow-up period*	*Outcome criteria*	*Control sample*
Treatment in Special Hospitals (contimued)									
Black (1982)	None	Men discharged; psychopaths not reported separately	41.5	125	Broadmoor	None	5 years	Readmission	None
Norris (1984)	MHA category	All men discharged to community; 104 psychopathic	–	330	Broadmoor	None	3 years	Police contact; offending; recall; imprisonment	Compare with mentally ill patients
Tennent & Way	MHA category (1984)	Men; 304 with personality disorder (no details); 202 psychopaths	–	617	All Special Hospital discharges	None	6 years	Any offence; violent offence	Compared with mentally ill patients
Dell & Robertson (1988) Robertson (1989)	MHA category	Males; 30 psychopaths released to secure facility	–	121	Broadmoor; admission 4 years or less	None	5–10 years	Convictions	Compared with mentally ill patients

Baily & MacCulloch (1992*a,b*)	MHA category	Discharged direct to community; 44% psychopaths, 46% personality disorder (clinician's view)	39.5	112	Park Lane; 42 months' stay	None	6 months to 14 years (no mean)	Discharge conditions; convictions; serious offences	None
Treatment at Patuxent									
Boslow & Kohlmeyer (1963)	State legislature "defective delinquent"	Male parolees	–	81	Patuxent 'milieu' therapy unit; maximum security	Some	Not given	Parole violation; offending	None
Hodges (1971)	As above	Released on parole	–	156	Patuxent 'milieu' therapy unit; maximum security	Some	3 years	Conviction; revocation of parole	Compared with 112 men released by courts early, and 129 untreated men
Steadman (1977)	As above	Paroled inmates	33	106	Patuxent 'milieu' therapy unit; maximum security	Some	5 years	Convictions; arrests (violence)	105 released by courts, 46 untreated, and 39 not accepted

at Park Lane Hospital had personality disorder; however, they rely upon the individual clinicians' diagnosis of personality disorder rather than using any standardised criteria or assessment.

Maximum-security institutions in other countries have also used the relevant legislation to define their population (e.g. Hervesteder, Patuxent). The studies from Henderson Hospital, apart from the two mentioned above (Copas *et al*, 1984; Murch & Dolan, 1992), require the reader to accept that the patients must be 'psychopaths' or 'personality disordered' by virtue of being accepted for treatment in a unit which specialises in the treatment of severe personality disorder.

Gunn *et al* (1978) recognise the problem of the diagnosis of psychopathy in their study at HMP Grendon. They note that in attempting to make such a diagnosis, based upon information from interviews and case-notes, they were unable to obtain acceptable inter-rater reliability. Therefore, they "largely eschewed the terms personality disorder and psychopathy" in their study as "people who are given the diagnosis are not a homogeneous group" (Gunn *et al*, 1978, p. 38).

It is not within the brief of this review to argue for the precedence of one diagnostic system for psychopathic disorder over another. However, it is clear that in treatment outcome research there is no universally accepted, or even predominant, diagnostic approach. Of course, it would have been impossible for researchers working before 1980 to make a DSM axis II personality disorder diagnosis, or to use Hare's PCL scale in research (Hare, 1980). Nevertheless, it seems that the conceptual difficulties with the term 'psychopath' may have led many researchers to avoid using any definition of psychopathy, even those definitions which were contemporary to their research study. It may be that it was too difficult to define the term precisely. This position might be tenable if, like Gunn *et al* (1978), workers then did not use the term psychopath in their writings, but simply described the demographic, behavioural and psychological characteristics of their sample in detail. However, many authors have classified their subjects as 'psychopaths', or as having 'psychopathic disorder', without any further elucidation of their meaning. In the absence of diagnostic measures, the clinical description of subjects in many studies is extremely poor. Samples are referred to as showing 'psychopathic' or 'sociopathic' traits or behaviour with no specification of the nature or degree of these features.

In the reviewed studies it seems that the 'elephant adage' predominates: "I can't describe a psychopath but I know one when I see one". However, in treatment outcome research it is essential to know that other researchers are able to perceive the 'psychopath' from the same viewpoint.

Aside from this lack of 'psychopathic' descriptor, many studies also omit other fundamental demographic features of the samples (such as age, gender and marital status). Except for IQ, descriptions of psychological features are almost totally absent unless the study is measuring change in that particular psychological aspect.

Many studies also give minimal information on the selection of subjects for treatment, or use treatment-selection methods or criteria which are not clearly defined and therefore are not readily replicable. Furthermore, the selection of those subjects included in follow-up investigation is often not clearly documented. It is not sufficient to describe 'all consecutive discharges' if no information is given about how those discharged differ from those who have not yet been discharged or those who terminated treatment in another way.

Particularly in the case of research from the Special Hospitals, many patient populations studied have been selected on the basis of discharge from treatment. Little information on how this group correspond to the admitted population is given. The discharged population may be wholly unrepresentative of the admitted patients (e.g. Black, 1982).

Random allocation of subjects

(c) Is random allocation possible or ethical?

The majority of studies (including all investigations of psychosurgery) have not reported *any* control or comparison sample. Without a control sample it is impossible to know whether any changes noted can be specifically attributed to the treatment intervention under investigation. Other spurious factors, such as the passage of time, could be accounting for any changes found. Although comparative samples partially address this issue, those studies which have used comparative groups still have several flaws in their methods of selecting the comparative samples which hinder accurate interpretation of treatment effects.

Controlled studies

Random allocation of a homogeneous group of subjects to two different conditions is the optimum method for showing group differences in treatment outcome studies. Subjects can be allocated to either a treatment and a no-treatment condition or to two different treatment conditions. However, only ten studies of psychological treatment of psychopaths have used a randomly allocated untreated control sample.

It is noteworthy that half of the studies that randomly allocated subjects to non-treatment conditions have been with juvenile delinquents rather than adult psychopaths, and that this is usually for short-term treatment interventions. Persons (1966) matched pairs of male adolescent delinquents and then randomly allocated one of each pair to 20 weeks of psychotherapy and the other to no treatment. Truax *et al* (1966) and Taylor (1967) randomly allocated female delinquents to group therapy or no treatment for three and six months respectively. Hendrix & Heckel (1982) also used random allocation in their two-week behavioural programme.

In studies of adult offender populations, Persons (1965) randomly allocated adult male 'sociopaths' to ten weeks of individual treatment or no treatment, and Maas (1966) randomly allocated female sociopaths to three months of actional group therapy. Stermac (1986) used six sessions of anger-management training in his controlled programme with soldiers. Two other studies of US military personnel with 'character disorder' have used random allocation for 10–16-week behavioural programmes (Colman & Baker, 1969; Jones *et al*, 1977).

The random-allocation controlled studies described above have employed a variety of different treatment methods (dynamic psychotherapy, behavioural programmes, cognitive–behavioural therapy). What they have in common is a very short duration of treatment intervention. One important issue for randomised controlled studies is the ethical consideration of withholding treatment, which may be effective, from a group of patients in need. It could be considered more ethically appropriate to randomly control in studies of short-term treatment with short-term follow-up, as the control group can subsequently be treated with the same intervention a short time after completion of the experimental study. In such instances, patients would not ultimately be having successful interventions withheld.

However, many interventions used with psychopathic patients are not short term: the duration of treatment is often years rather than weeks. In such cases, withholding what may be a successful method of treatment raises significant ethical questions. This may, in part, explain why random-allocation controlled studies of Therapeutic Community (TC) treatment and long-term hospitalisation are scarce.

For studies within Health Service settings or Special Hospitals, the ethics of random allocation to treatment are particularly problematic, since there is an obligation upon the professional to treat the referred patient. It is noteworthy that only one study in a Health Service setting used random allocation for long-term treatment (Craft, 1965). In this study randomisation was to one of two treatment modalities for 14 months. No subjects were left untreated because of the research study.

In their prison-based study, Fink *et al* (1969) were able to randomly allocate male inmates to TC treatment or to no intervention in prison. In this setting they were under no obligation to treat any of their subjects. However, in order to use random allocation for the purposes of evaluation, they were forced to modify what was normally a voluntary treatment programme. To enable methodologically acceptable randomisation, the subjects could no longer be admitted voluntarily to the Therapeutic Community which they were studying, and had to be admitted compulsorily for the first six weeks. Therefore an important aspect of the treatment programme under examination was substantially altered for the research programme. Although this may make for methodologically purer research, the results cannot then be generalised to the original TC treatment strategy.

Comparison samples

Those outcome studies which have used a two-group comparative design have used three main types of comparison sample:

(a) patients with a similar diagnosis or characteristics who do not receive treatment
(b) patients who receive the same treatment but who have a different psychiatric diagnosis
(c) subjects matched on demographic and historical variables, who do not have the same psychological or psychiatric profile and who do not receive treatment.

Although comparative studies are generally more methodologically correct than single-sample studies, problems remain when interpreting findings.

Patients with a similar diagnosis or characteristics who do not receive treatment

In the absence of random allocation, comparison patients are most often those who are referred to a service but who for some reason do not get treatment (e.g. Copas *et al*, 1984; Moyes *et al*,

1985; Wexler *et al*, 1990) or who drop out early (Jones, 1988; Cook *et al*, 1991). However, in most cases there is a specific reason why treatment was withheld (e.g. patients' clinical characteristics, level of violence or level of motivation to change). Such factors may be intrinsically linked to treatment success and therefore may have important differential effects upon the outcome of the two groups. For example, Dolan *et al* (1990) have shown how patients not accepted for treatment of personality disorder at Henderson Hospital differed significantly from those who were accepted on some psychological variables (levels of somatisation, phobic anxiety and obsessional–compulsive symptoms). These features were interpreted as indicative of a tendency to unconsciously deny or avoid feeling emotional distress. This incapacity to verbalise distress may indicate that such patients were less likely to benefit from the therapeutic community's psychotherapeutic approach and they would perhaps have had a worse outcome had they been admitted.

Comparison studies of patients not accepted for treatment cannot presume that the two populations are equivalent. Such studies should therefore consider population differences and how these may relate to predicted treatment outcome for each group.

Patients who receive the same treatment but who have a different psychiatric diagnosis or no diagnosis

Several studies have compared psychopathic or personality-disordered subjects with those who do not have any psychopathic or personality disorder, and they generally find a worse outcome for the psychopathic group. Unfortunately, when such studies do show a poorer outcome for psychopaths than for other diagnostic groups they are often used, erroneously, as evidence of the untreatability of psychopaths.

Studies have compared drug addicts with antisocial personality disorders with non-personality-disordered addicts (Woody *et al*, 1985); personality-disordered subjects with neurotic patients (Mehlum *et al*, 1991); and high PCL–R scorers with low PCL–R scorers (Ogloff *et al*, 1990). The use of a treated comparison group of patients who have a different psychiatric diagnosis is found in several reports from Special Hospitals. In these, outcome results of people held under the Mental Health Act category of psychopathic disorder are compared with those of mentally ill or learning-disabled patients (Norris, 1984; Tennent & Way, 1984; Dell & Robertson, 1988; Bailey & MacCulloch, 1992*a*,*b*). At best, such comparative studies can only reveal differences in the ways psychopaths and patients with other psychiatric illnesses respond to the given treatment.

Additionally, the fact that these different patient groups are treated within the same institution does not necessarily indicate that they have experienced similar treatment programmes during hospitalisation. Such comparison will not be able to demonstrate the efficacy of the treatment *per se*, as opposed to non-treatment of the psychopathic group.

Subjects matched on demographic and historical variables, who do not have the same psychological or psychiatric profile and who do not receive treatment

An untreated comparison group comprising subjects who are matched with the treated subjects on demographic and historical variables but do not have the same psychological or psychiatric profile seems to have been used most often in studies within penal systems (Gibbens *et al*, 1955; Newton, 1971; Jew *et al*, 1972; Gunn *et al*, 1978; Sewell & Clarke, 1982; Robertson & Gunn, 1987). In most of these studies the comparison group is well matched in terms of offending behaviour, which is also the study outcome measure. Several studies have carefully matched for index offence, number and severity of previous offences, previous imprisonment, etc. However, even when comparison groups are matched for criminological variables, and other demographic features have also been matched (age, marital status, etc.), the majority of studies do not then match their comparison group for the degree of psychopathy or psychological disturbance. Such studies can only state whether there is a difference between outcome of treated psychopaths and *non*-treated *non*-psychopaths.

Black (1982) has noted how the diagnosis of psychopathic disorder is associated with recidivism. Therefore, to be meaningful, evaluations of treatment outcome should include methodological control for diagnosis alongside other life-history or criminological factors. It is unknown how the effects of treatment interact with the psychopathic characteristics. Therefore any findings of a different outcome for psychopaths and the non-psychopathic comparison group do not reveal the efficacy or inefficacy of the treatment for psychopaths. It must first be established how psychopaths and non-psychopathic criminals fare when both are untreated. At the present time there are no satisfactory natural history studies to show this.

Descriptions of treatment

(d) What constitutes treatment?

Perhaps the feature of most concern to emerge from this review of treatment research is the fact that the nature of the treatment intervention is usually not mentioned at all, or is very poorly described. The three-level rating of treatment description in studies, as 'good' (treatment described sufficiently to be replicable), 'some' (brief description but treatment not replicable) and 'none' (no description of treatment at all), reveals that the majority of studies do not describe the treatment given sufficiently for an independent researcher to be able to replicate the study or for the clinician to apply the treatment to his or her own patients.

Generally, studies of physical and drug treatment of psychopaths do describe the treatment given well enough for the reader to replicate the study. These types of treatment are perhaps the easiest to describe within the context of a research report. Nevertheless, some still fail to give replicable treatment details (e.g. MacKay, 1948; Darling & Sandall, 1952).

Six of the 13 TCs which have produced outcome research have described their treatment fully enough for reproduction of the programme elsewhere to be possible (Henderson Hospital, HMP Grendon, HMP Wormwood Scrubs, van der Hoeven Clinic, Penetenguishene and Wexler's Stay N'Out programme). Apart from treatment at these six institutions, only *three* other psychological or hospital programmes are described adequately enough for replication (Cohen & Filipczak, 1971; Moyes *et al*, 1983; Woody *et al*, 1985). Other studies simply state the modality of treatment (e.g. out-patient cognitive group therapy), or give no description at all. This is particularly true of studies of long-term hospitalisation and is most noticeable in the case of British Special Hospitals, the places where most psychopaths are detained for treatment. None of the Special Hospital studies have reported on the treatment received by their psychopathic patients. Although elsewhere such studies have been described as "methodologically elegant" (Tidmarsh (1982) referring to Walker & Macabe (1973)), they actually say little about what constitutes effective treatment.

Perhaps in these retrospective research studies conducted in Special Hospitals it was impossible to determine or quantify the treatment given. Dell & Robertson (1988) found that for legal psychopaths in Broadmoor there was no standard package of individual therapy, group therapy, cognitive therapy, behavioural training and psychotropic medication. Most patients received some of these therapies in varying 'doses', but 16% of patients in their sample were documented as not receiving any of these types of treatment. Chiswick (1982) notes the paucity in the medical literature of accounts of the clinical methods in Special Hospitals, and McGrath (1968) has questioned to what extent a "benevolent custodial and expectant regime" can be justified as 'treatment' in hospital. Blackburn (1992) points out that although such approaches may be referred to as 'milieu therapy', this is usually a euphemism for an orderly regime within the hospital. Similarly, Gunn (1978) suggests that a structured disciplined environment within a hospital is not "a medical strategy; it is simply a prerequisite for making sure patients stay where they are told to stay".

Some studies (e.g. Black, 1982) only claim to investigate discharge decisions and it may not be fair to criticise them for not describing the treatment. However, other studies are invariably referred to as showing the outcome of treatment without providing any description of the treatment given to patients. These studies actually have little value as investigations of treatment outcome: in most cases they can only provide information about the outcome of discharging someone from hospital care. This may be important information in its own right, when issues about dangerousness and clinical responsibility are being considered. However, it does not aid the understanding of appropriate treatment strategies for psychopaths.

(e) What constitutes non-treatment?

For those studies which have compared their treated sample with an untreated comparison group, the issue of what constitutes non-treatment must also be addressed. In many cases of offender populations, the 'untreated group' also undergo a loss of liberty or incarceration which could be associated with changes in behaviour or psychological state. Certainly part of the philosophy behind penal incarceration is that a period of loss of liberty will bring about a change in future offending behaviour. Dell & Robertson (1988) revealed how consultant psychiatrists at Broadmoor Hospital expected time to play a greater part than treatment in bringing about change in psychopathic patients in 62% of cases.

Within a custodial or compulsory setting it may be possible to describe the limited number of alternative interventions which may impinge on a non-treated group. But in out-patient or community settings this is more problematic.

Studies of voluntary treatment settings have compared results with non-admitted patients, presuming they represent an untreated group (e.g. Copas *et al*, 1984; Moyes *et al*, 1985). Although the untreated group may not receive the study treatment, it is likely that they may be subject to some interventions in the study period. Personality-disordered patients are high service users and when in the community they continue to 'suck in' services in a reactive and unplanned way (Perry *et al*, 1985). For example, Murch & Dolan (1992) have shown how a proportion of personality-disordered patients who were not admitted to a voluntary treatment setting still received a variety of health care interventions, and a proportion had been held in custody in the year following referral. Such interventions may affect outcome of the 'untreated' group. Therefore it is important that researchers take some account of these other variables when reporting upon 'untreated' samples.

Therapist factors

Alongside the consideration of what actual treatment is 'received' by the patient, the issue of who 'gives' the therapy may also be importantly related to outcome. It is easy to check that subjects are given accurate doses of a drug in pharmacological therapy. However, there is often an unspoken assumption that the psychological therapy described is administered in the same way by everyone, that each therapist is delivering the same treatment to the patient.

Only two studies give details of the therapists involved in the treatment programme (Truax *et al*, 1966; Woody *et al*, 1983). Although some TC studies will have descriptions of the staff team on the unit, most studies make no reference at all to the personal or professional characteristics of therapists. This may be of particular importance in studies of individual and group therapies (whether psychodynamic, cognitive or behavioural) as it is important to know whether outcomes are attributable to the therapists' age, gender or competence. This feature may be particularly important with the difficult client group we are considering here. A vast amount of work has demonstrated how features of the therapist may affect the process and outcome of therapy (Garfield & Bergin, 1986). Therapists' characteristics and skills have been shown to affect not only the treatment outcome of those who complete therapy, but also the patients' motivation and treatment drop-out rate (Browne & Dolan, 1991).

Measures of outcome

(f) What constitutes an acceptable measure of outcome?

Several studies do not use any measures of outcome but instead refer to a subjective clinical impression of changes. This is particularly true of studies of psychosurgery (Green *et al*, 1944; MacKay, 1948; Darling & Sandall, 1952; Balasubramanian & Rammamurthi, 1970; Poblete *et al*, 1970). Other studies have used only subjective clinical assessment to assess outcome of psychotherapy (Reckless, 1970), TC treatment (Rapoport, 1960; Tuxford, 1961; Sandhu, 1970; Ogloff *et al*, 1990), and in-patient hospitalisation (Heaver, 1943; Gabbard & Coyne, 1987).

Recidivism as an outcome measure

The most frequently used measure of outcome is reconviction. This is the only, or main, measure of treatment success in over three-quarters of the reviewed studies which consider long-term outcome (41/54 = 76%). Two issues arise when considering reconviction as an outcome measure: firstly, whether criminal behaviour is an appropriate measure of outcome for psychopaths, and secondly whether reconviction is an accurate measure of criminal behaviour.

Appropriateness of criminal behaviour as an outcome measure for psychopathy

Gunn (1977) has pointed out the paradox of criminal behaviour being used to define psychopathic disorder and at the same time being considered to be the result of the disorder. Despite the arguments that psychopathy should not be diagnosed on the basis of criminal behaviour (Blair, 1975*a*; Chiswick, 1992), it seems that criminal behaviour assumes primary importance when researchers have considered successful treatment. Crawford (1984) argues that the concept of 'mental abnormality' has no utility for deterministic behavioural science and that an examination of the determinants of offending behaviour is more appropriate. Such a view is particularly noticeable in the 11 studies reviewed from the English Special Hospitals, where subsequent criminal behaviour and re-admission are the *only* measures of outcome applied.

Robertson (1989) has suggested that the use of "criminological criteria to assess the usefulness of psychiatric intervention is ...

mistaken in principle and impossible in practice". He notes how the criteria used to judge the success of treatment for mentally ill patients are the same for offenders and non-offenders, and are related to their psychiatric illness. This illness can remit or respond to treatment, and mental state is considered when making discharge decisions. However, for patients with psychopathic disorder, where the validity of the medical concept is dubious and the 'illness' undefined, the recourse is to criminal rather than clinical criteria. The admission offence becomes the centre of discussions about a patient's discharge (Robertson, 1992).

Of course it could be argued that the British law requires no psychiatric symptoms to be present for a person to be detained under the Mental Health Act category of psychopathic disorder. Aggressive or irresponsible behaviour is all that must be manifest, with the presumption that this arises from a "persistent disorder or disability of mind". Chiswick (1992) suggests that "it is possible for any violent offender to slip into the category". If such behaviour goes away it is then taken as evidence that the disorder of mind is no longer present. However, as it is the "disorder or disability of mind" and not the offending which justifies detention within the mental health system, surely it should be the alleviation of this mental disorder which is the outcome criterion. Until the mediators of offending and antisocial behaviour are established and clarified, criminal behaviour cannot be accepted as a sufficient criterion of outcome. Finally, even if one believes that the absence of seriously aggressive and irresponsible behaviour is an indication that the person is no longer a psychopath, reconviction is not a measure of aggressive or irresponsible behaviour, it is a measure of being found guilty of breaking the law.

It is perhaps understandable that prison studies rely upon recidivism as the outcome measure, given the Home Office statement that the prison's duty to prisoners is "to help them lead *law-abiding* lives in custody and after release" (HMSO, 1991). However, for psychiatric treatment studies it might be assumed that it is the patient's psychiatric disturbance rather than criminal offending that is being treated. Although the offending behaviour may have been the feature which brought the patient to the attention of the health care system, it is not a sufficiently accurate measure of mental state.

Accuracy of recidivism measures as behavioural indicators

Setting aside the conceptual difficulties of using criminal behaviour to identify the presence or absence of psychopathic disorder, the use of recidivism as an outcome measure also produces associated methodological problems which make it a scientifically invalid criterion of outcome.

In essence, the experimental model applied in treatment studies is that the independent variable (treatment) will effect changes in the dependent variable (reconviction). However, the treatment effect is only a very small factor among the multitude of other circumstances upon which reconviction will depend. For the offender to be convicted, he/she must:

(a) have the motivation and/or need to offend
(b) be in a position and have the opportunity to offend
(c) be identified by police as the offender
(d) be apprehended
(e) be charged
(f) be found guilty.

At each stage of this procedure several other factors, both personal to and external to the subject, can intervene and affect the final outcome. Many of these intervening factors can be neither measured nor controlled, and just because treatment is a more measurable factor the researcher cannot be sure that the treatment given relates to reconviction more specifically than these other intervening factors.

Some researchers have attempted to avoid the problem of using actual conviction rates by resorting to arrest records (Steadman, 1977). However, although cutting down some of the variance in being convicted of a crime, this brings the possibility that a previous offender, already known to police authorities, may be more likely to be suspected of a crime and then arrested, despite his/her innocence.

Robertson (1989) has succinctly described reconviction as failing "to meet the criteria necessary for scientific evaluation, as it is impossible to obtain sufficient control of the random or error variance contributing to the criterion measure".

In order to determine whether time spent in treatment does affect future offending, a huge number of observations would need to be made. This would involve looking at a large cohort of subjects over an extended time period. Robertson (1989), on the basis of previous research, notes that several variables would be found to relate to reoffending, but that each one would only influence outcome to a very small degree. This statistical information would be of little use to the person who must make a decision about an individual patient.

Rehospitalisation as an outcome measure

Rehospitalisation has also been used a measure of outcome in several reports. Particularly in Special Hospital studies where patients have been on conditional release or discharged under licence, rehospitalisation may actually result from further criminal or antisocial behaviour, although this behaviour may not have led to conviction (Tong & MacKay, 1959; Craft, 1965; Gathercole *et al*, 1968; Aarvold Committee, 1973; Acres, 1975; Dell, 1980; Black, 1982; Norris, 1984). In such cases, therefore, patients' return to a secure psychiatric hospital is a measure of antisocial or criminal behaviour and not any indication of psychiatric or psychological state. In this way, a measure of rehospitalisation is actually similar to the use of recall or revocation of parole as an outcome measure in several of the prison studies (Boslow & Kohlmeyer, 1963; Taylor, 1967; Fink *et al*, 1969; Hodges, 1971; Jessen & Roosenberg, 1971; McCord & Sanchez, 1982).

Other studies of voluntary treatment have considered the need for further psychiatric treatment and in those studies rehospitalisation may be more indicative of psychiatric state (e.g. Whiteley, 1970; Copas & Whiteley, 1976; Copas *et al*, 1984; Mehlum *et al*, 1991). Tucker (1987) has pointed out that rehospitalisation of personality-disordered patients is not necessarily a sign of treatment failure. It may be that a patient has sought treatment rather than follow some other course of action, such as attempt suicide. As with reconviction, factors other than the patient receiving a specific type of treatment may intervene in the process of being readmitted to hospital. To be admitted, a patient must first come to the attention of the health care authorities in some way. Following this, because of the pejorative attitudes and therapeutic pessimism towards people with personality disorders (Lewis & Appleby, 1988), some people still may not be admitted to psychiatric hospital, despite their need for further help. Others may refuse non-compulsory treatment although they would benefit from further admission. Because of all these variables affecting readmission, it is at best a very rough indication of a person's true psychiatric or mental state.

Life history measures of outcome

Other studies have used life-history variables such as employment (Tuxford, 1961; Craft *et al*, 1964; Taylor, 1966; Van Emmerik, 1987; Woody *et al*, 1985) and return to military service (Colman & Baker, 1969; Jones *et al*, 1977). Such measures are also problematic if taken as evidence of success of treatment. As with recidivism and rehospitalisation, many independent factors can contribute to these life-history measures. At best, life-history measures only provide a very rough indication of the level of mental disorder.

Psychological outcome measures

Very few studies have considered outcome of psychological variables in relation to treatment outcome. Even among those studies which do measure some aspect of psychological functioning, no one scale is commonly used. Twelve different psychological scales, measuring different aspects of personality or psychological states, have been applied in the reviewed studies. Many of these scales are developed from different theoretical stances. Only two scales have been used by more than three authors. The Minnesota Multiphasic Personality Inventory (MMPI) was used by Craft *et al* (1964), Persons (1966), Carney (1977), Gunn *et al* (1978), Skolnick & Zuckerman (1979), and Valliant & Antonowicz (1991). The Symptom Check-List (SCL–90) was used by Woody *et al* (1985), Vaglum *et al* (1990), Dolan *et al* (1992*c*), and Mehlum *et al* (1991).

Other scales which have been used in only one study or by one set of research workers are: the Beck Depression Inventory (BDI), used by Woody *et al* (1985); the Peterson Delinquency Scale (PDS), the Taylor Manifest Anxiety Scale (TMAS), and the Personal Experience and Attitudes Questionnaire (PEAQ), used by Persons (1965, 1966); the Novaco Provocation Inventory, used by Stermac (1986); the Block-Ego Identity Scale, used by Maas (1966); the Speilberger State Trait Anxiety Scale, used by Valliant & Antonowicz (1991); the Minnesota Counselling Inventory (MCI), used by Truax *et al* (1966); the General Health Questionnaire (GHQ), used by Gunn *et al* (1978); the Hostility and Direction of Hostility Questionnaire (HDHQ), used by Newton (1973) and Miller (1982); the Eysenck Personality Questionnaire (EPQ), used by Miller (1982); and the Sensation Seeking Scale (SSS), used by Skolnick & Zuckerman (1979). The IQ test has been used as an outcome measure by Craft *et al* (1964) and by Andy (1975) as evidence that psychosurgery did not detrimentally affect intelligence. Two additional studies have used a repertory grid approach to examining conceptual changes during TC treatment (Norris, 1985; Jones, 1990).

Grounds (1987) suggests that a "critical issue" for the detention of psychopathic patients in Special Hospitals is that, if "following treatment some psychopaths do show evidence of psychological and personality change, does such change imply that the patient's risk of reoffending is reduced?" However, to date, no studies have looked at change in any aspect of personality or psychological state following Special Hospital treatment and how this relates to reoffending, although Black (1982) did consider whether scores on any of a series of psychological tests administered while the patient was in hospital were predictive of outcome.

Length of follow-up

(g) How long term is follow-up?

The durability of change is one of the most important issues in treatment outcome research. Therefore whichever measures of outcome are used, psychological changes and/or life-history events should be evaluated over an extended time period. The study of Robertson & Gunn (1987) demonstrates how a long-term perspective should be taken on reoffending, as rates were considerably higher at ten years than at two years (92% v. 70%) in their sample of prison inmates. However, apart from three notable exceptions (McCord & Sanchez, 1982; Robertson & Gunn, 1987; Rice *et al*, 1992), all the studies reviewed followed up their subjects for less than ten years.

The follow-up period for the majority of outcome studies is between two and five years (Heaver, 1943; Craft, 1958; Tong & MacKay, 1959; Craft *et al*, 1964; Gathercole *et al*, 1968; Whiteley, 1970; Cohen & Filipczak, 1971; George, 1971; Hodges 1971; Jesen & Roosenberg, 1971; Newton, 1971; Sadoff *et al*, 1971; Jew *et al*, 1972; Kozol *et al*, 1972; Aarvold Committee, 1973; Acres, 1975; Copas & Whiteley, 1976; Steadman, 1977; Cavior & Schmidt, 1978; Dell, 1980; Black, 1982; Sewell & Clarke, 1982; Copas *et al*, 1984; Norris, 1984; Moyes *et al*, 1985; Van Emmerick, 1987; Jones, 1988; Wexler *et al*, 1990; Cook *et al*, 1991; Mehlum *et al*, 1991; Bailey & MacCulloch, 1992*a,b*; Cullen, 1992).

In many cases, studies have reported a significant improvement in the initial period after treatment or after a short-term follow-up. However, longer-term follow-up finds that the effect disappears (Cohen & Filipczak, 1971; Hendrix & Heckel, 1982). Several reports have used a follow-up period of less than a year, which is arguably too short to allow for any confidence in the stability of changes (Green *et al*, 1944; MacKay, 1948; Taylor, 1966, 1967; Colman & Baker, 1969; Fink *et al*, 1969; Carney, 1977; Skolnick & Zuckerman, 1979; Sleap, 1979; Woody *et al*, 1985; Dolan *et al*, 1992*c*).

It is noteworthy that, excepting Mehlum *et al* (1991), those studies which do have a follow-up period of longer than two years resort to offending behaviour or rehospitalisation as their outcome indicators. Obviously, following up a large cohort of subjects using self-report measures or observational data is extremely time-consuming and difficult. Gunn *et al* (1978) had to abandon their attempts to follow up their subjects with a self-report questionnaire because of the poor response rate. This may be one factor that discourages researchers from using such instruments to research psychological factors.

The natural history study of Gibbens *et al* (1959) indicates a levelling out of offending after five years. In contrast, Tong & MacKay (1959) found that relapse occurred soon after discharge from Rampton Hospital. Studies of time to relapse (or offending), rather than the categorical distinction of subjects who do and do not relapse, provide a more statistically powerful comparison. However, very few studies have looked at this aspect of outcome.

The power of statistical findings

(h) What is an adequate number of subjects to be sure of a difference? (What is an acceptable power for statistical tests?)

The power of the statistical findings reported in comparative studies depends upon the size of the sample studied, the nature of the measurement, and the criterion of significance (alpha level) used.

Confidence intervals of X^2 tests

The most common method of reporting outcome has been 2 x 2 contingency tables, analysed with a X^2 test (e.g. proportions of subjects who did and did not reoffended in each group). The criterion of significance (i.e. probability value) most often applied is 0.05. However, when using the X^2 test, no studies have reported the statistical power of the test.

The statistical power of a test is the probability that it will show a significant effect given a particular true treatment effect in the population from which the experimental samples are taken. One method of reporting power of tests is to calculate the confidence interval of the treatment effect (in the case of a X^2 test, for the differences in proportions) (Gardner & Altman, 1986). The use of confidence intervals is increasingly replacing statistical hypothesis tests. Although it is generally based on the same assumptions for any particular experimental design, the form of the answer is not 'significant/non-significant' but two values. For example, the 95% confidence interval for a study is an interval between two values, say between 20 and 74 for the drop in some personality measure with treatment. These intervals, calculated for many different studies, will contain the true population treatment effects for 95% of those studies. This approach dovetails exactly with the hypothesis test on an alpha of 0.05 for most tests: if the 95% confidence interval does not include no difference then there is a statistically significant effect.

However, the additional information in the confidence interval is that its width gives an indication of the accuracy with which the treatment effect has been pinned down by the study. Confidence intervals are being insisted upon by an increasing number of journals because they may change the widespread tendency for researchers not to consider statistical power, leading, in extreme cases, to non-significant results being presented as if they proved that there is a treatment effect in the population. For many studies considered in this review, the statistical power was so low that the finding of a non-significant result was more probable than a significant result, even if the population treatment effect was large enough to be of some real clinical utility.

To illustrate the importance of this, examples are recalculated below from three comparative outcome studies which used recidivism as a criterion of failure (Table 11.4). These are: Craft *et al*'s (1964) comparative study of 50 adolescents in an authoritarian programme and 50 in a group therapy programme; Robertson & Gunn's (1987) ten-year follow-up of 61 Grendon men and 61 matched inmates from the parole index; and Acre's (1975) study of 28 psychopathic and 43 mentally ill patients released from Special Hospitals.

Craft *et al* (1964) found no significant difference in the proportions of their two treated samples who were reconvicted. After 14 months, 78% of subjects in the authoritarian programme and 72% of those in the group therapy programme were not convicted; that is, the rate of conviction was 6% lower for the authoritarian treatment than for group therapy. However, with sample sizes of 50 subjects, the 95% confidence interval of this difference ranges from -11% to + 23%. This means that the study is only powerful enough to produce a 34% confidence interval for the population differences.

Robertson & Gunn (1987) also found no statistical difference in their two samples after ten years, with only 15% of the non-treated

TABLE 11.4

The 95% confidence intervals of X^2 analysis from three studies

	Not reconvicted	*Reconvicted*	*Total*
Craft et al (1964)			
Authoritarian group treatment	39 (78%)	11	50
TC therapy	36 (72%)	14	50
Difference in proportions	6%		
95% CI of difference	-11% to +23%		
Robertson & Gunn (1987)			
Untreated prisoners	9 (15%)	52	61
Grendon inmates	5 (8%)	56	61
Difference in proportions	7%		
95% CI of difference	-5% to +18%		
Acres (1975)			
Mental illness	23 (82%)	5	28
Psychopathic disorder	20 (47%)	23	43
Difference in proportions	36%		
95% CI of difference	+15% to +56%		

sample and 8% of the treated sample remaining free of conviction. The 95% confidence interval of this 7% difference in proportions is between -5% and +18%.

Acres (1975) found that significantly more of the mentally ill than the psychopathic disordered patients released from Special Hospitals did not reoffend (82% v. 47%). However, the 36% difference in proportions has a 95% confidence interval of between 15% and 56% in favour of the mentally ill group. Although a significant effect is demonstrated, with this sample size the confidence interval on the population difference is still very large.

Power of statistical tests

Figures 11.1 to 11.4 illustrate some of the statistical power issues raised by this review. All four show statistical power; that is, the probability of finding a significant result. All figures plot power on the y-axis against sample size on the x-axis. All calculations are based on a criterion of 0.05 for significance. Calculations and plots were performed using the SOLO power analysis program (Hintze, 1991).

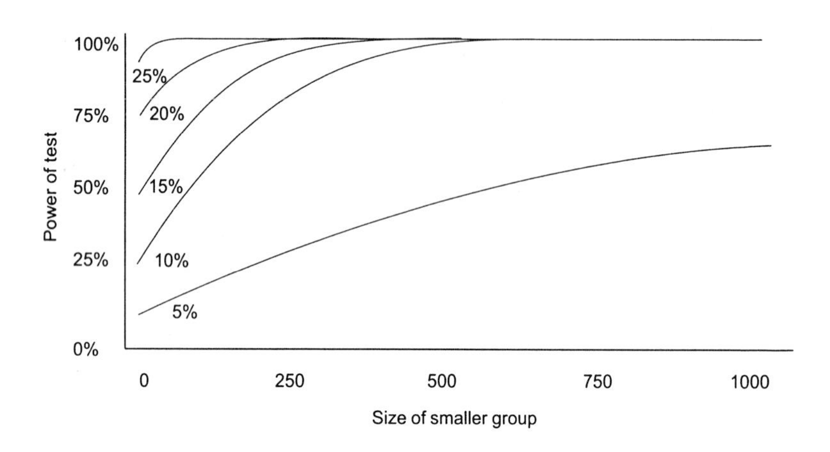

Fig. 11.1. Power by sample size. Lines indicate the power obtainable for various effects of treatment (i.e. various levels of difference in recidivism rates) from 5% to 25%. Larger group size held constant at n=810; control group recidivism rate held constant at 70%

Figure 11.1 shows how power depends both on the magnitude of the difference between groups and on sample size, assuming comparison of recidivism rates over a fixed period, a recidivism rate of 70% in the control group and reductions in recidivism of 5%, 10%, 15%, 20% and 25% in the treatment group. The control group size was kept constant at an unrealistic 810.

As shown in Fig.11.1, if the recidivism rate is 70% in the control group and 45% (i.e. 25% less) in the experimental group, then with only 50 subjects in the smaller group one can obtain 100% power. However, if the experimental group have a recidivism rate of 55% (i.e. 15% less) then one needs in the region of 250 subjects in the smaller group to obtain 100% power. If one has only 50 subjects in the smaller group with this 15% difference in recidivism rates the power is reduced to around 55%.

Figure 11.2 illustrates how the size of the smaller group limits the power that can be achieved by increasing the other group. Here the treatment effect difference between groups is kept constant at 10% and the curves show sizes for the smaller group, ranging from 30 to 810. The sample size of 30 in the smaller group limits the power achievable to about 15% even if the size of the other group (control or intervention group) is raised as high as 1000.

Figure 11.3 shows that the statistical power to detect a fixed difference of 10% in recidivism rates increases as the control

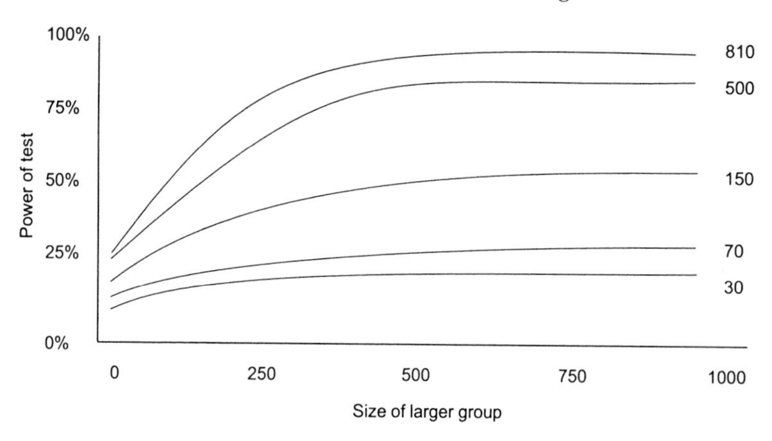

Fig. 11.2. Effect of smaller group size to limit power. Lines indicate power for different sizes of the smaller group (from n = *30 to* n = *810). Control group recidivism rate held constant at 70%; experimental group recidivism rate held constant at 60%*

group recidivism rate increases from 50% to 80% (i.e. it is easier to detect a difference between 80% and 70% than between 50% and 40%).

All of these models have considered the detection of differences in proportions over a fixed follow-up period, which was the most common comparison made in the studies reviewed. Statistical power to detect differences in continuous ratings is always higher than that for detection of dichotomies (such as 'reoffended/did not reoffend'), provided that the continuous and dichotomous measures are of approximately equal reliability. Hence it would be wise for future studies to supplement recidivism measures with continuous measures of psychopathy or liability to reoffend or behave antisocially if these can be formulated. The possible gains in power and capacity to explore change in sequences of treatment would justify some investment in further exploration of existing measures (interviews, questionnaires and repertory grids) and their refinement to address specific models of psychopathy and response to treatment.

What else can be done to improve the precision, the statistical power, of studies of treatment of personality disorder? A greater chance of showing a significant treatment effect can be achieved using more homogeneous groups (or aspects of personality which fluctuate less in within-subjects designs) than if much more diverse (or fluctuating) aspects are taken as the focus of the study.

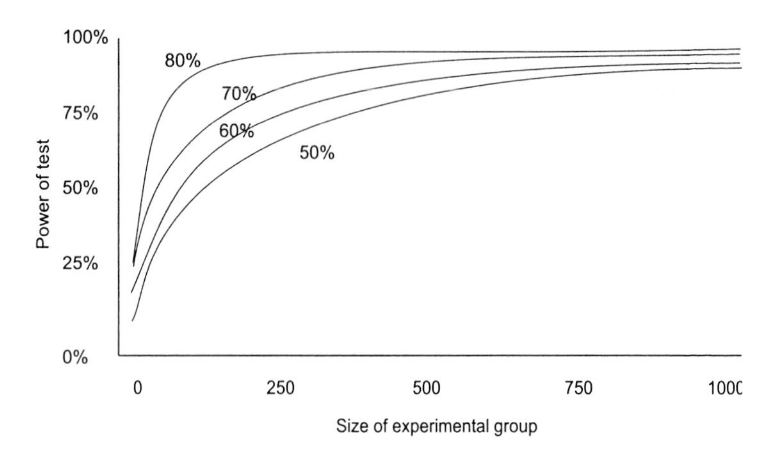

Fig. 11.3. Effect of control group recidivism rate. Control group size held constant at n = 810; difference in recidivism rate of control and experimental groups held constant at 10%

Statistical power is also improved by increasing the sample size (or number of repeated measurements in within-subjects designs), improving the accuracy of measurement (to reduce the non-treatment differences in scores) and using a lower alpha level.

However, all these methods of improving statistical power involve sacrifices. Greater homogeneity of study groups will limit the clinical situations to which the results can logically be extrapolated; larger numbers expose more patients to uncertainty and risk and involve increased costs, or may actually make a study so large or long drawn out as to be impractical or behind the times by the time the results are available. Improved measurement is generally only possible at considerable expense in terms of subject time and the employment of multiple raters, etc. Finally, a less stringent (larger) alpha level increases the risk that a random sampling effect will be misinterpreted as a treatment effect.

'Survival' or 'time to failure' analysis

Although more extensive and better informed use of continuous measures is desirable, dichotomous measures such as recidivism, time to relapse and even longevity will remain central to research on the treatment of psychopathic disorder. However, the use of simple comparison of proportions in fixed follow-up periods is a very limited, and potentially inappropriate, statistical analysis of these dichotomous indicators of response to treatment. One very big methodological improvement would be the use of 'survival' or 'time-to-failure' analytic methods, now ubiquitous in trials of treatment in cancer and other parallel situations in which time to relapse may vary widely and loss to follow-up occurs at varying times after treatment. Survival analysis allows for the occurrence of 'censored observations' which may arise because patients have not reached the end-point of interest (e.g. relapse, recidivism, etc.) by the end of the study period. For example, often the final 'survival' time is unknown: all that is known is that the patient has not relapsed *yet* when the study ends. Alternatively, in some cases the patient may be lost to follow-up for some reason, but it is known that he/she had been free from relapse up to some point, and this information could be utilised. Survival analyses use information about time to relapse or loss from the study, so that the much longer time that earlier recruits can be studied is not lost in order to preserve a fixed follow-up period (Everitt, 1989).

Figure 11.4 shows the statistical power for such a study, in which patients were entered at a uniform rate over six years and the total study time was 10 years, with an overall loss to follow-up of 10%. The power curves against total sample size in the two groups are

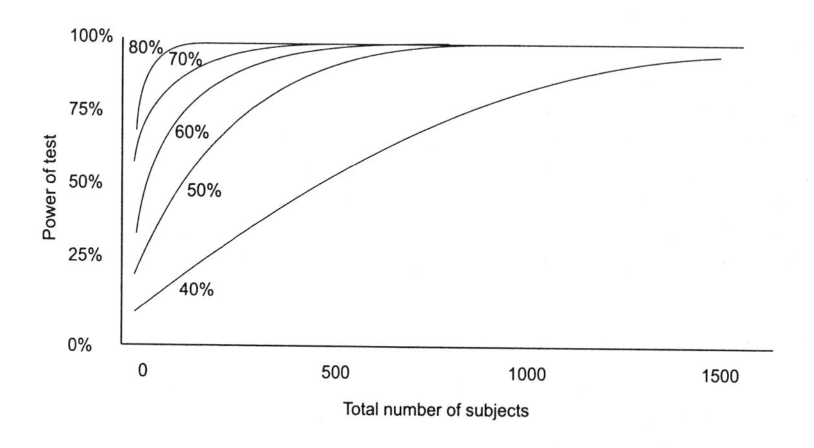

Fig. 11.4. Survival analysis plots of power against sample size. Plot of six years of subject accrual plus four years of follow-up; control group recidivism rate held constant at 70%. Recidivism rates from 40% to 80% in experimental group; loss to follow-up 10%

shown for overall recidivism rates of 80%, 70%, 60%, 50%, and 40%, against a comparison rate of 70%. For the 50% rate (i.e. an improvement with treatment of 20%) 122 in each group provides 80% power to detect this difference and 160 in each group provides 90% power. This is markedly greater than the power that could be achieved in the same time for any fixed follow-up period, assuming that the treatment centre sees the same number of patients regardless of the design of the study.

12 Summary of findings and recommendations for future research

After the many methodological criticisms of the studies reviewed in the previous chapter, it could be argued that to go ahead and review the overall findings from such flawed studies is of limited value. However, this would be an unsatisfactory review if it did not attempt to pull together the findings of studies, draw some conclusions from the work available, and suggest some directions for future research. This chapter therefore presents the basic findings and inferences which can be taken from the reviewed studies of treatment of psychopathic and antisocial personality disorders. This chapter should not be read independently of the previous chapter which outlines why, in many cases, the conclusion must be that there is no evidence for the efficacy of a specific treatment. This should not be taken to mean that the treatment itself is ineffective, but rather that efficacy cannot be demonstrated from the available evidence.

Summary of reviewed research

Pharmacological treatment

As there have been no controlled studies of the pharmacological treatment of the 'core' features of psychopathic disorder, there is consequently no reliable evidence of the efficacy of this treatment modality for psychopathy. Nevertheless, there are studies indicating that a range of different medications may be effective, firstly on associated forms of axis II psychopathology, particularly borderline and schizotypal personality disorder, and secondly on associated forms of behavioural dyscontrol.

Physical treatment

One non-controlled study of electro-shock therapy in 24 'criminal psychopaths' reported no change or only slight improvement in the majority of cases (Green *et al*, 1944). There is no reliable evidence of the efficacy of electro-shock therapy for treating psychopathic disorder.

Six studies of psychosurgery are reviewed, all of which have claimed that psychosurgery (including leucotomy, thalamotomy, amygdalotomy and lobotomy) reduces aggressive and impulsive in behaviour 'psychopathic' patients who did not respond to other methods of treatment. Five studies were of fewer than 30 patients. Only one study used recognised diagnostic criteria for psychopathy. No studies carried out controlled investigations and all have used only subjective clinical reports as their measure of improvement. There is no reliable evidence of the efficacy of psychosurgery for treating psychopaths.

Dynamic psychotherapeutic approaches

There are very few studies which evaluate the use of psychotherapy with psychopaths independent of other treatment modalities.

Reports of short-term out-patient psychotherapy have shown only limited effectiveness in treating psychopathic or antisocial personality disorder. The follow-up periods for empirical studies of personality-disordered patients is generally short. The two reviewed studies which did show some long-term reduction in recidivism were of enforced group therapy with sex offenders.

Some short-term studies of in-patient psychotherapy with adolescent delinquents have demonstrated short-term improvements in psychological state and behaviour compared with untreated controls (Persons, 1966; Truax *et al*, 1966; Taylor, 1967) but evaluations have not been made over periods longer than one year.

One study of in-patient psychotherapy with adult psychopaths has shown a short-term reduction in recidivism which is not maintained on long-term follow-up (Jew *et al*, 1972).

Following a combined individual and group therapy approach, 'dangerous psychopathic offenders' showed less serious recidivism than those deemed dangerous but released by courts over a 3.5-year follow-up (Kozol *et al*, 1972).

Cognitive–behavioural psychotherapy

Some initial reduction in recidivism has been noted after behavioural programmes for young offenders (Stermac, 1986; Valliant & Antonowicz, 1991). These effects have not been shown to be maintained in the long term (Cohen & Filipczak, 1971; Moyes *et al,* 1985).

A reduction in behaviour problems, self-mutilation, and temper outbursts was maintained up to two years after treatment of personality-disordered adolescents in a behavioural programme (Moyes *et al,* 1985)

In-patient behavioural programmes have shown behavioural improvements, which were maintained on follow-up, for "character disordered" soldiers (Colman & Baker, 1969; Jones *et al,* 1977).

Several of the cognitive programmes reviewed are of short-term treatment (Stermac, 1986; Valliant & Antonowicz, 1991). Most cognitive–behavioural approaches attend to a specific aspect of behaviour or attitude (such as aggression, social skills) and do not claim to treat the entire 'personality-disordered' aspect of the patient.

There is only limited evidence for the long-term efficacy of cognitive–behavioural programmes alone for treating psychopathic disorder in adults.

Therapeutic community approaches

Uncontrolled studies of changes during Therapeutic Community (TC) treatment have generally demonstrated an improvement on psychological measures (Newton, 1973; Gunn *et al,* 1978; Miller, 1982; Norris, 1985).

Those studies which consider the management of violent offenders within prison TCs report fewer serious incidents than in the normal prison system (suicide, violence, riot, etc.) (Sandhu, 1970; Gray, 1974; Cooke, 1989).

Two uncontrolled studies have shown significant reduction in distress due to psychological symptoms as measured by the Symptoms Check-List questionnaire following TC treatment of personality-disordered patients (Vaglum *et al,* 1990; Dolan *et al,* 1992*c*).

Only two TC studies have a ten-year follow-up period, and both showed no difference in recidivism in treated male offenders compared with matched control samples of untreated non-psychopaths (Robertson & Gunn, 1987; Rice *et al,* 1992).

A five-year follow-up study of TC treatment at Henderson Hospital indicates significantly less recidivism and readmission in a treated group of psychopaths compared with untreated referrals (Copas *et al*, 1984).

Three reviewed studies which suggest a less favourable outcome for psychopaths after treatment did not allow voluntary participation in the TC treatment (Craft *et al*, 1964; Fink *et al*, 1969; Rice *et al*, 1992).

Length of stay in TC therapy has been shown to be positively related to improved outcome (Newton, 1971; George, 1971; Copas *et al*, 1984; Cullen, 1992).

Studies of TC treatment have shown the most promising results of any treatment modality for psychopathy in terms of psychological and behavioural changes during treatment, reduction of violent incidents in treatment settings, and significant improvements following treatment in life-history variables (recidivism, rehospitalisation etc.) and psychological states. In some cases these changes have been maintained at follow-up. In general the actual treatment provided in TC studies is well described. However, there is a dearth of controlled research studies into TC treatment.

Milieu therapies and long-term hospitalisation

Reports of outcome after long-term in-patient treatment in hospitals rarely describe the treatment received by the patients. Therefore outcome cannot be related to the actual type of treatment given.

Of those reviewed studies considering compulsory hospital treatment, none have reported on changes in psychological factors following or during treatment.

Approximately half of discharged psychopathic or personality-disordered patients will reoffend within three years; serious or violent offences will be committed by around a quarter of psychopaths (Norris, 1984; Tennent & Way, 1984; Bailey & MacCulloch, 1992*a,b*).

Comparison of psychopaths with mentally disordered offenders generally shows a worse outcome for psychopaths in terms of recidivism and readmission. However, one study of patients hospitalised for a short period (less than four years) found no difference in the recidivism rates of psychopathic and mentally ill patients discharged from Broadmoor Special Hospital (Dell & Robertson, 1988).

A variety of life-history factors have been associated with a good outcome after release for psychopathic patients. These include fewer previous hospitalisations (Black, 1982; Norris, 1984; Dell &

Robertson, 1988); fewer previous criminal convictions (Black, 1982; Norris, 1984); a previous conviction for homicide (Aarvold Committee, 1973); not having been institutionalised as a juvenile (Tennent & Way, 1984); fewer previous convictions for violent offences (Tennent & Way, 1984); longer length of admission (Norris, 1984); supervision and after-care (Acres, 1975; Norris, 1984); and being on conditional discharge (Aarvold Committee, 1973).

There have been no adequately controlled studies of in-patient secure hospital treatment. Even in uncontrolled studies, no attempts have been made to link the type of treatment received to outcome variables. Therefore there is little conclusive evidence for the efficacy of long-term 'milieu' hospital treatment of psychopaths.

Community supervision

The evidence for the efficacy of community supervision in prevention of recidivism in patients with 'psychopathic disorder' is limited and inconclusive. There is some evidence that patients who have been detained under the legal categories of 'psychopathic disorder' and 'subnormality' and who have a high risk of reoffending are less likely to offend in the two years after discharge when receiving community supervision than those who receive no supervision at all (Walker & McCabe, 1973).

One further study reports a positive effect for conditional discharge of Special Hospital patients when serious recidivism rates of mentally ill and psychopathic patients are analysed together (Bailey & MacCulloch 1990*a,b*). However, the significant effect of community supervision was not found when results for psychopathic patients were reanalysed separately.

Conclusions and recommendations

The preceding summary of research findings in the treatment of psychopathic and antisocial personality disorders is based upon a small number of studies, themselves limited by poor methodology, with vaguely defined samples followed up for relatively short periods of time and with inadequate measures. Despite this pessimistic summary of the available research, it is important to point out that there is still no convincing evidence that psychopaths can or cannot be successfully treated.

The collapse of the rehabilitative ideal reconsidered

This conclusion is of major importance in the light of similar findings in a series of reviews by criminologists of the effects on subsequent reoffending of treatment programmes in penal settings and correctional facilities for juveniles. Firm conclusions based on apparently negative findings should only be made with extreme caution in view of the misleading and potentially negative effects they might have upon the decisions of policy-makers. Academics have a considerable responsibility in this area, as not only may a programme which is beneficial for a subgroup of individuals be terminated, but negative results may have profoundly negative effects on the attitudes and philosophy of correctional and hospital staff towards treatment and rehabilitation.

Palmer (1992) describes how Martinson's (1974) negative evaluation of treatment programmes in correctional settings played its part in the collapse of the rehabilitative ideal. This review had a considerable impact in the USA at a time of rising crime, growing public concern, and political pressures for tougher approaches to criminals. Having concluded that rehabilitation programmes had not achieved their goals of reducing offender recidivism, 'nothing works' became accepted wisdom. Determinate sentencing increasingly replaced indeterminate sentencing in the courts as the 'justice' model gained prominence, and incapacitation and deterrence were seen as more important goals than rehabilitation. Increased spending on prison capacity in the 1980s became official policy in the UK as well as the USA, where many similar changes in penal and sentencing policy can be observed. Martinson (1979) subsequently retracted his 'nothing works' thesis, but this had little impact on the momentum of the change in the attitudes of policy-makers. More recently, however, a series of meta-analyses and literature reviews have indicated that a cautious return to the rehabilitative approach is overdue: not 'nothing works', but 'what works?'

It is now proposed that approximately 25–50% of properly conducted experimental treatment programmes in penal settings do appear to work in significantly reducing recidivism in treated subjects compared with control subjects, although 10% of programmes achieve worse results for the 'treated' group (Davidson *et al*, 1984; Garrett, 1985; Gendreau & Ross, 1987; Whitehead & Lab, 1989; Lipsey, 1991; Pannizzon *et al*, 1991; Palmer, 1992). Several conclusions of these reviews of research are very similar to our own. For example, no single type of treatment programme in an institutional setting is found to be uniformly successful with inmates, and the reviews point to a need for better-designed studies, more replications of apparently successful programmes, and more attempts to build theoretical models based on successful programmes. In the case of serious and multiple reoffenders, a subgroup which overlap with the subjects we have studied, the reviewers concluded that multi-modal treatment programmes are more appropriate, that these programmes should be more intensive than previous ones, and that appropriate matching of the offender to the programme should be improved.

Treatability

It is a curious observation that the failure of researchers to develop investigative strategies which could prove or disprove the efficacy of a particular treatment modality has been transferred to psychopathic and personality-disordered patients and is often perceived in clinical settings as the patients' own failure to be treatable. The 'untreatability of psychopaths' may, in part, result from the professionals' inadequate assessment in the first place, followed by an inability to develop, describe, research and adequately demonstrate the efficacy of treatment strategies. It cannot be said that the psychopath is untreatable until we are satisfied that all possible treatment interventions have been tried, adequately evaluated, and then shown to fail.

The Mental Health Act 1983 added a new caveat for the detention of persons in hospital under the category of psychopathic disorder, that "medical treatment must be likely to alleviate, or prevent the deterioration of, the mental condition". Ashworth & Gostin (1985) describe this as meaning that "the court must find that it is likely that treatment will effect some change in the offender's mental condition" (cure, remedy or prevent from becoming worse). This has been considered by most to mean that it must be demonstrated that the person must be 'amenable to treatment'. However, the issue of whether the individual is treatable would seem redundant until it can be shown that *any* treatment can effect change in *any* patient's mental condition.

In general, the 'treatability test' is applied to the patient and not to the treatment offered. However, it seems from the studies reviewed in this volume that most treatment methods currently being provided for people suffering from psychopathic disorder could not prove their efficacy in order to pass a treatability test.

We began by quoting a series of statements from different workers from 1941 onwards who commented upon the lack of evidence of efficacious treatment for psychopathy and the need for further research (see pages 3–6). It seems strange, then, that little advance has been made over the subsequent 50 years.

There are several major factors which have contributed to the lack of published research into treatment outcome. These include the unpopularity of this patient group (Lewis & Appleby, 1988); the self-fulfilling factor of therapeutic pessimism surrounding treatment; the disinclination of many psychiatrists outside Special Hospitals to take the risk of treating personality-disordered or psychopathic patients (Coid & Cordess, 1992); the lack of funding for research into psychopathic disorder; the long-term nature of any treatment and follow-up studies which need to be undertaken; and the previous unreliability and lack of consensus regarding diagnosis. Publication bias in clinical research, which results in studies with statistically significant results being more often published than those finding no differences between study groups, may also detract from the knowledge base (Easterbrook *et al*, 1991).

However, this review has demonstrated that developments have taken place in the areas of diagnosis, epidemiology, and the natural history of psychopathic disorder, if not in more effective treatment. These developing areas should perhaps be consolidated first. At a later stage, the investment of additional resources in empirical trials of treatment can be targeted more appropriately. But investment of time and resources should only be in studies with properly assessed and defined samples of subjects, followed up for an adequate period, and with validated measures of treatment effectiveness and operational definitions of outcome.

Part of the problem of untreatability inevitably stems from the diagnostic construct itself. This is largely based on criteria of behavioural features and personality traits which in themselves imply the failure of the individual to respond to normal sanctions on his or her antisocial behaviour over a prolonged period and up to the point of assessment when the diagnosis is made. Thus, if an individual is partly defined on the basis of the failure of a series of other professionals, including social workers, child psychiatrists, teachers, law enforcement officers, and correctional staff, to effect change in personality and behaviour over the life-span, it is perhaps unreasonable to then expect health care professionals to be more effective at a later stage of the process. There will be little progress until more is understood about the underlying nature of the condition itself.

Research into aetiology

Despite shortcomings in the current diagnostic constructs, there have nevertheless been major developments in this area over the last decade. Researchers now have a choice of validated research instruments with which to assess psychopathic subjects. Preliminary data are also available on the epidemiology of these conditions (see review by Coid, 1993*a*), which should promote further use of the relevant diagnostic instruments in future large-scale population surveys.

Chapter 3 has reviewed the growing database on the longitudinal development of psychopathic disorder and its potential for treatment interventions. These studies are expensive and difficult to carry out, and take a long time to yield results. Nevertheless, it is clear that the area that now requires most intense investigation is aetiology. It could therefore be argued that it is premature to invest large resources in treatment programmes for a condition, or series of conditions, where aetiological factors remain so poorly understood. We have argued that the core features of psychopathy, as defined by the PCL–R or DSM–III–R ASPD, could be a final common pathway for a series of different conditions. These may in turn have more than one aetiology and therefore require more than one treatment modality. This may apply to several individuals with apparently similar diagnostic presentations. Longitudinal studies have now demonstrated a series of potential aetiological factors which require prospective evaluation in more sophisticated studies. Research which has examined the interaction of both risk and protective factors has been particularly enlightening. Such research examined broad groups of subjects with adverse outcomes such as criminal history and presentation to mental health services in early adulthood, rather than core features of psychopathic disorder. However, preliminary research might retrospectively trace the life course of psychopathic individuals in relation to potential aetiological factors with a view to identifying areas of importance for a future prospective study. At a later stage, it is essential to accurately identify the predictive factors that might be used to guide intervention strategies, particularly those directed towards prevention.

Strengths and limitations of randomised clinical trials

The random clinical trial is still considered the most effective tool for the assessment of different treatment methods within the tradition of the medical model. The randomising process reduces the individual characteristics of the patients so that evaluation of the benefits received in specific groups can be attributed to the treatment itself rather than unusual characteristics of the patient. To avoid placebo effects, the double-blind randomised trial is usually employed, where neither patient nor physician knows the composition of treatment groups for the range of treatment methods being tested. This minimises the impact of bias in the thinking of the therapist when the patient is treated and when the effectiveness of various treatment modalities is evaluated (Cochrane, 1972).

Overviews of this approach range from a general acceptance of its benefits to the insistence that unless it has been employed, any decision made with regard to the effectiveness of treatment cannot be ultimately justified and may even be unethical. Over time, random clinical trials have revealed the ineffectiveness of many treatment methods that had been long considered essential in the care of patients in all branches of medicine (Antman *et al*, 1992). Similarly, other work has shown that if systematic reviews of randomised trials had been conducted, recommendations for treatment could have been made earlier to the benefit of a number of patients (Lau *et al*, 1992; Chalmers *et al*, 1992).

It has become particularly clear from this review that the randomised double-blind controlled trial of treatment outcome is not yet appropriate for studying psychopathic disorder. It should be unsurprising that an experimental model based upon the concept of the treatment of medical illness has failed to be extrapolated successfully to the treatment of psychopathy, a concept which does not so readily fit the illness model (Chiswick, 1992). Vigorous methodological approaches derived from the medical model of treatment evaluation may not be entirely appropriate when applied to a construct that is partially socially defined. Certainly, progress in identifying suitable treatment methods within this conventional model has been slow.

Traditional medical models of treatment are based upon the assumption that one can administer a particular intervention for a certain period of time and then terminate the treatment, after which the problem is eliminated. However, psychopathic and antisocial personality disorders are chronic conditions which do not fit neatly into this medical model. When using a conventional medical model, the absence of long-term effects after termination of treatment has been taken as failure. However, as with other chronic conditions, psychopathic and antisocial personality disorders may require continued, but varied, treatment interventions over the course of life (as examples see the case histories presented in the Appendix). Therefore a major issue when considering treatment outcome is that treatment of psychopathy or severe personality disorder is rarely, if ever, something which involves just one treatment modality or therapist. Treatment is usually a multi-agency reshaping procedure extending over a long period of time. Several different strategies of treatment will be involved at different periods in the patient's recovery. This makes traditional notions of 'cure' following a specific treatment intervention somewhat unhelpful. It can be artificial to distinguish between different treatment methods (in the way in which this review is divided) as if they were discrete entities which did not impinge upon each other. It would therefore be wrong to suggest that one method of treatment alone will prove to be the most efficacious for this group of subjects. Furthermore, while psychopaths are defined by incompatible legal and psychiatric systems, research studies will inevitably include a heterogeneous group of people. Different levels of severity of personality disorder, symptoms, behaviour and dangerousness will be demonstrated by individual subjects.

Kazdin (1987) has noted how an assumption seems to be made in experimental research that it is the specific technique that is applied to a clinical problem which makes an important difference. However, this presumes that any change is independent of factors other than the treatment given. He describes how the 'amenability-to-treatment model' has not been sufficiently exploited. This model first identifies where interventions are likely to be effective (i.e. it identifies subjects thought to be most amenable to treatment). Once treatment methods are shown to work in amenable patients they can then be extended to less amenable patients. But if treatment methods do not even produce change in those deemed amenable, the probability of the approach working with more intractable subjects is low. Within a naturalistic study paradigm, this amenability-to-treatment model could be applied. Certainly those institutions which are able to select patients, rather than take them under legal obligation, may already be choosing admissions on the basis of presumed treatment amenability.

Many examples of the research we have reviewed in this volume were carried out with an intention of validating the institution under study. Thus, prisons have concentrated upon recidivism rates, Special Hospitals have concentrated upon the risk involved in the decision to discharge, etc. However, the object of future research should be not to determine the efficacy of one particular treatment or institutional setting for the whole of the heterogeneous category of 'personality disorder' or 'psychopaths', but to consider which patients benefit most from which setting at which time in their recovery. In this context, 'setting' not only includes the type of institution and its level of security, but also refers to the type or modality of treatment given and the characteristics of the therapist(s) involved in the treatment.

There are many schools of psychiatric and psychological treatment, each of which has its own notions of success. The development of objective criteria has therefore been difficult to achieve, especially with modalities such as individual and group psychotherapy, unless there is rigid adherence to more easily observed behavioural changes such as reduction in institutional infractions and subsequent recividism. In the case of psychotherapy directed at the restructuring of a psychopath's basic patterns of relating, it inevitably becomes more difficult to determine whether success has been achieved. However, our review has indicated that, whatever measures are finally chosen, the major question that must ultimately be answered is whether or not a treatment modality alters the life-course of the condition. This will need to be evaluated comparatively along the lines of what is already known about the longitudinal course in the absence of treatment, and will require an adequate period for follow-up. It also poses major problems if treatment modalities are to be evaluated solely on the basis of the model of the random clinical trial.

Naturalistic studies: an interim paradigm

We suggest that there is a need for new research strategies which take a naturalistic approach by following large cohorts of patients through a number of types of statutory and voluntary treatment, with differing levels of security, within health, social and penal services. Transition probabilities and features associated with good outcome for the different settings could then be established. Naturalistic studies which examined in depth the types of treatment offered for patients in different settings and the characteristics of patients who do and do not respond to such treatment would lay the groundwork for the future application of the experimental study. Within this paradigm, the amenability-to-treatment approach could also be adopted and tested. However, until further naturalistic studies are completed which give better indications of appropriate treatment, the more methodologically rigorous studies of comparative and controlled treatment cannot be designed.

Such an approach would necessitate a large study in a variety of settings and would require professionals from a variety of disciplines to work together. This type of naturalistic study can be very threatening as it may show differential responses of certain subjects to certain treatment strategies and it opens each institution up to scrutiny. However, it must be pointed out that some institutions have continued to apply individual treatment modalities to psychopaths with the presumption that they are effective but without any evaluation of the possibility that they are not, and with considerable resistance to proper scrutiny.

Nevertheless, the naturalistic research we are proposing should be based not on institutions but on patients, asking the following questions:

(a) Which patients find their way back to the community after treatment?
(b) How soon do they relapse?
(c) What treatment did they receive?
(d) What, if anything, is typical about their diagnostic presentations?

The ultimate objective would not be to find out which institutions function and which do not, but to examine all possibilities for each patient. Thus variables recognised at an assessment stage could be examined in relation to final outcome. Data collected should also emphasise the search for a better understanding of the underlying aetiology of psychopathic disorder and its associated conditions. This would provide information in terms of patients rather than institutions, but it is, after all, the patient who should be at the centre of investigations of treatment strategies.

Promotion of such a naturalistic paradigm should not be interpreted as a retrograde step of returning to uncontrolled retrospective studies. Since the 1940s an extraordinary amount of research money and effort has produced very little conclusive evidence. We believe this is a result of applying a premature paradigm. Competent naturalistic studies, involving just one specific location at each of Special Hospital, prison, medium-secure, open ward and community settings may well provide more information pertinent to our current resource-allocation decisions than the interim 50 years' work which we have assessed in this review.

We advocate that prospective naturalistic studies should take account of the limitations of other studies reviewed here and pay particular attention to descriptions of the subjects and the methods of treatment. Failure to use recognised or replicable diagnostic criteria in describing subjects as psychopathic or antisocial personality disordered has plagued treatment outcome research. Interpretation and generalisation of outcome findings is impossible without clear descriptions of subjects, and information about the characteristics of those who succeed and those who fail in a treatment programme is essential for the clinician and/or researcher to make future recommendations in individual cases.

When reporting on any treatment method, even within a naturalistic study, it must be specified both what the planned treatment procedure was, and whether the treatment was actually carried out as planned. Luborsky & DuRubeis (1984) have suggested that, where possible, treatment should be delineated in a treatment manual which guides the therapist in the procedures, techniques and themes to attain the specific goals of therapy. Obviously, it is more difficult to give specific strategies with psychodynamic therapy, as opposed to drug or behavioural treatment. However, some delineation and specification of the treatment must be given for it to be possible to evaluate the treatment or train others to administer similar treatment. Clear specifications of the conceptualisation of the disorder, the treatment model, and treatment targets are also important, as they will help clarify what the aim of treatment is and point to those specific aspects or processes in treatment which are judged to alter the target psychopathology or behaviour.

There is also room for single-case design methodology to be employed within the naturalistic approach, in tandem with group evaluation of subjects. In certain situations single-case methodology could be a more ethical research method; for example, where subjects are receiving treatment with some degree of compulsion. Flexibility and modifications to original treatment plans can be accommodated in single-case designs in a way which is impossible within group summary comparison designs.

A naturalistic approach would also have the enormous advantage of building on the existing resources and, in the light of a new understanding of them, identifying where to expand resources and how to focus them for maximum efficiency. Developments from the proposed interim paradigm may later facilitate a return to the controlled experimental model of treatment evaluation. Once identified through naturalistic research, the treatable components of the condition (or group of conditions), and/or those individuals identified as most amenable to specific treatment approaches, could then be targeted more appropriately.

Prevention

Primary prevention strategies will ultimately have to be addressed for this group of conditions, particularly when the effectiveness of many tertiary interventions evaluated in this report have proved largely unimpressive. Primary prevention strategies no longer assume a simple, linear, unidirectional causal model. This suggests that such models of intervention may be particularly appropriate to psychopathic disorder. Longitudinal research has produced a reasonable base of generative knowledge to establish the need and rationale for some prevention programmes. These could be directed at the promotion of normal development as well as the reduction of new cases of the disorder. However, the database on the linkage between specific antecedent conditions and psychopathy in adulthood is, it must be conceded, still relatively small. For example, adverse early experiences such as sexual and physical abuse do not inevitably lead to an adverse adult outcome without intervening factors, many of which have yet to be identified with total accuracy. Thus, the mathematical models which we optimistically predicted in Chapter 3 are still far from development. To some extent, this becomes less problematic if there is less preoccupation with the reduction and elimination of adverse adult outcomes at the expense of attention to health promotion. But this would require the development of alternative methods to achieve positive outcomes at more complex levels of social organisation as well as at the level of the individual.

Seidman (1987) argues that in primary prevention the target of intervention may be the overall population as well as individuals, their setting, and the 'mesosystem'. Thus, high-risk individuals, such as those with multiple forms of conduct disorder and persisting aggression in childhood, could initially be selected. However, instead of attention being directed solely to these individuals, primary prevention could also apply to their family, peers, school, and religious, neighbourhood and voluntary organisations. These interventions are ultimately aimed at averting the final adult outcome. But the more immediate object is to alter the setting in which the individual lives. Similarly, a more complex intervention can impact on a mesosystem, referring to connections between systems, settings, and people. These can include policy initiatives and creating brand new systems. For example, a mesosystem alternative to targeting direct interventions on the children of poor, single-parent mothers might involve increased financial provision for preschool child care or improved preschool education in a certain geographic location, such as the inner city. Intervening at the mesosystem level clearly involves political and economic considerations. The individual effects are also more remote. But such an approach could be considered if the need for a mass-orientated prevention is greater. Thus, a condition such as ASPD, which is believed to affect at least 2% of the US population, with higher levels in inner-city areas, may require a broader approach than the establishment of more TCs in hospitals, secure-hospital beds, etc.

Some preventive interventions indicated by longitudinal studies could ultimately pose serious ethical dilemmas, however, with inevitable demands for additional resources. We believe that improvements in treatment and management of psychopaths will require more accurate and detailed assessment, which in turn requires better training and, in some situations, more staff. If better predictive indicators for early intervention are to be developed, this will include not only the fields of psychiatry and psychology, but disciplines such as paediatrics, developmental psychology and social work. Many adverse factors leading to poor outcome relate to social living conditions, which in themselves must bear some relationship to the general economic conditions in the wider community. However, the more important factors of parenting and other behavioural patterns that can be observed within the individual's family, along with cultural values, will question when and to what extent professionals, or indeed the state, should intervene to prevent the predicted adverse outcome. This in turn will question whether predictive methods are truly reliable. Energetic interventions, such as the removal of a child from what is considered to be a high-risk environment, cannot be justified in the absence of a truly beneficial alternative. Similarly, the question of preventive detention for those where the estimated risk of recidivism is high, or where the chance of 'burn-out' appears unlikely, cannot be justified according to the current state of knowledge due to the unacceptable risk of false positives. It is likely that increasing research in this area may considerably improve predictive methods. But this may not resolve the ethical dilemmas posed by such developments.

Appendix. Towards a standardised assessment of psychopathic disorder

In an attempt to overcome many of the problems identified in Chapter 2, a two-dimensional conceptualisation of psychopathic disorder has been proposed which incorporates three overlapping elements: personality disorder, clinical syndromes and behavioural disorder. Each will interact with the other two along one dimension, with a life-span perspective taken of each along the second dimension (Coid, 1993*a*). Thus, a comprehensive clinical assessment of psychopathic disorder would include the following.

Element 1: Personality disorder

A diagnostic assessment should involve one or more of the following constructs:

(a) DSM–III–R axis II categorisation
(b) ICD–10 categorisation
(c) Psychopathy Check-List (PCL–R) score
(d) Minnesota Multiphasic Personality Inventory (MMPI) or Special Hospital Assessment of Personality and Socialisation (SHAPS) profile
(e) structured clinical interview to provide a psychodynamic formulation of the subject's characterological disorder.

Element 2. Clinical syndromes (axis I)

A detailed psychiatric history should cover all major mental disorders, including paraphilias and substance abuse. Both research instruments and routine clinical history-taking should include a lifetime perspective, stating age of onset and the time of any resolution of symptoms, rather than eliciting present mental state alone.

Element 3. Behavioural disorder

A detailed assessment of the patient's behaviour in relation to culturally determined social norms should include as a minimum:

(a) criminal history
(b) non-criminalised antisocial and aggressive behaviour
(c) ability to form and maintain relationships with others
(d) occupational functioning.

A longitudinal approach should also include the recording of the time of appearance and resolution of different forms of behavioural disorder.

Diagnostic formulation

A diagnostic formulation would thus consist of these three main elements. In routine clinical practice, this could be based on a standardised history taken from the patient, to include components such as history of presenting complaint (including criminal behaviour in a forensic setting), family and developmental history, marital and psychosexual history, substance abuse, psychiatric history, history of physical illness, present mental state, etc., supplemented with a history from friends or relatives, observations from staff in institutional settings, and additional investigative procedures. For research purposes there is a range of standardised instruments to diagnose both personality disorder and clinical syndromes.

Four clinical examples are given to demonstrate this approach.

Case 1

A 30-year-old male prisoner serving 12 years for armed robbery and possession of a firearm presented with complaints of hearing voices, and interference with his thoughts, insisting that the Home Office had engineered a plot to kill him. Prison staff observed bizarre posturing and regressed behaviour in his cell, with faecal smearing of walls and his body. He was midway through his sentence, which had been characterised by several assaults on staff and other prisoners, frequent moves of prison, and long periods in solitary confinement. He was admitted to a maximum-security hospital during his previous prison sentence under the legal category 'psychopathic disorder' but was returned to prison after wrecking the patients' social club, requiring restraint by nurses armed with riot shields. His criminal history began at the age of eight years and progressed from burglaries and thefts of cars to increasingly serious violent offences, including the malicious wounding of a former common-law wife and the attempted murder of another prisoner during his previous sentence.

His personal history included abandonment by his mother in infancy when she ran off with another man. She is known to have given birth to four half-siblings subsequently by two different fathers and to have convictions for shoplifting, alcohol offences, and a recent admission to psychiatric hospital suffering from depression. Father was unable to cope with the prisoner during infancy due to his own periods of incarceration and is thought to have neglected and at times physically abused him.

The prisoner had several placements in children's homes and brief periods of foster care. All attempts at adoption or fostering failed due to his behavioural disorder. During late childhood and early adolescence he truanted frequently, ran away from the children's homes, from which he had frequent moves, fought with other children, and abused solvents and alcohol. He has never held a job for more than four months, and from the age of 16 has spent increasing periods in custody, first in detention centres, then in borstals and prisons. He has never resided in the community for longer than 14 months since the age of 16 and during that period he was arrested twice. He has had two periods of cohabitation and believes that he has four children by three different women. All relationships with women have been characterised by violence and repeated separations, often in the context of unfounded jealousy of his partners, and with violence exacerbated by his heavy drinking.

Assessment

Increasing seriousness of behavioural disorder over time can be observed from this man's criminal history and record of adjudications in prison. Two convictions of violence have occurred while he was serving a sentence for other offences. He has shown a worrying trend to attack home-owners or shopkeepers in the course of committing thefts or robberies in recent years.

The interview had to be conducted with great caution due to his extreme suspiciousness. Besides the florid psychotic symptoms, a history was elicited of lifelong suspiciousness of others which he attributed to living for most of his life among criminals. In addition, he described brief mood swings, when he becomes extremely tense and irritable. In the community he will resort to substance abuse or commission of offences during these episodes. In prison his moods are relieved by assaults on others, smashing up his cell, or deliberate self-injury. Staff have described him as an "arrogant, self-centred bully who enjoys the status of 'hard man', and who is suspected of intimidating weaker individuals for tobacco and possibly sexual favours".

Diagnostic formulation

Element 1. Personality disorder

He has DSM–III–R diagnoses of antisocial, borderline, narcissistic, paranoid personality disorder.

He has a score of 33 on the 20-item PCL–R scale, designating him as a psychopath for research purposes.

Previous psychological assessment with the MMPI showed a profile of Blackburn's type 2 'secondary' psychopath.

Element 2. Clinical syndromes

He has acute schizophrenia (from the age of 30).

He has a lifetime history of alcohol abuse disorder (from age 20); depressive disorder (age 21) treated with antidepressants during a previous period of imprisonment; and panic disorder (age 29) but possibly this was the prodromal phase of his current condition.

Element 3. Behavioural disorder

His criminal history started at age eight, his longest period in the community was 14 months, and there has been an increase in the seriousness of his convictions for both violence and acquisitive offending. He has had a total of 15 court appearances for 40 separate offences.

He has a custodial history of repeated discipline offences and adjudications, including assaults on prisoners and staff. He has been found in possession of home-made weapons, and illegal possession of drugs, and has brewed alcohol. His last two sentences have been characterised by increasing periods in the segregation unit due to the increasing seriousness of his disciplinary offences in prison.

He has had no contact with either of his previous cohabitees but writes to his children from the second relationship. He receives visits from an older sister and, rarely, from his father.

He has never held a job for more than four months. He considers crime to be 'work'. He is currently refusing to work in prison.

Discussion

This diagnostic formulation breaks down the subject's formidable range of psychopathology into discrete and more manageable components. Taking this piecemeal approach allows further refinement such as examining the potential relationship of diagnostic categories to possible aetiological factors: for example, the probable relationship between his own history of depressive disorder and borderline personality disorder and the similar history that is available to describe his mother; similarly, his history of several forms of early deprivation and emotional trauma and the later diagnosis of antisocial personality disorder in adulthood. More importantly, in the context of this review, it presents the clinician with a basis for proceeding further and formulating a programme of treatment and management, targeting each component individually. Thus, the first step in the prisoner's management was to move him to the prison hospital for observation in a more therapeutic setting following the development of psychotic symptoms. In view of his refusal to accept medication he was then assessed by a consultant from a Special Hospital to which he was transferred under the legal category 'mental illness' instead of 'psychopathic disorder'. He made a complete response to treatment after six months of neuroleptic medication. However, he was subsequently transferred back to prison to continue his sentence at his own insistence and because his behaviour had deteriorated within the hospital setting. He had begun to exploit and intimidate his fellow patients and threatened to take a nurse or doctor hostage if he was not returned to prison. Following his return, he continued to accept neuroleptic medication, to the relief of prison staff, recognising that it was necessary to prevent a recurrence of his psychotic symptoms. In view of his need for medication and the risk of further relapse and regression, he was not considered suitable for transfer to Grendon Underwood Prison, despite the additional diagnosis of severe personality disorder. He was subsequently referred for admission to a prison Special Unit (see Coid, 1991) but ultimately may not be accepted as his behaviour has shown some recent improvement. He appears to have settled in another prison where he had never previously been, and where other prisoners and staff were not acquainted with him, although his reputation had preceded him.

Case 2

A 33-year-old man was originally admitted to a Special Hospital at the age of 19 years, having been convicted of manslaughter due to diminished responsibility following the killing of his girlfriend. He was detained under the legal category 'psychopathic disorder'. The body had been found gagged and bound on his aunt's bed and strangled with a silk scarf. She was also dressed in certain articles of his aunt's clothing. Forensic examination indicated that he had masturbated over the body after death.

His own mother died during his infancy and he had two unhappy foster placements along with his elder sister, where he claims they were both ill-treated. He returned briefly to live with his father, who had remarried, before being placed in the care of his aunt, whom he alleges showed more affection towards her own children. He never had a close relationship with his sister, who left home to cohabit as soon as she was allowed to.

At school he had difficulty concentrating and was a loner, with few friends. He did not show serious conduct disorder but was generally mistrusted by teachers and had two minor convictions for theft prior to the homicide. He had remained unemployed after leaving school with no qualifications and had no previous girlfriends except the deceased, who was considered to be very immature for her age. There had been an episode when he had followed girls in the neighbourhood and their parents had complained to his on several occasions prior to the index offence. He had explained that this was a prank and that it had been due to his drinking.

Following his arrest, pornographic material was found of women in bondage poses and writings involving the tying-up and strangulation of girls in his neighbourhood. Following admission to a maximum-security hospital, he admitted to sadistic masturbatory fantasies that preoccupied him for much of his waking life and which had been present in various forms since his early teens. They had been particularly intrusive when he felt miserable or under stress. He remembered them increasing in intensity in his teenage years when he was punished by his aunt. Arousal to fantasies of strangulation and the power of life or death over a victim were subjectively the most exciting features. His general demeanour was of cocky unconcern once his court case was over. He was considered immature and untrustworthy by staff and other patients. He became involved in homosexual liaisons with older, more aggressive psychopathic patients, whom he tended to play off one against another for his favours.

Diagnostic formulation

Element 1. Personality disorder

His DSM–III–R diagnoses were of narcissistic, histrionic, borderline personality disorder.

He scored 22 on the 20-item PCL–R scale, placing him in the medium range. He was therefore not designated a psychopath for research purposes.

Element 2. Clinical syndromes

He presented with a syndrome of sexual sadism (with specific arousal to fantasies involving homicide, mainly by strangulation).

Element 3. Behavioural disorder

His previous criminal history was not indicative of his underlying personality and psychosexual disturbance.

He showed no overt serious behavioural disorder in the community or in institutional settings. He had a worrying tendency to be on the periphery of serious incidents within the maximum-security institution.

He showed an inability to sustain close friendships with others. Further assessment of his relationship with the deceased suggested a lack of true commitment and a series of behavioural try-outs of his bondage fantasies leading up to the homicide.

He showed an inability to work in the hospital setting except when given considerable guidance and supervision. He showed no motivation for further education.

Discussion

Rigid adherence to 'core' constructs such as DSM–III–R ASPD or Hare's PCL–R would not strictly diagnose this patient as a psychopath. Furthermore, it might be argued that axis I sexual sadism was the primary condition within the DSM–III–R framework. However, he was still detained under the legal category 'psychopathic disorder' and underwent treatment for a long period within the maximum-security hospital where, from a clinical viewpoint, his general diagnostic designation as a psychopath was in little doubt. Furthermore, the presence of additional personality disorder psychopathology was one of the major factors in the prolongation of his stay in the therapeutic setting and was assumed to be the reason for the slow place of his treatment progress. Initial assessment was shaped by the predominating features of his sexual sadism. He was encouraged to keep a diary of his fantasies and their intensity. Penile plethysmography showed indiscriminate arousal to both males and females, but most strongly to scenes depicting violence, especially towards adult females. Initial treatment involved sex education followed by a behavioural programme of covert sensitisation and a self-administered procedure for reducing his spontaneous urges, accompanied by masturbatory reconditioning. However, response to treatment remained very slow after an initial marked drop in the intensity of the deviant fantasies. Repeated penile plethysmography measures over several years still revealed arousal to deviant visual stimuli. Group therapy in the early stages of hospitalisation appeared to convey little benefit as he was unable to conform in a sensible manner during these treatment sessions, tending to undermine therapy for others in a childish manner. Over time, a gradual process of maturation seemed to occur and at a later stage he appeared to benefit from insights conveyed by individual interpretive psychotherapy. Although this form of therapy initially resulted in a brief exacerbation of his deviant fantasies, these then subsided, aided by his self-initiated reintroduction of the behavioural techniques he had learned earlier. He was eventually transferred to a less secure hospital and allowed increasing freedom in the community. Discharge to a hostel remains delayed due to the relative behavioural immaturity still demonstrated by the patient, now in his late 30s, and the anxieties his case arouses in those responsible for him. In particular, anxieties have been further aroused by his recent relationship with a female patient and his stated wish to have sexual intercourse.

Interaction of elements

Both the above cases have been selected to demonstrate the complex interaction between personality-disorder, clinical syndromes and behavioural disorder, and the changes that take place within these interactions over the life-span. Both cases were deliberately selected as difficult examples in which there was a limited degree of optimism for treatment success when they were initially assessed. However, a systematic assessment finally produced a diagnostic formulation in each case, and from this a treatment programme and plan of management could be devised. At the same time, the multi-category approach also indicated multiple treatment modalities for each single patient. Closer examination also shows how interactions can occur between treatment components in a single case, sometimes of an adverse nature. For example, the personality disorder of the second patient appeared to contribute to the poor response both to group psychotherapy and, in the early stages, to behavioural treatment of his sexual sadism. Furthermore, interpretative psychotherapy initially led to a resurgence of his deviant fantasies as painful early memories were reawakened.

It is proposed that in future the treatment and management of psychopaths should make use of this approach. It has become apparent from our review of the different forms of treatment that few authors have done so in the context of empirical research.

Two additional cases illustrate how the assessment of multiple areas of psychopathology is essential for a successful treatment outcome and ultimate return to the community. In these cases the severity of the patients' psychopathology was not as marked as in cases 1 and 2. Both patients were initially detained at a medium level of security. Nevertheless, they could not have been treated without starting their clinical programme within secure conditions, and both required the additional resources of multidisciplinary teamwork.

Case 3

A 20-year-old African-Caribbean woman was admitted to a medium-secure unit under the legal category 'psychopathic disorder' following a conviction of criminal damage. She and a female friend had smashed windows after a bout of heavy drinking because they felt "bored". She was already on probation for criminal damage, and had several previous convictions for assault on the police, criminal damage, and being drunk and disorderly. Criminal convictions only dated from the age of 18, but the police had responded over the previous two years by initially taking her home to her mother and later to hospital under Section 136 (Place of

Safety Order) of the Mental Health Act, 1983. As her behaviour persisted the police had begun to press charges.

Her parents were divorced and she described her father as a violent alcoholic who had had several periods of imprisonment. She considered a foster mother her true mother and had an ambivalent relationship with her biological mother. She was brought up in material poverty in a deprived, delinquent, inner-city area. She was taken into care with her sisters during infancy when the family were in severe financial debt, and when her mother was unable to cope with the children due to depression. The children were considered physically and emotionally neglected.

She was initially thought to have learning disability, but made rapid improvement, with consolidation of the gains in her intellectual and physical development when she was placed with a white foster family. Attempts to 'rehabilitate' her to her original family were initially unsuccessful. Police were repeatedly called to domestic violence in the family home. On occasions the patient had been reluctantly separated from her foster mother. She finally remained with her biological mother from the age of eight, after the latter had separated from her father, but showed a progressive deterioration in her conduct, with truanting, drunkenness, frequent fighting, and disruption of class in school. When aged 13 she was briefly excluded from the family home during which time she lived with her father as his 'wife'. She was subsequently expelled from school after a serious assault on another pupil and received home tuition. When aged 17 she was excluded from the family home again, after her alcohol and cannabis abuse had deteriorated to the extent that she would contribute nothing to her upkeep. She slept rough and moved between friends' addresses.

She became pregnant when aged 18, the paternity uncertain. After the birth she was placed in a children's home with mother-and-baby facilities, but began to demonstrate a pattern of staying out late, neglecting the child, abusing alcohol, and threatening staff with violence. She was observed to handle the baby roughly, and the child was later placed with foster parents. Her behaviour deteriorated further and she mutilated her face, and had a series of brief admissions to psychiatric hospitals. She failed to comply with a probation order or to attend regularly for out-patient psychiatric treatment.

On admission she appeared a small, waif-like woman, who seemed younger than her 20 years. She related her history of antisocial behaviour with total unconcern or else childlike amusement. She described frequent self-mutilation, beginning from the age of 12, which gave her a sense of relief from symptoms of mood disorder and seemed a way of 'punishing' herself. She described mood swings which would come on for no explainable reason, when she would feel angry, tense, and depressed. Drinking would improve her moods, but also disinhibited her. She admitted that she enjoyed setting fires and had fantasies of what it might be like to strangle her co-defendant.

Following admission she presented a pattern of highly disturbed behaviour associated with brief episodes of affective disturbance. During these moods she would damage ward furniture, mutilate herself, threaten female staff, and persuade other patients to smuggle alcohol on to the ward for her. A trial of carbamazepine followed by lithium carbonate conveyed no benefit. Depot neuroleptic medication was partly effective in reducing the intensity of her moods and behavioural disorder.

At the six-month stage of treatment she was considered to have shown considerable improvement as a result of the depot neuroleptic, but placement in secure conditions was still considered necessary. She still became involved in altercations with other patients, had a variety of hyperchondriacal complaints, and admitted to a continuing craving for alcohol. The brief affective mood swings were still detectable, albeit without the previous secondary behavioural disturbance. Several major deficits were now revealed in her interactions with others, her level of self-care, and her attitudes towards herself, her criminal behaviour, and her sexuality. She had few skills in independent living, her style of interacting with other patients inevitably led to isolation, and she expressed doubts over her sexual identity and orientation. Treatment was prolonged over a further two years. This was carried out in a private hospital with a wider range of resources. It was still considered necessary for the patient to remain in a highly structured in-patient setting, the first ten months in the private hospital being spent on a locked ward due to fights with other patients and attempts to abscond. She then began to address her psychosexual difficulties through individual counselling from a clinical psychologist. Participation in group activities, including group psychotherapy, and training in social skills improved her tendency to alienate others. After two years, her mood swings had resolved and neuroleptic medication was gradually withdrawn. There was no resurgence of the affective symptoms and she was moved to a hostel within the hospital grounds. This had a lower level of supervision and she coped well, but again became pregnant.

She was transferred to a supervised hostel for mothers and babies halfway through the pregnancy. Following the birth of her child she coped better with the infant, who continues to remain in her care. She was placed in a council flat, where she resides with her friend and the baby. She receives regular visits from social workers, attends a forensic psychiatric out-patient clinic, and shows no current affective symptoms or behavioural disturbance. Her daughter appears to be developing normally.

Diagnostic formulation

Element 1: personality disorder

The patient's DSM–III–R diagnosis is antisocial and borderline personality disorder.

She scored 30 on the 20 item PCL–R Scale, designating her as a psychopath for research purposes.

Element 2: Clinical syndromes

The patient has had recurrent mood disorder since the age of 16 (see Coid, 1993*b*).

She has a lifetime history of alcohol abuse disorder (from age 17).

Element 3: behavioural disorder

Criminal history began at age 18. Previous similar behaviour, dating from age 16, did not lead to arrest. She had increasing frequency of convictions leading up to current admission, involving minor offences of violence, criminal damage, and possession of drugs. Most offences occurred when she was drunk. She has had a total of six court appearances for ten separate offences.

She has had a series of behavioural problems associated with brief episodes of mood disorder. These include self-mutilation, substance abuse, assaults and intimidation of those she considers weaker than herself. She has a self-reported history of fire-setting for a pleasurable sense of excitement and morbid violent ruminations.

Her psychosexual history is characterised by a history of incest, uncertain sexual orientation, and inability to form stable relationships with others without alternating hostility and overdependence. She has manifested an inability to parent her first child, to whom she showed a pattern of abusive behaviour similar to that experienced by herself, including physical injury and neglect, resulting in fostering.

She has never had a job. She experienced two brief periods on a Youth Training Scheme in her mid-teens, when she showed no aptitude.

Discussion

The subject's in-patient treatment lasted for more than three years and she still requires considerable support and supervision in the community. Although the antipsychotic medication made an impact upon her mood disorder and antisocial behaviour, it could be argued that the underlying affective disturbance showed a spontaneous resolution rather than a direct response to the medication. Placing her initially in a secure unit, followed by an open, but still highly structured, in-patient setting was essential for the maintenance of her slow progress. It was only at a time when her mood disorder had sufficiently improved that she could begin the treatment programme designed to improve her interactions with others and to address her psychosexual dysfunction, the experience of incest, and her poor level of self-care. Her case illustrates the importance of a resource-intensive approach to the management of severe personality disorders, flexibility in the use of several treatment modalities, and acceptance and agreement from health-care staff and the health authority (who funded her stay in the private hospital) that her in-patient treatment would be prolonged.

Case 4

A 23-year-old man was admitted from prison for assessment in a medium-secure unit under the legal category 'psychopathic disorder', charged with robbery. He had snatched a handbag and had been apprehended after a chase by police and passers-by. He had two minor juvenile convictions, then none until his late teens, when he was sentenced to three years imprisonment for manslaughter. Although living with his wife and child, he had engaged in regular homosexual liaisons and had killed one of his male partners. It had been successfully argued at his trial that he had been provoked by the victim's threats to telephone his wife and expose their relationship. While on remand for the current offence, he had pleaded for admission to hospital to help with his multiple problems. He expressed a deep sense of remorse for both his present and previous offences and presented with clinical symptoms of depression. His psychiatric history included an admission to hospital following an overdose, when he had been treated with tricyclic antidepressants.

In-patient assessment confirmed the depressive illness, which required further treatment with a tricyclic antidepressant. However, he was also observed to have a chronic pattern of brief mood disturbance, bouts of alcohol abuse, and highly ambivalent relationships with members of his family and his wife, alternating from overdependence to hostility, and a self-reported pattern of destructiveness to other persons with whom he formed close relationships. He also described considerable confusion as to his sexual orientation.

He came from a large family and was brought up in an inner-city area with high rates of delinquency. Both parents were heavy drinkers and his mother had suffered from episodes of depression. He had a history of persistent truanting during his school years and had been expelled, but otherwise did not merit a diagnosis of conduct disorder. He had frequently been bullied by other children and therefore avoided school. He left without qualifications and had a series of short-lasting jobs, most of which he was sacked from due to a general lack of application. He would subsequently leave home in the morning pretending that he was going to work. He cohabited with his girlfriend when she became pregnant, but found the responsibility of their relationship difficult to cope with, drank increasingly heavily, and engaged in homosexual liaisons which gave him a feeling of relief and freedom. At the time of his arrest she was again pregnant, a further source of anxiety, and at a time when his other child was demonstrating increasing signs of unruliness and disruption at primary school.

After the four-month assessment he received a Hospital Order from the Court. His behaviour then underwent a dramatic deterioration. He became involved in fights with other patients, and threatened violence to staff. He absconded from an escorted walk in the hospital grounds, returning to the unit with a large sum of money, and admitted to another robbery. Although his depressive illness had resolved with antidepressant medication, his mood swings intensified and were characterised by symptoms of anger and tension, which he described as being accompanied by intense destructive urges. He then admitted that the offence of manslaughter had been a premeditated murder at a time when he was experiencing a similar episode of affective disturbance. Neuroleptic medication and carbamazepine produced little improvement. But while consideration was being given to a referral for admission to a maximum-security hospital, he was given a trial of lithium carbonate. His behaviour and mood disorder improved dramatically.

This clinical improvement facilitated a second phase of treatment. He underwent individual supportive psychotherapy with a clinical psychologist to explore his psychosexual difficulties and the remorse he persistently described for the victim he had killed, and whom he otherwise considered a close friend. Nevertheless, it proved impossible to explore with him the true motivation for the homicide. Over the last six months of in-patient treatment he was counselled with regard to his alcohol abuse. In addition, he received marital counselling together with his common-law wife from a male and a female nurse. This also included a practical course of more appropriate management strategies for his child, whose difficult behaviour he had been observed to encourage on visits to the unit.

He has continued to attend the out-patient clinic of a forensic psychiatrist over a two-year period. He misses over half of the scheduled appointments and admits to ambivalent feelings towards his doctor. During the follow-up period there have been three brief relapses into affective disturbance, accompanied by bouts of alcohol abuse and violent altercations with his family. Each relapse occurred 2–4 weeks after he had stopped taking lithium carbonate. Although he denied this on two occasions, serial recordings of serum lithium have demonstrated this to be the most likely explanation. He remains stable, but feels unable to cope with regular employment, spending his time watching TV or visiting relatives. His wife administers his lithium carbonate.

Diagnostic formulation

Element 1: personality disorder

The DSM–III–R diagnosis for this patient was borderline and avoidant personality disorder.

He scored 20 on the 20-item PCL–R, scale placing him in the medium range. He was therefore not designated a psychopath for research purposes.

Element 2: clinical syndromes

He had depressive disorder (from age 22) requiring treatment with tricyclic antidepressant; he also abused alcohol (from age 17).

He had a chronic pattern of brief affective disturbances resulting in impulsive behavioural disorder (Coid, 1993*b*).

Element 3: behavioural disorder

His previous criminal history included two minor juvenile offences, after which he desisted from delinquent activities until the manslaughter at the age of 19. Motivation remains undetermined for this offence, but it was thought that this reflected his psychosexual disturbance (which was a component of his borderline personality disorder) and was at a time when he was experiencing intense violent urges secondary to the mood disorder described under element 2 above.

He demonstrated assaultiveness in the hospital setting secondary to mood disturbance; when he was in the community such behaviour was accompanied by bouts of alcohol abuse. He explained the second robbery as an attempt to obtain money for drink. He was not prosecuted for this offence.

He could maintain a relationship with his wife but required considerable support from family members and tolerance from herself. He admitted to distressing urges to undermine and destroy this relationship, as he had experienced in relationships with others. His sexual orientation was uncertain, but he expressed a wish to become exclusively heterosexual.

He had never worked consistently. This had been further exacerbated by the increasing presentation of affective disturbance and alcohol abuse from his late teens onwards. He showed no motivation for further education or any desire to seek further employment.

Discussion

The in-patient treatment of this subject lasted a total of 16 months. It was of some concern to the clinical team that the initial assessment phase, which was carried out under Section 38 of the Mental Health Act 1983, did not give any indication of his underlying potential dangerousness. The subsequent emergence of dangerous behaviour following his return to hospital from Court, on a Hospital Order under Section 37, remains unexplained. This deterioration poses the worrying question of what might have happened had he not received a trial of lithium carbonate and shown a dramatic improvement. This case would suggest that a flexible treatment programme is essential for the management of such patients, with an ability to arrange transfer from one level of security to another according to appropriate secur ity needs. By implication, this would require close cooperation between different institutions.

The case also indicates the importance of setting realistic goals of treatment. Three years later, he is still unable to work consistently and the true motivation of the homicide has never been uncovered. A clinical decision was made during the course of treatment that neither of these factors should be involved in the goal of treatment. It was decided that the fragility of his defences (considered in psychodynamic terms) indicated that he could tolerate only structured and supportive psychotherapy as a more intensive approach risked further behavioural and affective disturbance.

References

Aarvold Committee (1973) *Report on the Review Procedures for the Discharge and Supervision of Psychiatric Patients Subject to Restrictions*, Cmnd 5191. London: HMSO.

Acres, D. I. (1975) The aftercare of Special Hospital patients. In *Report of the Committee on Mentally Abnormal Offenders*, Cmnd 6244 (Home Office and Department of Health and Social Security), Appendix 3, pp. 291–302. London: HMSO.

Akiskal, H. S. (1983) Dysthymic disorder: psychopathology of proposed chronic depression subtypes. *American Journal of Psychiatry*, **140**, 11–20.

—, Hirschfield, R. M. A. & Yerevanian, B. I. (1983) The relationship of personality to affective disorders: a critical review. *American Journal of Psychiatry*, **40**, 801–810.

—, Rosenthal, T. L., Haykal, R. F., *et al* (1980) Clinical and sleep EEG findings separating 'subaffective dysthymias' from 'character spectrum disorders'. *Archives of General Psychiatry*, **37**, 777–793.

American Psychiatric Association (1980) *Diagnostic and Statistical Manual of Mental Disorders* (3rd edn). Washington, DC: APA.

— (1987) *Diagnostic and Statistical Manual of Mental Disorders* (3rd edn, revised). Washington, DC: APA.

— (1989) *Treatment of Psychiatric Disorders*. Vol. 3. Washington, DC: APA.

Andrew, D. A., Zinger, I., Hodge, R. D., *et al* (1990) Does correctional treatment work? A clinically relevant and psychologically informed meta-analysis. *Criminology*, **28**, 369–404.

Andy, O. J. (1975) Thalamotomy for psychopathic behaviour. *Southern Medical Journal*, **68**, 437–442.

Angst, J. (1990) Recurrent brief depression: a new concept of depression. *Pharmacotherapy*, **23**, 63–66.

— & Dobler-Mikola, A. (1984) The Zurich study. II. The continuum from normal to pathological depressive mood swings. *European Archives of Psychiatry and Neurological Sciences*, **234**, 21–29.

Antman, E. M., Lau, J., Kupelmick, B., *et al* (1992) A comparison of results of meta-analysis of randomized control trials and recommendations of clinical experts. Treatment for myocardal infarction. *Journal of the American Meedical Asociation*, **268**, 240--248.

Anton, R. F., Waid, C. R., Fossey, M., *et al* (1986) Case report of carbamazepine treatment of organic brain syndrome with psychotic features. *Journal of Clinical Pharmacology*, **6**, 232–234.

Applezweig, M. H., Dibner, A. S. & Osbourne, R. T. (1958) PEAQ: a measure of psychopathic behaviour. *Journal of Clinical Psychology*, **14**, 26–30.

Aschenbach, T. M. & Edelbrock, C. S. (1981) Behavioral problems and competencies reported by parents of normal and disturbed children aged four through sixteen. *Monographs of the Society for Research in Child Development,* **46**, 1–82

Ashworth, A. & Gostin, L. (1985) Mentally disordered offenders and the sentencing process. In *Secure Provision* (ed. L. Gostin). London: Tavistock.

Bach-y-Rita, G., Coin, J. R., Climent, C. E., *et al* (1971) Episodic dyscontrol: a study of 130 violent patients. *American Journal of Psychiatry,* **127**, 1473–1478.

Bailey, J. & MacCulloch, M. (1992*a*) Characteristics of 112 cases discharged directly to the community from a new Special Hospital and some comparisons of performance, *Journal of Forensic Psychiatry,* **3**, 91–112.

— & — (1992*b*) Patterns of reconviction in patients discharged directly to the community from a Special Hospital: implications for after-care. *Journal of Forensic Psychiatry,* **3**, 445–461.

Balasubramanian, V. & Rammamurthi, B. (1970) Stereotaxic amydalotomy in behaviour disorders. *Confina Neurologica,* **32**, 367–373.

Barkley, R. (1977) A review of stimulant drug research with hyperactive children. *Journal of Child Psychology and Psychiatry,* **18**, 137–166.

Barnes, R. J. (1977) Mesoridazine (Serentil) in personality disorders – a controlled trial in adolescent patients. *Diseases of the Nervous System,* 258–264.

Basson, J. V. & Woodside, M. (1981) Assessment of a secure/intensive care/forensic ward. *Acta Psychiatrica Scandinavica,* **64**, 132–141.

Bauer, G. & Clark, J. (1976) Personality deviance. *Journal of Clinical Psychology,* **6**, 118–120.

Beck, A. T. (1976) *Cognitive Therapy and the Emotional Disorders.* New York: International Universities Press.

—, Rush, J., Shaw, B., *et al* (1979) *Cognitive Therapy of Depression.* New York: Guilford Press.

— & Freeman, A. (1990) *Cognitive Therapy of Personality Disorders.* New York: Guilford Press.

Bender, L. (1947) Psychopathic disorders in children. In *Handbook of Correctional Psychology* (eds M. Linder & R. V. Seliger). New York: Phil. Lib.

Berner, P., Musalek, M. & Walter, H. (1987) Psychopathological concepts of dysphoria. *Psychopathology,* 20, 93–100.

Berner, W. & Karlick-Bolten, E. (1986) *Verlaufsformen der Sexualkriminalität,* Kriminologie 23. Stuttgart: Ferdinand Enke Verlag.

Bernstein, D. P., Cohen, P., Velez, C. N., *et al* (1993) Prevalence and stability of DSM–III–R personality disorders in a community-based survey of adolescents. *American Journal of Psychiatry,* **150**, 1237–1243.

Bick, P. A. & Hannah, A. L. (1986) Intramuscular lorazepam to restrain violent patients. *Lancet, i,* 206.

Black, D. A. (1982) A 5-year follow-up study of male patients discharged from Broadmoor Hospital. In *Abnormal Offenders, Delinquency and the Criminal Justice System* (eds J. Gunn & D. P. Farrington). Chichester: Wiley.

Black, D. W., Bell, S., Hulbert, J., *et al* (1988) The importance of axis II in patients with major depression. *Journal of Affective Disorders,* **14**, 115–122.

Black, T. (1984) Treatment in maximum security settings. In *Mentally Abnormal Offenders* (eds Craft & Craft), pp. 350–383. Bailliere Tindall.

— & Spinks, P. (1985) Predicting outcomes of mentally disordered and dangerous offenders. *Prediction in Criminology* (eds Farrington & Tarling), pp. 174–192.

Blackburn, R. (1971) Personality types among abnormal homicides. *British Journal of Criminology,* **11**, 14–31.

— (1975) An empirical classification of psychopathic personality. *British Journal of Psychiatry,* **127**, 456–460.

— (1983) Are personality disorders treatable? *Issues in Criminology and Legal Psychology*, **4**, 23–26.

— (1986) Patterns of personality deviation among violent offenders: replication and extension of an empirical taxonomy. *British Journal of Criminology*, **26**, 254–269.

— (1992) Clinical programmes with psychopaths. In *Clinical Approaches to the Mentally Disordered Offender* (eds K. Howells & C. Hollis). Chichester: Wiley.

— , Crellin, M. C., Morgon, E. M., *et al* (1990) Prevalence ofpersonality Disorder in a Special Hospital population. *Journal of Forensic Psychiatry*, **1**, 43–52.

Blair, D. (1975*a*) The medicolegal implications of the terms 'psychopath', 'psychopathic personality' and 'psychopathic disorder'. *Medicine, Science and the Law*, **15**, 51–61.

— (1975*b*) The medicolegal implications of the terms 'psychopath', 'psychopathic personality' and 'psychopathic disorder'. *Medicine, Science and the Law*, **15**, 110–123.

Bland, R. C., Newman, S. C., Dyck, R. J., *et al* (1990) Prevalence of psychiatric disorders and suicide attempts in a prison population. *Canadian Journal of Psychiatry*, **35**, 407–413.

Block, J. (1961) Ego, identity, role variability and adjustment. *Journal of Consulting Psychology*, **25**, 392–397.

Bluglass, R. (1988) Psychiatric approaches to aggression and violence. *Issues in Criminology and Legal Psychology*, **12**, 24–33.

Blumstein, A. & Cohen, J. (1979) Estimation of individual crime rates from arrest records. *Journal of Criminal Law and Criminology*, **70**, 561–585.

— & Cohen, J. (1987) Characterizing criminal careers. *Science*, **237**, 985–991.

Borriello, J. (1979) Group therapy with acting-out patients: specific problems and techniques. *American Journal of Psychotherapy*, **33**, 275–285.

Boslow, H. M. & Kohlmeyer, W. (1963) The Maryland defective delinquency law: an eight year follow-up. *American Journal of Psychiatry*, **120**, 118–124.

Brett, T. R. (1992) The Woodstock approach: one ward in Broadmoor Hospital for the treatment of personality disorder. *Criminal Behaviour and Mental Health*, **2**, 152–158.

Brinkley, J. R., Beitman, B. D. & Friedal, R. O. (1979) Low dose neuroleptic regimes in the treatment of borderline patients. *Archives of General Psychiatry*, **36**, 319–326.

Brown, G. L., Goodwin, F. K., Ballenger, J. C., *et al* (1979) Aggression in humans correlates with cerebrospinal fluid amine metabolites. *Psychiatry Research*, **1**, 131–139.

—, Ebert, M. H., Goyer, P. F., *et al* (1982) Aggression, suicide, and serotonin: relationships to CSF amine metabolites. *American Journal of Psychiatry*, **139**, 741–746.

— & Goodwin, F. K. (1986) Cerebrospinal fluid correlates of suicide attempts and aggression. *Annals of the New York Academy of Sciences*, **487**, 175–186.

Browne, A. & Dolan, B. M. (1991) Counsellors' responses to clients' non-attendance at counselling sessions. *Counselling Psychology Quarterly*, **4**, 105–114.

Buck, O. D. & Harvey, P. (1986) Combined carbamazepine and lithium therapy for violent behaviour (letter). *American Journal of Psychiatry*, **143**, 1487.

Buckstein, O. G., Brent, D. A. & Kaminer, Y. (1989) Comorbidityof substance abuse and other psychiatric disorders in adolescents. *American Journal of Psychiatry*, **146**, 1131–1141.

Buss, A. H. (1966) *Psychopathology*. New York: Wiley.

Butler (1975) *Report of Committee on Mentally Disordered Offenders*. Home Office and Department of Health and Social Security, Cmnd 6244. London: HMSO.

Cantwell, D. P. (1972) Psychiatric illness in the families of hyperactive children. *Archives of General Psychiatry*, **27**, 414–417.

— & Carlson, G. A. (1978). Stimulants. In *Paediatric Psychopharmacology* (ed. J. S. Werry). New York: Brunner/Mazel.

Carney, F. L. (1972) Some recurring therapeutic issues in group psychotherapy with criminal patients. *American Journal of Psychotherapy*, **26**, 34–41.

— (1976) Treatment of aggressive patients. In *Rage, Hate, Assault and other Forms of Violence* (ed. Madden). New York: Spectrum Publications.

— (1977) Out-patient treatment of the aggressive offender. *American Journal of Psychotherapy*, **31**, 265–274.

— (1978) In-patient treatment programmes. In *The Psychopath: a Comprehensive Study of Antisocial Disorders and Behaviours* (ed. W. H. Reid). New York: Bruner Mazel.

— (1981) Residential treatment programs for antisocial personality disorders. In *The Treatment of Antisocial Syndromes* (ed. W. H. Reid), ch. 5. Van Nostrand Reinhold.

Cavior, H. E. & Schmidt, A. (1978) A test of the effectiveness of a differential treatment strategy. *Criminal Justice and Behaviour*, **5**, 131–139.

Chalmers, I., Dickerson, K. & Chalmers, T. C. (1992) Getting to grips with Archi Cochrane's agenda. *British Medical Journal*, 305–306.

Charney, D. S., Nelson, C. & Quinlan, O. M. (1981) Personality traits and disorder in depression. *American Journal of Psychiatry*, **138**, 1601–1604.

Cheney, C. O. (1934) *Outlines for Psychiatric Examinations*. New York: New York State Hospitals Press.

Chiswick, D. (1982) The Special Hospitals: a problem of clinical credibility. *Psychiatric Bulletin*, **6**, 130–132.

— (1992) Compulsory treatment of patients with psychopathic disorder: an abnormally aggressive or seriously irresponsible exercise. *Criminal Behaviour and Mental Health*, **2**, 106–113.

—, McIsaac, M. W. & McClintock, F. (1984) *Prosecution of the Mentally Disturbed*. Aberdeen: Aberdeen University Press.

Clark, L. A. (1992) Resolving taxonomic issues in personality disorders: the value of large-scale analyses of symptom data. *Journal of Personality Disorders*, **6**, 360–376.

Clarke, C. & Glatt, M. (1985) Wormwood Scrubs Annexe - a Therapeutic Community within a prison: discussion paper. *Journal of the Royal Society of Medicine*, **78**, 656–662.

Clear, T. R. & O'Leary, V. (1983) *Controlling the Offender in the Community*. Lexington, Massachusetts: D. C. Heath and Co.

Cleckley, H. (1941) *The Mask of Sanity* (1st edn). St Louis: C. V. Mosby Co.

— (1952) Comment on Darling and Sandall (1952) (op. cit.). *Journal of Clinical and Experimental Psychology*, **13**, 180.

— (1964) *The Mask of Sanity* (4th edn). St. Louis: C. V. Mosby Co.

— (1976) *The Mask of Sanity* (5th edn). St. Louis: C. V. Mosby Co.

Coccaro, E. F., Siever, C. J., Klar, H., *et al* (1989*a*) Serotonergic studies of patients with affective and personality disorders: correlates with suicidal and impulsive aggressive behaviour. *Archives of General Psychiatry*, **46**, 587–599.

— , —, Kavouss, R., *et al* (1989*b*) Impulsive aggression in personality disorders: evidence for involvement of 5-HT-1 receptors. *Biological Psychiatry*, **25**, 86A.

— , Gabriel, S. & Siever, C. J. (1990*a*) Buspirone challenge: preliminary evidence for a role for central 5-HT-1a receptor function in impulsive aggressive behaviour in humans. *Psychopharmacology Bulletin*, **26**, 343–405.

— , Astill, J. L., Herbert, J. L., *et al* (1990*b*) Fluoxetine treatment of impulsive aggression in DSM–III–R personality disorder patients. *Journal of Clinical Psychopharmacology*, **10**, 373–375.

Cochrane, A. L. (1972) *Effectiveness and Efficiency: Random Reflections on Health Services*. London: Nuffield Provincial Hospitals Trust.

Cohen, H. & Filipczak, J. (1971) *A New Learning Environment*. San Francisco: Jossey-Bass.

Coid, J. W. (1991) Psychiatric profiles of difficult/disruptive prisoners. In *Special Units for Difficult Prisoners* (eds K. Bottomley & W. Hay). Hull: Centre for Criminology and Criminal Justice, University of Hull.

— (1992) DSM–III diagnosis in criminal psychopaths: a way forward. *Criminal Behaviour and Mental Health*, **2**, 78–79.

— (1993*a*) Current concepts and classifications of psychopathic disorder. In *Personality Disorder Reviewed* (eds P. Tyrer & G. Stein). London: Gaskell, Royal College of Psychiatrists.

— (1993*b*) An affective syndrome in psychopaths with borderline personality disorder? *British Journal of Psychiatry*, 162, 641–650.

— & Cordess, C. (1992) Compulsory admission of dangerous psychopaths. *British Medical Journal*, **304**, 1581–1582.

Cole, J. O., Salomon, M., Gunderson, J. G., *et al* (1984) Drug therapy in borderline patients. *Comprehensive Psychiatry*, **25**, 249–262.

Collard, J. (1976) Pimozide in the treatment of some 'social maladjustments' in 'personality disorders'. *Acta Belgica Psychiatrica*, **79**, 686–703.

Collins, P. (1991) The treatability of psychopaths. *Journal of Forensic Psychiatry*, **2**, 103–110.

Colman, A. D. & Baker, S. L. (1969) Utilization of an operant conditioning model for the treatment of character and behaviour disorders in a military setting. *American Journal of Psychiatry*, 125, 1395–1403.

Conte, H. R, Putchik, R., Picard, S., *et al* (1991) Can personality traits predict psychotherapy outcome? *Comprehensive Psychiatry*, **32**, 66–72.

Cook, D. A. G., Fox, C. A., Weaver, M., *et al* (1991) The Berkeley group: ten years' experience of a group for non-violent sex offenders. *British Journal of Psychiatry*, **158**, 238–243.

Cooke, D. J. (1989) Containing violent prisoners: an analysis of Barlinnie special unit. *British Journal of Criminology*, **129**, 129–143.

Copas, J. B. & Whiteley, S. (1976) Predicting success in the treatment of psychopaths. *British Journal of Psychiatry*, **129**, 388–392.

— , O'Brien, M., Roberts, J., *et al* (1984) Treatment outcome in personality disorder: the effect of social, psychological and behavioural variables. *Personality and Individual Differences*, **5**, 565–573.

Cope, R. & Ward, M. (1993) What happens to Special Hospital patients admitted to medium security? *Journal of Forensic Psychiatry*, **4**, 13–24.

Cornelius, J. R., Solott, P. H., Pevel, J. M., *et al* (1990) Fluoxetine trial in borderline personality disorder. *Psychopharmacology Bulletin*, **26**, 151–154.

Cote, G. & Hodgin, S. (1990) Co-occurring mental disorders among criminal offenders. *Bulletin of the American Academy of Psychiatry and Law*, **18**, 271–281.

Cowdry, R. & Gardner, D. C. (1988) Pharmacotherapy of borderline personality disorder. *Archives of General Psychiatry*, **45**, 111–119.

Cox, M. (1976) Group psychotherapy in a secure setting. *Proceedings of the Royal Society of Medicine*, **69**, 215–220.

— (1986) The 'holding function' of dynamic psychotherapy in a custodial setting: a review. *Journal of the Royal Society of Medicine*, **79**, 162–164.

Craft, M. (1958) *Mental Disorder in the Defective*. Starcross, Devon: Royal Institution. (Reported in Craft (1966) op cit.), p. 217.

— (1965) *Ten Studies in Psychopathic Personality*. Bristol: Wright.

— (1966) *Psychopathic Disorders and their Assessment*. Oxford: Pergamon Press.

— (1968) Psychopathic disorder: a second trial of treatment. *British Journal of Psychiatry*, **114**, 813–820.

—, Stephenson, G. & Granger, C. (1964) A controlled trial of authoritarian and self-governing regimes with adolescent psychopaths. *American Journal of Orthopsychiatry*, **34**, 543–554.

—, Ismail, I. A., Krishinamurth, D., *et al* (1987) Lithium in the treatment of aggression in mentally handicapped patients: a double blind trial. *British Journal of Psychiatry*, **150**, 685–689.

Crawford, D. A. (1984) Behaviour therapy. In *Mentally Disorded Abnormal Offenders* (eds M. Craft & A. Craft). London: Bailliere, Tindall.

Cullen, E. (1992) The Grendon reconviction study. Unpublished internal document, Psychology Department, HMP Grendon.

CURRAN, D. & PARTRIDGE, M. (1963) *Psychological Medicine* (5th edn). London: E. S. Livingstone Ltd.

DALE, P. G. (1980) Lithium therapy in aggressive mentally subnormal patients. *British Journal of Psychiatry*, **137**, 469–474.

DARLING, H. F. & SANDALL, J. W. (1952) A psychopathologic concept of psychopathic personality. *Journal of Clinical and Experimental Psychology*, **13**, 175–180.

DAVIDSON, W., GOTTSCHALK, R., GENSHEIMER, L., *et al* (1984) *Interventions with Juvenile Delinquency: A Meta-analysis of Treatment Efficacy*. Washington, DC: National Institute of Juvenile Justice and Delinquency Prevention.

DAVIES, W. & FELDMAN, P. (1981) The diagnosis of psychopathy by forensic specialists. *British Journal of Psychiatry*, **138**, 329–331.

DAVIS, D. R. (1967) *Introduction to Psychopathology*. Oxford: Oxford University Press.

DAVIS, D. L. & BOSTER, L. (1988) Multifaceted therapeutic interventions with the violent psychiatric in-patient. *Hospital and Community Psychiatry*, **39**, 867–869.

DELL, S. (1980) Transfer of Special Hospital patients to the NHS. *British Journal of Psychiatry*, **136**, 222–234.

— (1982) Transfer of Special Hospital patients into national health service hospitals. In *Abnormal Offenders, Delinquency and the Criminal Justice System* (eds. J. Gunn & D. P. Farrington), ch. 17. Chichester: Wiley.

— , ROBERTSON, G. & PARKER, E. (1987) Detention in Broadmoor: factors in length of stay. *British Journal of Psychiatry*, **150**, 824–827.

— & — (1988) *Sentenced to Hospital: Offenders in Broadmoor*. Oxford: Oxford University Press.

DEPARTMENT OF HELATH & HOME OFFICE (1992) *Review of Health & Social Services for Mentally Disordered Offenders and Others Requiring Similar Services*, Cmd 2088. London: HMSO.

DEROGATIS, L. R. (1983) *SCL–90R, Administration, Scoring and Procedures Manual* (2nd edn). New York: Clinical Psychometric Research.

DEYKIN, E. Y. & DIMASCIO, A. (1972) The relationship of patient background characteristics to efficacy of pharmacotherapy in endogenous depression. *Journal of Nervous and Mental Disease*, **155**, 209–215.

DIGUER, L., BARBER, J. P. & LUBORSKY, L. (1993) Three concomitants: personality disorder; psychiatric severity and outcome of dynamic psychotherapy of major depression. *American Journal of Psychiatry*, **130**, 1246–1248.

DOCHERTY, J. P., FIESTER, S. J. & SHEA, T. (1986) Syndrome diagnosis and personality disorder. In *American Psychiatric Association Annual Review*, Vol. 5 (eds. A. J. Frances & R. E. Hales). Washington, DC: American Psychiatric Press.

DOLAN, B. M., MORTON, A. & WILSON, J. (1990) Selection of admissions to a Therapeutic Community using a group setting: association with degree and type of psychological distress. *International Journal of Social Psychiatry*, **36**, 265–271.

— & NORTON, K. (1992) One year after the NHS Bill: the extra-contractual referral system at Henderson Hospital. *Psychiatric Bulletin*, **16**, 745–747.

— , EVANS, C. D. & NORTON, K. (1992*a*) Never mind the quality feel the width: multiple axis II diagnoses of personality disorder. *Proceedings Royal College of Psychiatrists Annual meeting, Dublin.*

— , — & — (1992*b*) The separation–individuation inventory: association with borderline phenomena. *Journal of Nervous and Mental Diseases*, **180**, 529–533.

— , — & WILSON, J. (1992*c*) Therapeutic community treatment for personality disordered adults. 1 Changes in neurotic symptomatology on follow-up. *International Journal of Social Psychiatry*, **38**, 243–250.

— , — & — (1992*d*) Neurotic symptomatology and length of stay in a Therapeutic Community. *Therapeutic Communities*, **13**, 171–177.

—, EVANS, C. D. & NORTON, K. (1993) Multiple axis II diagnoses of personality disorder. (Submitted.)

— & Glaister, A. (1993) Personality disorders and attribution of blame for criminal acts. (Submitted.)

— & Mitchell, E. (1993) Personality disorders, psychological and behavioural characteristics in women in the psychiatric wing of HMP Holloway and HMP Holloway Psychology Department. (Submitted.)

Dolan, M., Coorey, P. & Kulupana, S. (1993) An audit of recalls to a Special Hospital. *Journal of Forensic Psychiatry*, **4**, 249–260.

Drug and Therapeutics Bulletin (1992) Fluoxetine, suicide and Aggression. *Drug and Therapeutics Bulletin*, **30**, 5–6.

Du Fort, G. G., Newman, S. C. & Bland, R. (1993) Psychiatric comorbidity and treatment seeking: sources of selection bias in the study of clinical populations. *Journal of Nervous and Mental Disease*, **181**, 467–474.

Easterbrook, P. J., Berlin, J. A., Gopalan, R., *et al* (1991) Publication bias in clinical research. *Lancet*, **337**, 867–872.

Elliot, F. A. (1978) Neurological aspects of antisocial behaviour. In *The Psychopath: A Comprehensive Study of Antisocial Disorders and Behaviors* (ed. W. Reid). New York: Bruner/Mazel.

Elphick, M. (1989) Clinical issues in the use of carbamazepine in psychiatry: a review. *Psychological Medicine*, **19**, 591–604.

Emmerick, van (1987) Detention at the government's pleasure: a follow up study of patients released from the Dr. Henri Van Der Hoeven Clinic. In *Studies on the Dutch Prison System* (ed. M. J. M. Brand-Koolen), ch. 9. Kuger Publications.

Eppright, T. D., Kashani, J. H., Robinson, B. D., *et al* (1993) Co-morbidity of conduct disorder and personality disorders in an incarcerated juvenile population. *American Journal of Psychiatry*, **150**, 1233–1236.

Essa, M. (1986) Carbamazepine in dementia. *Journal of Clinical Psychopharmacology*, **6**, 234–236.

Everitt, B. S. (1989) *Statistical Methods for Medical Investigations.* New York: Oxford University Press.

Falconer, M. A. & Shur, P. (1959) Surgical treatment of mental illness. *Recent Progress in Psychiatry*, Vol. 3. New York: Grove Press.

Faltus, F. J. (1984) The use of alprazolam in the treatment of three patients with borderline personality disorder. *American Journal of Psychiatry*, **141**, 802–803.

Farrington, D., Loeber, R. & Van Kammen, W. B. (1990) Long-term criminal outcomes of hyperactivity–impulsivity–attention deficit and conduct problems in childhood. In *Straight and Devious Pathways from Childhood to Adulthood* (eds L. N. Robins & M. Rutter). Cambridge: Cambridge University Press.

Fava, M., Rosenblaum, J. F., Pava, J. A, *et al* (1993) Anger attacks in unipolar depression, Part 1: Clinical correlates and response to fluoxetine treatment. *American Journal of Psychiatry*, **150**, 1158–1163.

Fawcett, J. & Siomopouloo J. (1971) Dextroamphetamine response as a possible predictor of improvement with tricyclic therapy in depression. *Archives of General Psychiatry*, **25**, 244–247.

Feldbrugge, J. T. T. M. (1992) Rehabilitation of patients with personality disorders: patient–staff collaboration used as a working model and a tool. *Criminal Behaviour and Mental Health*, **2**, 169–177.

Fenwick, P. (1986) Aggression and epilepsy. In *Aspects of Epilepsy and Psychiatry* (eds M. R. Trimble & T. G. Bolwig). Chichester: Wiley.

Fink, L., Derby, W. N. & Martin, J. P. (1969) Psychiatry's new role in corrections. *American Journal of Psychiatry*, **126**, 124–128.

Franklin, J. L., Solovitz, B., Mason, M., *et al* (1987) An evaluation of case management. *American Journal of Public Health*, **77**, 674–678.

Frosch, J. P. (1983) The treatment of antisocial and borderline personality disorders. *Hospital Community Psychiatry*, **34**, 243–248.

Gabbard, G. O. & Coyne, L. (1987) Predictors of response of antisocial patients to hospital treatment. *Hospital Community Psychiatry*, **38**, 1181-1185.

Gaind, R. & Jacoby, R. (1978) Benzodiazepines causing aggression. In *Current Themes in Psychiatry*, Vol. 1 (eds R. Gaind & B. C. Hudson). London: Macmillan.

Gallwey, P. (1992) The psychotherapy of psychopathic disorder. *Criminal Behaviour and Mental Health*, **2**, 159–168.

Gardner, D. C. & Cowdry, R. W. (1985) Alprazolam-induced dyscontrol in borderline personality disorder. *American Journal of Psychiatry*, **142**, 98–100.

— & — (1986) Positive effects of carbamazepine on behavioral dyscontrol in borderline personality disorder. *American Journal of Psychiatry*, **143**, 519–522.

—, Lucas, P. B. & Cowdry, R. W. (1990) CSF metabolites in borderline personality disorder compared with normal controls. *Biological Psychiatry*, **28**, 247–254.

Gardner, M. J. & Altman, D. G. (1986) Confidence intervals rather than p values: estimation rather than hypothesis testing. *British Medical Journal*, **292**, 746–750.

Gardos, G., Di Mascio, A., Sulzman, C., *et al* (1968) Differential actions of chlordiazepoxide and oxazepam on hostility. *Archives of General Psychiatry*, **18**, 757–760.

Garfield, S. L. & Bergin, A. E. (1986) *Handbook of Psychotherapy and Behavior Change* (3rd edn). New York: Wiley.

Garrett, C. J. (1985) Effects of residential treatment of adjudicated delinquents: a meta-analysis. *Journal of Research in Crime and Delinquency*, **22**, 287–308.

Gathercole, C. E., Craft, M. J., McDougall, J., *et al* (1968) A review of 100 discharges from a Special Hospital. *British Journal of Criminology*, **8**, 419–424.

Genders, E. & Player, E. (1994) *The Therapeutic Prison: A Study of Grendon*. Oxford: Oxford University Press.

Gendreau, P. & Ross, R. (1979) Effective correctional treatment: bibliography for cynics. *Crime and Delinquency*, **25**, 463–489.

— & — (1987) Revivification of rehabilitation: Evidence from the 1980s. *Justice Quarterly*, **4**, 349–407.

— & Andrews, D. A. (1994) What the meta-analyses of the offender treatment literature tells us about 'what works'. *Canadian Journal of Criminology* (in press).

Gerstley, L. J., Alterman, A. I., McLellan, A. T., *et al* (1990) Antisocial personality disorder in patients with substance abuse disorders: a problematic diagnosis. *American Journal of Psychiatry*, **147**, 173–178.

Gibbens, T. C. N. (1961) Treatment of psychopaths. *Journal of Mental Science*, **107**, 181–186.

—, Pond, D. A. & Stafford-Clark, D. (1955) A follow- up study of criminal psychopaths. *British Journal of Delinquency*, **6**, 126–36.

—, — & — (1959) A follow-up study of criminal psychopaths. *Journal of Mental Science*, **105**, 108–115.

Goddard, P. & Lokare, V. G. (1970) Diazepam in the management of epilepsy. *British Journal of Psychiatry*, **117**, 213–214.

Goldberg, S., Schulz, S., Schulz, P., *et al* (1986) Borderline and schizotypal personality disorders treated with low-dose thiothixene versus placebo. *Archives of General Psychiatry*, **43**, 680–690.

Golombek, H., Marton P., Stein B., *et al* (1986) Personality dysfunction and behavioural disturbance in early adolescence. *Journal of the American Academy Child Psychiatry*, **25**, 697–703.

Gorenstein, E. E. (1982) Frontal lobe functions in psychopaths. *Journal of Abnormal Psychology*, **91**, 368–379.

Gough, H. G. (1948) Sociological theory of psychopathy. *American Journal of Sociology*, **53**, 359–366.

— (1961) Theory and measurement of socialisation. In *Studies in Behavior Pathology* (ed. T. R. Sarbin). New York: Holt, Reinhart, Wilson.

Gray, H. C. & Hutchinson, H. C. (1964) The psychopathic personality: a survey of Canadian psychiatrists' opinions. *Canadian Psychiatric Association Journal*, **9**, 452–461.

Gray, W. J. (1974) Grendon Prison. *British Journal of Hospital Medicine*, September, 299–308.

Green, E., Silverman, D. & Geil, G. (1944) Petit mal electro shock therapy of criminal psychopaths. *Journal of Criminal Psychopathology*, **5**, 667–695.

Grendon Psychology Unit (1966) *A Pilot Study of the Subsequent Progress of Former Grendon Inmates Discharged July–Dec. 1964*, Grendon Psychology Unit Reports, Series C, C/23. London: Directorate of Psychological Services, Home Office.

Griffiths, J. L. (1985) Treatment of episodic behavioural disorders with rapidly acting benzodiazepines. *Journal of Nervous and Mental Disease*, **173**, 312–315.

Gross, A. M. & Brigham, T. A. (1980) Behaviour modification in the treatment of juvenile delinquency: a review and proposal for future research. *Criminal Justice and Behaviour*, **26**, 98–108.

Grounds, A. T. (1987) Detention of 'psychopathic disorder' patients in Special Hospitals: critical issues, *British Journal of Psychiatry*, **151**, 474–478.

— , Quayle, M. T., France, J., *et al* (1987) A unit for 'psychopathic disorder' patients in Broadmoor Hospital. *Medicine, Science & the Law*, **27**, 21–31.

Gunderson, J. G. (1984) *Borderline Personality Disorder.* Washington, DC: American Psychiatric Press.

Gunn, J. (1977) Forensic psychiatry and psychopathic patients. *British Journal of Psychiatry*, 302–307.

— (1978) The treatment of psychopaths. In *Current Themes in Psychiatry* (eds Gaind & Hudson). London: Macmillan.

— (1992) Personality disorder and forensic psychiatry. *Criminal Behaviour and Mental Health*, **2**, 202–211.

— & Robertson, G. (1976) Psychopathic personality: a conceptual problem. *Psychological Medicine*, **6**, 631–634.

— , — , Dell, S., *et al* (1978) *Psychiatric Aspects of Imprisonment.* London: Academic Press.

Gupta, B. K., Fish, D. N. & Tereranian, B. I. (1987) Carbamazepine for intermittent explosive disorder in the Prader-Willi syndrome patient. *Journal of Clinical Psychiatry*, **48**, 423.

Guze, S. (1964) A study of recidivism based upon a follow-up of 217 consecutive criminals. *Journal of Nervous and Mental Disease*, **138**, 575–580.

Goodwin, D. W. & Crane, J. B. (1969) Criminality and psychiatric disorders. *Archives of General Psychiatry*, **20**, 583–591.

Hall, R. C. W. & Joffe, J. R. (1972) Aberrant response to diazepama new syndrome. *American Journal of Psychiatry*, **129**, 738–742.

Hamilton, J. (1990) Special Hospitals and the state hospitals. In *Principles and Practice of Forensic Psychiatry* (eds R. Bluglass & P. Bowden). Edingburgh: Churchill Livingstone.

Hamilton, M. (1976) Development of a rating scale for primary depressive illness. *British Journal of Social and Clinical Psychology*, **6**, 278–296.

Hann, R. G., Harman, W. G. & Pease, K. (1991) Does parole reduce the risk of reconviction? *Howard Journal*, **30**, 66–75.

Hare, R. D. (1980) A research scale for the assessment of psychopathy in criminal populations. *Personality and Individual Differences*, **1**, 111–117.

— (1983) Diagnosis of antisocial personality disorder in two prison populations. *American Journal of Psychiatry*, **140**, 887–890.

— (1984) Performance of psychopaths in cognitive tasks related to frontal lobe function. *Journal of Abnormal Psychology*, **93**, 133–140.

— (1985) *The Psychopathy Check-List.* University of Columbia, Vancouver, Canada.

— (1990) *Manual for the Revised Psychopathy Check-List.* University of British Columbia, Vancouver, Canada.

— (1991) *The Hare Psychopathy Checklist – Revised.* Toronto: Multi Health Systems.

—, McPherson, L. M. & Forth, A. E. (1988) Male psychopaths and their criminal careers. *Journal of Consulting and Clinical Psychology*, **56**, 710–714.

—, Hart, S. D. & Harpur, T. J. (1991) Psychopathy and the DSM–IV criteria for antisocial personality disorder. *Journal of Abnormal Psychology*, **100**, 391–398.

Harris, G. T., Rice, M. E. & Cormier, C. A. (1989) Violent recidivism among psychopaths and non-psychopaths treated in a Therapeutic Community. *Research Reports, Mental Health Centre, Penetanguishene, Ontario*, **6**, 1–34.

Hart, S. D., Kropp, P. R. & Hare, R. D. (1988) Performance of male psychopaths following conditional release from prison. *Journal of Consulting and Clinical Psychology*, **56**, 227–232.

Haynes, R. B. (1992) Clinical review articles. *British Medical Journal*, **304**, 330–331.

Heaver, W. L. (1943) A study of 40 male psychopathic personalities before, during and after hospitalisation. *American Journal of Psychiatry*, **100**, 342–346.

Hechtman, L. (1991) Resilience and vulnerability in long-term outcome of attention deficit hyperactive disorder. *Canadian Journal of Psychiatry*, **36**, 415–421.

—, Perlman, T., Hopkins, J., *et al* (1991) Hyperactives as young adults: prospective ten year follow-up. In *Psychosocial Aspects of Drug Treatment for Hyperactivity* (eds K. D. Gadow & J. Loney). Boulder, CO: Westview Press.

Heckmatt, J. K., Houston, A. B., Clow, D. J., *et al* (1976) Failure of phenobarbitone to prevent febrile convulsions. *British Medical Journal*, *i*, 559–561.

Hedberg, D. L., Houck, K. H. & Glucck, B. L. (1971) Tranyleypromine–trifluoperazine combination in the treatment of schizophrenia. *American Journal of Psychiatry*, **127**, 1141–1146.

Hellekson, C., Buckland, R. & Price, T., (1979) Organic personality disturbance: a case of apparently atypical cyclical affective disorder. *American Journal of Psychiatry*, **136**, 833–835.

Henderson, D. K. (1939) *Psychopathic States.* London: Norton.

Henderson, M. (1982) An empirical classification of convicted violent offenders. *British Journal of Criminology*, **22**, 1–22.

Henderson, D. & Batchelor, I. (1962) *Henderson and Gillespies Textbook of Psychiatry* (9th edn). Oxford: Oxford University Press.

Hendrix, C. E. & Heckel, R. V. (1982) The effects of a behavioral approach on modifying social behavior in incarcerated male delinquents. *Journal of Clinical Psychology*, **38**, 77–79.

Her Majesty's Stationary Office (1989) *Caring for People.* London: HMSO.

Herbert, M. (1987) *Conduct Disorders of Childhood and Adolescence: a Social Learning Perspective* (2nd edn). Chichester: Wiley.

Hesselbrock, M. N. (1986) Childhood behaviour problems and adult antisocial personality disorder in alcoholism. In *Psychopathology and Addictive Disorders* (ed. R. E. Myer). New York: Guilford Press.

Hickey, P. (1973) Grendon: further comment (letter). *Prison Services Journal.*

Hill, D. (1944*a*) Cerebral dysrhythmia: its significance in aggressive behaviour. *Proceedings of the Royal Society of Medicine*, **37**, 317–328.

— (1944*b*) Amphetamine in psychopathic states. *British Journal of Addiction*, **44**, 50–54.

— & Waterson, D. (1942) Electroencephalographic studies of psychopathic personalities. *Journal of Neurology, Neurosurgery and Psychiatry*, **5**, 47–65.

Hintze, J. L. (1991) *SOLO Statistical System Power Analysis.* Los Angeles, California: BMDP Statistical Software.

Hirschi, T. & Gottfredson, M. (1983) Age and the explanation of crime. *American Journal of Sociology*, **89**, 552–584.

HODGE, J. E. (1992) Addiction to violence: a new model of psychopathy. *Criminal Behaviour and Mental Health*, **2**, 212–223.

HODGES, E. F. (1971) Crime prevention by the indeterminate sentence law. *American Journal of Psychiatry*, **128**, 71–75.

HOLLAND, T. R. & HOLT, N. (1975) Personality patterns among short-term prisoners undergoing presentence evaluations. *Psychological Reports*, **37**, 827–836.

—, LEVI, M. & BECKETT, G. (1981) Associations between violent and non-violent criminality. *Multivariate Behavioral Research*, **16**, 237–242.

—, HOLT, N. & BECKETT, G. E. (1982) Prediction of violent versus non-violent recidivism from prior violent and non-violent criminality. *Journal of Abnormal Psychology*, **91**, 178–182.

—, —, Levi, M., *et al* (1983) Comparison and combination of clinical and statistical predictions of recidivism among adult offenders. *Journal of Applied Psychology*, **68**, 203–211.

HOLLIN, C. R. (1990) *Cognitive–Behavioural Interventions with Young Offenders*. Elmsford, NY: Pergamon Press.

— & HENDERSON, M. (1984) Social skills training with young offenders: false expectations and the 'failure of treatment' *Behavioural Psychotherapy*, **12**, 331–341.

HOME OFFICE (1987) *Prison Department Circular Instruction*, 21/1987. London: Home Office.

— (1993) *Life Licensees and Restricted Offenders Reconvictions: England and Wales 1990*, Home Office Statistical Bulletin 3/93. London: Home Office Research and Statistics Department.

HOOVER (1968) *Uniform Crime Reports for the United States*. Washington, DC: US Government Printing Office.

HOWELLS, K. (1976) Interpersonal aggression. *International Criminology and Penology*, **4**, 319–330.

— (1986) Social skills training and criminal antisocial behaviour in adults. In *Handbook of Social Skills Training*, Vol. 1 (eds C. R. Hollin & P. Trower). Oxford: Pergamon.

— (1988) The management of angry aggression: a cognitive behavioural approach. In *Developments in Cognitive Psychotherapy* (eds W. Dryden & P. Trower). London: Sage.

HUDSON, J. I. & POPE, H. G. (1990) Affective spectrum disorder: does anti-depressant response identify a family of disorders with a common pathophysiology? *American Journal of Psychiatry*, **147**, 552–564.

HYLER, S., REIDER, R., SPITZER, R. L., *et al* (1987) *Personality Diagnostic Questionnaire*. New York: New York State Psychiatric Institute.

INGRAM, G. I., GERARD, R. I., QUAY, H. C., *et al* (1970) Looking in the correctional wastebasket: an experimental programme with psychopathic delinquents. *Journal of Research in Crime and Delinquency*, January, 24-30.

INGRAM, I. M. & TIMBURY, G. C. (1960) Side effect of Librium (letter). *Lancet, ii*, 766.

INTAGLIATA, J. (1982) Improving the quality of community care of the chronically mentally disabled: the role of case management. *Schizophrenia Bulletin*, **8**, 655–674.

IZZO, R. L. & ROSS, R. R. (1990) Meta-analysis of rehabilitation programs for juvenile delinquents: a brief report. *Criminal Justice and Behaviour*, **17**, 134–142.

JESSEN, J. L. & ROOSENBERG, A. M. (1971) Treatment results at the Dr Henri van der Hoeven Clinic, Utrecht, The Netherlands. *Excerpta Medica International Congress Series No. 274, Proceedings of the V World Congress of Psychiatry*.

JEW, C. C., CLANON, T. L. & MATTOCKS, A. L. (1972) The effectiveness of group psychotherapy in a correctional institution. *American Journal of Psychiatry*, **129**, 602–605.

JONES, M. (1953) *The Therapeutic Community*. London: Tavistock Press.

— (1962) *Social Psychiatry*. Springfield, Ill. : Charles C. Thomas.

JONES, L. (1988) *The Hospital Annexe: a Preliminary Evaluation Report*. DPS report, Series II, No. 164 London: Directorate of Psychological Services Home Office.

— (1990) *The Use of a Repertory Grid as a Tool for the Evaluation of a Therapeutic Community.* MSc Applied Criminology Dissertation.

Jones, F. D., Stayer, S. J., Wichlaz, C. R., *et al* (1977) Contingency management of hospital diagnosed character and behaviour disordered soldiers. *Therapy and Experimental Psychiatry,* **8**, 333.

Kagan, R. (1986) The child behind the mask: sociopathy as a developmental delay. In *Unmasking the Psychopath* (eds W. Reid, D. Dorr, J. Walker, *et al*). New York: Norton.

Kaila, K. (1972) Uber die Behandlung von Asocialen in einer geschlossenen psychotherapeutischen Abteilung. *Psychotherapie und Psychosomatik,* **20**, 139–142.

Kalnia, R. K. (1964) Diazepam: its role in a prison setting. *Diseases of the Nervous System.* **25**, 101–107.

Kammen, D. P., van & Murphy, D. L. (1979) Prediction of antidepressant response to lithium carbonate by a one day administration of d-amphetamine in unipolar depressed woman. *Neuropsychobiology,* **5**, 261–266.

—, Docherty, J. P., Marder, S. R., *et al* (1982) Antipsychotic effects of pimozide in schizophrenia: treatment response prediction with acute dextro-amphetamine response. *Archives of General Psychiatry,* **39**, 261–266.

Kanter, J. (1989) Clinical case management: definition, principles, components. *Hospital and Community Psychiatry,* **40**, 361–368.

Karpman, B. (1961) The structure of neurosis: with special differentials between neurosis, psychosis, homosexuality, alcoholism, psychopathy, and criminality. *Archives of Criminal Psychodynamics,* **4**, 599–646.

Karterud, S., Vaglum, S., Friis, S., *et al* (1992) Day hospital Therapeutic Community treatment for patients with personality disorders: an empirical evaluation of the containment function. *Journal of Nervous and Mental Diseases,* **180**, 238–243.

Kazdin, A. E. (1987) Treatment of antisocial behaviour in children: current status and future directions. *Psychological Bulletin,* **102**, 187–203.

Kelly, D. (1976) Psychosurgery in the 1970's. *British Journal of Hospital Medicine,* 165–174.

Kendell, R. E. (1989) Clinical validity. *Psychological Medicine,* **19**, 45–56.

Kennard, D. & Wilson, S. (1979) The modification of personality disturbance in a Therapeutic Community for drug abusers. *British Journal of Medical Psychology,* **52**, 215–219.

Kernberg, O. (1968) The treatment of patients with borderline personality organisation. *International Journal of Psychoanalysis,* **49**, 600–619.

— (1975) *Borderline Conditions and Pathological Narcissism.* New York: Aronson.

— (1984) *Severe Personality Disorders: Psychotherapeutic Strategies.* New Haven: Yale University Press.

Kiger, R. S. (1967) Treating the psychopathic patient in a Therapeutic Community. *Hospital and Community Psychiatry,* 191–196.

Kiresuk, W. J. & Sherman, R. B. (1968) Goal attainment scaling: a general method for evaluating comprehensive community mental health programmes. *Community Mental Health Journal,* **4**, 443–453.

Klein, D. D. (1967) Importance of psychiatric diagnosis in prediction of clinical drug effect. *Archives of General Psychiatry,* **16**, 118–126.

— & Fink, M. (1962) Psychiatric reaction patterns to imipramine. *American Journal of Psychiatry,* **119**, 432–438.

Klein, D. F. (1968) Psychiatric diagnosis and typology of clinical drug effects. *Psychopharmacalogia,* **13**, 359–386.

Klein, R. G. & Mannuzza, S. (1991) Long-term outcome of hyperactive children: a review. *Journal of the American Academy of Child and Adolescent Psychiatry,* **30**, 383–387.

Kozol, H. L., Boucher, R. J. & Garofalo, R. F. (1972) The diagnosis and treatment of dangerousness. *Crime and Delinquency,* **18**, 371–392.

LACEY, J. H. (1983) Bulimia nervosa, binge eating, and psychogenic vomiting: a controlled treatment study and longterm outcome. *British Medical Journal,* **286**, 1609–1613.

LANGAN, P. A. & GREENFIELD, L. A. (1983) *Career Patterns in Crime.* Bureau of Criminal Statistics Special Report NCJ-88672. Washington, DC: Bureau of Justice Statistics.

LAU, J., ANTMAN, E. M., JIMENEZ-SILVA, J., *et al* (1992) Cumalative meta-analysis of therapeutic trials for myocardial infarction. *New England Journal of Medicine,* **327**, 248–54.

LEBLANC, M. & FRECHETTE, M. (1989) *Male Criminal Activity from Childhood Through Youth: Multilevel and Developmental Perspectives.* New York: Springer-Verlag.

LEFKOWITZ, M. (1969) Effects of diphenylhydantoin in disruptive behaviour: a study of male delinquents. *Archives of General Psychiatry,* **20**, 643–651.

LEJINS, P. P. (1977) The Patuxent experiment. *Bulletin of the American Academy of Psychiatry and the Law,* **5**, 116–133.

LEON, G., DE & ZIEGENBUSS, J. L. (1986) *Therapeutic Communities for Addictions.* Springfield Illinois: Charles C. Thomas.

LEONE, N. F. (1982) Response of borderline patients to Ioxapine and chlorpromazine. *Journal of Clinical Psychiatry,* **43**, 148–150.

LEVEY, S. & HOWELLS, K. (1990) Anger and its management. *Journal of Forensic Psychiatry,* **1**, 305–27.

LEWIS, A. (1974) Psychopathic personality: a most elusive category. *Psychological Medicine,* **4**, 133–140.

LEWIS, D. O., PINCUS, J. H. & BARD, B. (1988) Neuropsychiatric, educational and family characteristics of 14 juveniles condemned to death in the United States. *American Journal of Psychiatry,* **145**, 584–588

LEWIS, G. & APPLEBY, L. (1988) Personality disorders: the patients psychiatrists dislike. *British Journal of Psychiatry,* **153**, 44–49.

LIEBOWITZ, M. R. & KLEIN, D. F. (1979) Hysteroid dysphoria. *Psychiatric Clinics of North America,* **2**, 555–575.

— & — (1981) Inter-relationship of hysteroid dysphoria and borderline personality disorder. *Psychiatric Clinics of North America,* **4**, 67–87.

— , STONE, M. H. & TURKAT, I. D. (1986) Treatment of personality disorders. In *American Psychiatric Association Annual Review,* Vol. 5 (eds. A. J. Frances & R. E. Hales). Washington, DC: American Psychiatric Press.

— , QUITKIN, F. M., STEWART, J. W., *et al* (1988) Antidepressant specificity in atypical depression. *Archives of General Psychiatry,* **45**, 129–137.

LION, J. R. (1979) Benzodiazepines in yhe treatment of aggressive patients. *Journal of Clinical Psychiatry,* **40**, 70–71.

— & BACH-Y-RITA, G. (1970) Group psychotherapy with violent out-patients. *International Journal of Group Psychotherapy,* 185–191.

LIPPER, S., DAVIDSON, J. R., GRADY, T. A., *et al* (1986) Preliminary study of carbamazepine in post-traumatic stress disorders. *Psychosomatics,* **27**, 849–854.

LIPSEY, M. (1991) Juvenile delinquency treatment: A meta-analytic inquiry into the viability of effects. In *Meta-analysis for Explanation: A Casebook* (eds T. Cook, H. Cooper, D. Corday, *et al*). New York: Russell Sage Foundation.

LIPTON, D., MARTINSON, R. & WILKS, J. (1975) *The Effectiveness of Correctional Treatment: A Survey of Treatment Evaluation Studies.* New York: Praeger.

LISHMAN, W. A. (1978) *Organic Psychiatry.* Oxford: Blackwell.

LITTAUER, J. & KJÆRGÅRD, J. (1971) Invalidepensionens resocialiserende betydning for strafuegnede kriminelle karakterafvigere. *Nord T. f. Kriminalvidenskab,* **59**, 210–238.

LOEBER, R. (1982) The stability of antisocial and delinquent child behaviour: a review. *Child Development,* **53**, 1431–1446.

LAHEY, B. B. & THOMAS, C. (1991) Diagnostic conundrum of oppositional defiant disorder and conduct disorder. *Journal of Abnormal Psychology,* **100**, 379–390.

Luria, A. R. (1980) *Higher Cortical Function in Man* (2nd edn). New York: Basic.

Maas, J. (1966) The use of actional procedures in group psychotherapy with sociopathic women. *International Journal of Group Psychotherapy*, **16**, 190–197.

MacCulloch, M. & Bailey, J. (1993) Issues in the management and rehabilitation of patients in maximum secure hospitals. *Journal of Forensic Psychiatry*, **4**, 25–44.

— , — , Jones, C., *et al* (1993) Nineteen male serious reoffenders who were discharged direct to the community from a Special Hospital: general characteristics. *Journal of Forensic Psychiatry*, **4**, 237–248.

MacKay, G. W. (1948) Leucotomy in the treatment of psychopathic feeble-minded patients in a state mental deficiency institution. *Journal of Mental Science*, **94**, 834–842.

Maddocks, P. D. (1970) A five year follow-up of untreated psychopaths. *British Journal of Psychiatry*, **116**, 511–515.

Main, T. (1983) The concept of a theraputic community: variations and vicissitudes. In *The Evolution of Group Analyses* (ed. M. Pines). London: Routledge and Kegan Paul.

Maletsky, B. M. (1973) The episodic dyscontrol syndrome. *Diseases of the Nervous System*, **34**, 178–185.

Mandell, A. J. (1976) Dr Hunter S. Thompson and the new psychiatry. *Psychiatry Digest*, **37**, 12–17.

Marcus, E. (1987) Relationship of illness and intensive hospital treatment to length of stay. *Psychiatric Clinics of North America*, **10**, 247–255.

Mark, V. H. & Ervin, F. (1970) *Violence and the Brain.* New York: Harper and Rowe.

Markovitz, P. J., Calabrese, J. R., Schulz, S. C., *et al* (1991) Fluoxetine in the treatment of borderline and schizotypal personality disorders. *American Journal of Psychiatry*, **148**, 1064–1067.

Martin, R. L., Cloniger, C. R., Guze, S. B., *et al* (1985) Mortality in a follow-up of 500 psychiatric out-patients: II. Cause-specific mortality. *Archives of General Psychiatry*, **42**, 58–66.

Martinson, R. (1974) What works? Questions and answers about Prison Reform. *The Public Interest*, **35** (Spring), 22–54.

Martinson, R. (1979) Symposium on sentencing: Part II. *Hofstra Law Review*, **7**, 243–258.

Mattes, J. A., Boswell, L. & Oliver, H. (1984) Methylphenidate effects on symptoms of attention deficit disorder in adults. *Archives of General Psychiatry*, **41**, 1059–1063.

McAllister, T. W. (1985) Carbamazepine in mixed frontal lobe and psychiatric disorders. *Journal of Clinical Psychiatry*, **46**, 393–394.

McClelland, R. J. (1988) Psychosocial sequelae of head injury: anatomy of a relationship. *British Journal of Psychiatry*, **153**, 141–146.

McCord, J. (1978) A thirty-year follow-up of treatment effects. *American Psychologist*, 284–289.

— (1979) Some child-rearing antecedents of criminal behavior in adult men. *Journal of Personality and Social Psychology*, **37**, 1477–1486.

— (1982*a*) A longitudinal view of the relationship between paternal absence and crime. In *Abnormal Offenders, Delinquency and the Criminal Justice System* (eds J. Gunn & D. P. Farrington), ch. 7. Chichester: Wiley.

— (1982*b*) *The Psychopath and Milieu Therapy: a Longitudinal Study.* New York: Academic Press.

— & Sanchez, J. (1982) The Wiltwyck–Lyman project: a twenty-five-year follow-up study of milieu therapy. *The Psychopath and Milieu Therapy: a Longitudinal Study.* New York: Harcourt Brace Jovanovich.

McDonagh, J. D. (1988) Motivational dominance in psychopaths. *British Journal of Clinical Psychology*, **27**, 153–158.

McGowan, M. E. C., Neville, B. G. R. & Reynolds, E. H. (1983) Comparative monotherapy trial in children with epilepsy. *British Journal of Clinical Practice* (Symposium Supplement), **27**, 115–118.

McGrath, P. G. (1966) The English Special Hospital System. In *Psychopathic Disorder* (ed. M. Craft). Oxford: Pegamon Press.

— (1968) The psychopath as a long stay patient. In *Psychopathic Offenders* (ed. D. West). Cambridge: Institute of Criminology.

McGurk, B. J. (1978) Personality types among normal homicides. *British Journal of Criminology*, **18**, 146–161.

— (1980) *An Attempt to Evaluate the Efficiency of Relaxation Training, Desensitisation and Biofeedback in the Treatment of Violent Behaviour.* DP5 report, Series II, No 81. London: Directorate of Psychological Services Home Office.

— & McGurk, R. E. (1979) Personality types among prisoners and prison officers. *British Journal of Criminology*, **19**, 31–49.

Mehlum, L., Friis, S., Irion, T., *et al* (1991) Personality disorders 2–5 years after treatment: a prospective follow-up study. *Acta Psychiatrica Scandinavica*, **84**, 72–77.

Mellsop, G., Varghese, F., Joshua, T., *et al* (1982) The reliability of axis II of DSM–III. *American Journal of Psychiatry*, **139**, 1360–1361.

Miles, A. E. (1969) The effects of a Therapeutic Community on the interpersonal relationships of a group of psychopaths. *British Journal of Criminology*, **9**, 22–38.

Miller, L. (1988) Neuropsychological perspectives on delinquency. *Behavioural Sciences and the Law*, **6**, 409–428.

Miller, Q. J. (1982) *Preliminary Consideration of Psychological Test/Retest Scores and Their Bearing Upon Criminal Reconviction.* Grendon Psychology Unit Report, Series D, D/13.

Millon, T. & Everly, G. S. (1985) *Personality and its Disorders.* New York: Wiley.

Ministrie van Justice (1992) TBS: *a Special Measure Within the Criminal Code.* Leiden, Netherlands: Zorn Publishing Co.

Mohr, P. (1947) Die Forensiche Bedetung der Psychopathen. *Schweizer Archive Neurologie und Psychiatrie*, **60** (Quoted in McCord (1982*b*)).

Monroe, R. R. (1970) *Episodic Disorders.* Cambridge, Masachusetts: Harvard University Press.

Montgomery, S. A. & Asberg, M. (1979) A new depression scale designed to be sensitive to change. *British Journal of Psychiatry*, **134**, 382–389.

— & Montgomery, D. (1982) Pharmacological prevention of suicidal behaviour. *Journal of Affective Disorders*, **4**, 291–298.

—, Montgomery, D., Baldwin, D., *et al* (1989) Intermittent 3-day depressions and suicidal behaviour. *Neuropsychobiology*, **22**, 128–134.

Morris, N. (1974) The failure of imprisonment: toward a punitive philosophy. *Michigan Law Review*, **72**, 305–315.

Morrison, J. R. & Stewart, M. A. (1971) A family study of the hyperactive child syndrome. *Biological Psychiatry*, **3**, 189–195.

Moss, H. B., Yao, J. K. & Panzuk, G. L. (1990) Serotonergic responsivity and behavioural dimensions in antisocial personality disorder with substance abuse. *Biological Psychiatry*, **28**, 325–338.

Moyes, T., Tennent, T. G. & Bedford, A. P. (1985) Long-term follow-up of a ward based behaviour modification programme for adolescents with acting out and conduct problems. *British Journal of Psychiatry*, **147**, 300–305.

Mullen, P. E. (1984) Mental disorder and dangerousness. *Australia and New Zealand Journal of Psychiatry*, **18**, 8–17.

Mulrow C. D. (1987) The medical review article: state of the science. *Annals of Internal Medicine*, **106**, 485–488.

Murch, L. & Dolan, B. M. (1992) Are short term savings worth long term costs? Service usage of personality disordered patients one year after a non-successful referral for specialist treatment. Society for Psychotherapy Research Audit Meeting, London.

Nathan, P. E. (1988) The addictive personality is the behaviour of the addict. *Journal of Consulting and Clinical Psychology*, **56**, 183–188.

National Institute of Mental Health (1985) Rating scales and assessment instruments for use in pediatric psychopharmacology research. *Psychopharmacology Bulletin,* **21**.

Nestor, P. G. (1992) Neuropsychological and clinical correlates of murder and other forms of extreme violence in a forensic psychiatric population. *Journal of Nervous and Mental Disease,* **180**, 418–23.

Newton, M. (1971) *Reconviction after Treatment at Grendon.* CP Report, Series B, No. 1. London: Office of Chief Psychologist, Prison Department, Home Office.

— (1973) *Progress of Follow-up Studies and Comparison with Non-patients Carried out at HMP Oxford.* Grendon Psychology Unit Report, Series A, A/15.

Newton, A. (1980) The effects of imprisonment. *Criminal Justice Abstracts,* **12**, 405–411.

Norden, M. J. (1989) Fluoxetine in borderline personality disorder. *Progress in Neuro-Psychopharmacology and Biological Psychiatry,* **13**, 885–893.

Norris, M. (1984) *Integration of Special Hospital Patients into the Community.* London: Gower.

— (1985) Changes in patients during treatment at Henderson Hospital Therapeutic Community during 1977–1981. *British Journal of Medical Psychology,* **56**, 135–143.

Norton, K. (1992*a*) A culture of enquiry – its preservation or loss. *International Journal of Therapeutic Communities,* **13**, 3–25.

— (1992*b*) Personality disordered individuals: the Henderson Hospital model of treatment. *Criminal Behavior and Mental Health,* **2**, 180–191.

Novaco, R. W. (1975) *Anger Control.* Lexington, Mass. : Lexington.

Nurnberg, H. G., Raskin, M., Levine, P. E., *et al* (1991) The comorbidity of borderline personality disorder and other DSM–III–R axis II personality disorders. *American Journal of Psychiatry,* **148**, 1371–1377.

O'Brien, M. (1976) *The Diagnosis of Psychopathy – A Study of Some Characteristics in Personality and Behaviour of Psychopaths Referred for Treatment to a Therapeutic Community.* PhD thesis, University of London.

O'Donnell, M. (1991) Trial by anecdote. *British Medical Journal,* **302**, 56–57.

Offord, D. R. (1982) Family backgrounds of male and female delinquents. In *Abnormal Offenders, Delinquency and the Criminal Justice System* (eds J. Gunn & D. P. Farrington). Chichester: Wiley.

Ogloff, J. R. P., Wong, S. & Greenwood, A. (1990) Treating criminal psychopaths in a Therapeutic Community programme. *Behavioral Sciences and the Law,* **8**, 181–90.

Palmer, T. (1992) *The Reemergence of Correctional Intervention.* Newbury Park: Sage.

Pannizon, A., Olson-Raymer, G. & Guerra, N. (1991) *Delinquency Prevention: What Works/What Doesn't.* Sacramento: Office of Criminal Justice Planning.

Parsons, B., Quitkin, F. M., McGrath, P. J., *et al* (1989) Penelzine, impramine, and placebo in borderline patients meeting criteria for atypical depression. *Psychopharmacology Bulletin,* **25**, 524–534.

Perkins, D. (1991) Clinical work with sex offenders in secure settings. In *Clinical Approaches to Sex Offenders and their Victims* (eds C. Hollins & K. Howells). Chichester: Wiley.

Perry, J. C. (1985) Depression in borderline personality disorder: lifetime prevalence at interview and longitudinal course of symptoms. *American Journal of Psychiatry,* **142**, 15–21.

Persons, R. W. (1965) Psychotherapy with sociopathic offenders: an empirical evaluation. *Journal of Clinical Psychology,* **21**, 205–207.

— (1966) Psychological and behavioural change in delinquents following psychotherapy. *Journal of Clinical Psychology,* **22**, 337–340.

Petersilia, J., Greenwood, P. W. & Lavin, M. (1978) *Criminal Careers of Habitual Felons.* Washington, DC: US Government Printing Office.

Peterson, D. R., Quay, H. C. & Cameron, G. R. (1959) Personality and background factors in juvenile delinquency as inferred from questionnaire responses. *Journal of Consulting Psychology,* **23**, 395–399.

Peterson, M. A. & Braiker, H. B. (1980) *Doing Crime: A Survey of California Prison Inmates.* Santa Monica, Cal. : RAND.

Pfohl, B., Staugh, D. & Zimmerman, M. (1984) The implication of DSM– III personality disorders for patients with major depression. *Journal of Affective Disorders,* **7**, 309–318.

Pichot, P. (1978) Psychopathic behaviour: a historical overview. In *Psychopathic Behaviour* (eds R. D. Hare & D. Schalling). Chichester: Wiley.

Plenge, P., Mellerup, E. T., Bolwig, T. G., *et al* (1982) Lithium treatment: does the kidney prefer one daily dose instead of two? *Acta Psychiatrica Scandinavica,* **66**, 121–128.

Poblete, M., Palestini, M., Figueroa, E., *et al* (1970) Stereotaxic thalamotomy in aggressive psychiatric patients. *Confina Neurologica,* **32**, 326–331.

Poulton, R. G. & Andrews, G. (1992) Personality as a cause of adverse life events. *Acta Psychiatrica Scandinavica,* **85**, 35–38.

Powell, G. E. (1984) Personality. In *The Scientific Principles of Psychopathology* (eds P. McGuffin, M. F. Shanks, R. J. Hodgson). London: Grune and Stratton.

— & Stewart R. A. (1978) The relationship of age, sex and personality to social attitudes in children aged 8–15 years. *British Journal of Social and Clinical Psychology,* **17**, 307–317.

Powers, E. & Whitmer, H. (1951) *An Experiment in the Prevention of Delinquency: The Cambridge–Somerville Youth Study.* New York: Columbia University Press.

Prins, H. (1980) *Offenders, Deviants, or Patients?* London: Tavistock.

Quality Assurance Project (1991) Treatment outlines for antisocial personality disorder. *Australian and New Zealand Journal of Psychiatry,* **25**, 541-547.

Quay, H. C. (1964*a*) Dimensions of personality in delinquent boys as inferred factor analysis of case history data. *Child Development,* 484.

— (1964*b*) Personality dimensions in delinquent males as inferred factor analysis of behavior ratings. *Journal of Research in Crime and Delinquency,* **1**, 33–37.

Quinsey, V. L. & Maguire, A. (1983) Offenders remanded for a psychiatric examination: perceived treatability and disposition. *International Journal of Law and Psychiatry,* **6**, 193–205.

Rampling, D. (1978) Aggression – a paradoxical response to tricyclic antidepressant. *American Journal of Psychiatry,* **135**, 117–118.

Rapaport, J. L. (1983) The use of drugs: trends in research. In *Developmental Neuropsychiatry* (ed. M. Rutter). Edinburgh: Churchill Livingstone.

— , Bucksbaum, M., Weingartner, H., *et al* (1978) Dextroamphetamine: behavioural and cognitive effects in normal prepubertal boys. *Science,* **199**, 560–563.

Rapoport, R. N. (1960) *Community as Doctor.* London: Tavistock.

Ravndal, E. & Vaglum, P. (1991) Changes in antisocial aggressive- ness during treatment in a hierarchical Therapeutic Community: a prospective study of personality changes. *Acta Psychiatrica Scandinavica,* **84**, 524–530.

Reckless, J. B. (1970) Enforced out-patient treatment of advantaged pseudosociopathic neurotically disturbed young women. *Canadian Psychiatric Association Journal,* **15**, 335–345.

Redfering, D. L. (1972) Group counseling with institutionalised delinquent females. *American Corretional Journal,* **26**, 160–163.

— (1973) Durability of effects of group counselling with institutionalised delinquent females. *Journal of Abnormal Psychology,* **69**, 83–86.

Reich, J. H. & Green, A. I. (1991) Effect of personality disorders on outcome of treatment. *Journal of Nervous and Mental Disease,* **179**, 74–82.

— & Vasile, R. G. (1993) Effect of personality disorders on treatment outcome of axis I conditions: an update. *Journal of Nervous and Mental Disease,* **181**, 475–484.

Reid, W. H. (1986) Antisocial personality. In *Psychiatry,* Vol. 1 (eds J. O. Cavenar *et al*). Philadelphia: J. B. Lippincott & Co.

Reid, A. H., Naylor, C. J. & Kay, D. S. (1981) A double-blind, placebo controlled cross-over trial of carbamazepine in overactive, severely mentally handicapped patients. *Psychological Medicine*, **11**, 109–113.

Renshaw, J. (1988) Care in the community: individual care planning and case management. *British Journal of Social Work*, **18** (suppl.), 74–105.

Reyntjens, A. M. (1972) A series of multicentre trials with pimozide in psychiatric practice. *Acta Psychiatrica Belgica*, **72**, 653–661.

Rice, M. E., Harris, G. T. & Cormier, C. A. (1992) An evaluation of a maximum security Therapeutic Community for psychopaths and other mentally disordered offenders. *Law and Human Behavior*, **16**, 399–412.

Rifkin, A., Quilkin, F., Carrillo, C., *et al* (1972) Lithium carbonate in emotionally unstable character disorders. *Archives of General Psychiatry*, **27**, 519–523.

Robbins, T. W. & Sahakian, B. J. (1979) 'Paradoxical' effects of psychomotor stimulant drugs in hyperactive children from the standpoint of behavioural pharmacology. *Neuropharmacology*, **18**, 931–950.

Robertson, G. (1987) Mentally abnormal offenders: manner of death. *British Medical Journal*, **295**, 632–634.

— (1989) Treatment of offender patients: How should success be measured? *Medicine, Science and Law*, **29**, 303–307.

— (1992) Objections to the present system. *Criminal Behaviour and Mental Health*, **2**, 114–123.

— & Gunn, J. (1987) A ten-year follow-up of men discharged from Grendon prison. *British Journal of Psychiatry*, **151**, 674–678.

Robins, L. N. (1966) *Deviant Children Grown up: a Sociological and Psychiatric Study of Sociopathic Personality*. Baltimore: Williams and Wilkins.

— (1970) Follow-up studies of childhood conduct disorder. In *Psychiatric Epidemiology* (eds Hare & Wing) .

— (1974) Antisocial behaviour disturbances of childhood. In *The Child in His Family* (eds Anthony & Koupernik). London: Wiley.

— (1978) Sturdy childhood predictors of adult antisocial behaviour: replications from longitudinal studies. *Psychological Medicine*, **8**, 611–622.

— (1981) Epidemiological approaches to natural history research: antisocial disorders in children. *Journal of the American Academy of Child Psychiatry*, **20**, 556–580.

— (1985) Epidemiology of antisocial personality. In *Psychiatry*, vol. 1 (ed. J. O. Cavenar). Philadelphia: Lippincott & Co.

— (1986) The consequences of conduct disorders in girls. In *Development of Antisocial and Prosocial Behaviour: Research, Theories and Issues* 24 (eds D. Olweus, J. Block & M. Radke-Yarrow). Orlando: Academic Press.

Robins, E. & Guze, S. B. (1970) Establishment of diagnostic validity in psychiatric illness: its application to schizophrenia. *American Journal of Psychiatry*, **126**, 983–987.

— & Price, R. K. (1991) Adult disorders predicted by childhood conduct problems: results from the NIMH Epidemiological Catchment Area Project. *Psychiatry*, **54**, 116–132.

Robins, L. N., Helzer, J. E., Weissman, M. M., *et al* (1984) Lifetime prevalence of specific psychiatric disorders in three sites. *Archives of General Psychiatry*, **41**, 949–958.

— & Regier, D. A. (1991) *Psychiatric Disorder in America: the ECA Study*. New York: Free Press.

Rodger, J. J. (1988) Social work as social control reexamined. Beyond the discipline thesis. *Sociology*, **22**, 563–581.

Rosenblatt, S., Schaiffer, D., Rosenthal, J. S. (1976) Effects of diphenylhydantoin on child-abusing parents: a preliminary report. *Current Therapeutic Research*, **19**, 332–336.

Rosenblaum, J. F., Fava, M., Pava, J. A., *et al* (1993) Anger attacks in unipolar depression, Part 2: Neuroendocrine correlates and changes following fluoxetine treatment. *American Journal of Psychiatry*, **150**, 1164–1175.

Ross, D. R., Lewin, R., Gold, K., *et al* (1988) The psychiatric uses of cold wet sheet packs. *American Journal of Psychiatry*, **145**, 242–245.

Ross, R. R. & Fabiano E. A. (1985) *A Time to Think: A Cognitive Model of Delinquency Prevention and Offender Rehabilitation.* Johnson City Institute of Social Science & Arts.

Rubin, S. (1979) New sentencing proposals and laws in the 1970's. *Federal Probation*, **2**, 80–89.

Rumgay, J. (1990) Taking rehabilitation out of after-care? The post-release supervision of young adult offenders. *British Journal of Criminology*, **30**, 36–50.

Rutter, M. (1987) Temperament, personality and personality disorder. *British Journal of Psychiatry*, **150**, 443–458.

—, Cox, A., Tupling, C., *et al* (1975) Attainment and adjustment in two geographical areas: I. The prevalence of psychiatric disorder. *British Journal of Psychiatry*, **126**, 493–509.

— & Giller, H. (1983) *Juvenile Delinquency: Trends and Perspectives.* Harmondsworth: Penguin.

Ryan, H. F., Merrill, F. B., Scott, G. E., *et al* (1968) Increases in suicidal thoughts and tendencies, association with diazepam therapy. *Journal of the American Medical Association*, **203**, 1137–1139.

Rydelius, P. A. (1988) The development of antisocial behaviour and sudden violent death. *Acta Psychiatrica Scandinavica*, **77**, 398– 403.

Sadoff, R. L., Roether, H. A. & Peters, J. J. (1971) Clinical measure of enforced group psychotherapy. *American Journal of Psychiatry*, **128**, 116–119.

Sandhu, H. S. (1970) Therapy with violent psychopaths in an Indian prison community. *International Journal of Offender Therapies*, **14**, 138–144.

Schalling, D. (1978) Psychopathy-related personality variables. In *Psychopathic Behaviour: Approaches to Research* (eds R. Hare & D. Schalling). Chichester: Wiley.

Schmideburg, M. (1959) The borderline patient. In *American Handbook of Psychiatry*, Vol. 1 (ed. S. Arieti), pp. 398–416. New York: Basic Books.

Schulz, S. C., Cornelius, J., Schulz, P. M., *et al* (1988) The amphetamine challenge test in patients with borderline personality disorder. *American Journal of Psychiatry*, **145**, 809–814.

Scott, P. D. (1960) The treatment of psychopaths. *British Medical Journal*, May, 1641–1646.

— (1963) Psychopathy. *Postgraduate Medical Journal*, **39**, 1–7.

Scott-Johnson, V. (1975) *The Kennedy Youth Center.* Paper presented at the National Criminology Conference, University of Cambridge, Institute Criminology.

Seidman, E. (1987) Towards a framework for primary prevention research. In *Preventing Mental Disorders. A Research Perspective* (eds J. A. Steinberg & M. M. Silverman). Rockville, Maryland: US Department of Health and Human Services, NIMN.

Sellars, C. (1992) The use of the Luria Nebraska neuropsychological battery in the assessment of mentally abnormal offenders: a preliminary study as to the nature of impairment and its relation to readmission rates. Unpublished paper, Broadmoor Hospital.

—, Brown, B., Clark, F., *et al* (1992) The treatability of psychopaths. Unpublished paper, Psychology Department, Broadmoor Hospital.

Sewell, R. & Clark, C. (1982) An evaluation study of "The Annexe" – a therapeutic community in Wormwood Scrubs prison. Unpublished report from the Home Office Prison Department.

Serban, G. & Siegel, S. (1984) Response of borderline and schizotypal patients to small doses of thiothixene and haloperidol. *American Journal of Psychiatry*, **141**, 1455–1458.

Serin, R. C., Peters, R. De V. & Barbaree, H. (1990) Predictors of psychopathy and release outcome in a criminal population. *Psychological Assessment*, **2**, 419–422.

Shawcross, C. R. & Tyrer, P. (1985) The influence of personality on response to monoamine oxidase inhibitors and tricyclic antidepressants. *Journal of Psychiatric Research*, **19**, 557–562.

SHEARD, M. H. (1971) Effect of lithium on human aggression. *Nature,* **230**, 113–114.

— , MARINI, J. L., BRIDGES, C. I., *et al* (1976) The effect of lithium on unipolar aggressive behaviour in man. *American Journal of Psychiatry,* **133**, 1409–1413.

SHEKIM, W. O., MASTERSON, A., CANTWELL, O. P., *et al* (1989) Nomifensine maleate in adult attention deficit disorder. *Journal of Nervous and Mental Disease,* **177**, 296–299.

SHEPHERD, G. (1990) Case management. *Health Trends,* **2**, 59–61.

SHORVON, J. J. (1947) Benzedrine in psychopaths and behaviour disorders. *British Journal of Addiction,* **44**, 58–62.

SINGER, N. M. & BLOOM, H. S. (1977) A cost-effectiveness analysis of Patuxent Institution. *Bulletin of the American Academy of Psychiatry and the Law,* **5**, 161–1790.

SKOLNICK, N. J. & ZUCKERMAN, M. (1979) Personality change in drug abusers: a comparison of Therapeutic Community and prison groups. *Journal of Consulting and Clinical Psychology,* **47**, 768–770.

SLEAP, H. (1979) *Goal Attainment Scaling: The Technique and Some Initial Findings.* Grendon Psychology Unit Reports, Series B,B/15. London: Directorate of Psychological Services, Home Office.

SMITH, D. R., SMITH, W. R. & NOMA, E. (1984) Delinquent career lines: a conceptual link between theory and juvenile offences. *Sociological Quarterly,* **25**, 155–172.

SMITH, R. (1984) Grendon, Barlinnie and Wormwood Scrubs Annexe: experiments in penology. *British Medical Journal,* **288**, 472–475.

SOLOFF, P. H. (1981) Pharmacotherapy of borderline disorders. *Comprehensive Psychiatry,* **22**, 535–543.

—, GEORGE, A., NATHAN, R. S., *et al* (1986*a*) Progress in pharmacotherapy of borderline disorders: a double-blind study of amitriptyline, haloperidol and placebo. *Archives of General Psychiatry,* **43**, 691–697.

—, ANSELUM, G., NATHAN, S., *et al* (1986*b*) Paradoxical effects of amitriptyline on borderline patients. *American Journal of Psychiatry,* **143**, 1603–1605.

—, CORNELIUS, J., ANSELM, G., *et al* (1993) Efficacy of phenelzine and haloperidol in borderline personality disorder. *Archives of General Psychiatry,* **50**, 377–385.

SPELLACY, F. (1978) Neuropsychological discrimination between violent and non-violent men. *Journal of Clinical Psychology,* **34**, 49–52.

STAFFORD-CLARK, D., POND, D. & DOUST, J. W. L. (1951) The psychopath in prison: a preliminary report of a co-operative research. *British Journal of Delinquency,* **2**, 117–129.

STEADMAN, H. J. (1977) A new look at recidivism among Patuxent inmates. *Bulletin of the American Academy of Psychiatry and the Law,* **5**, 200-209.

STEIN, G. (1992) Drug treatment of the personality disorders. *British Journal of Psychiatry,* **161**, 167–184.

STEIN, L. I. & TEST, M. A. (1980) Alternative to mental hospital treatment – 1. Conceptual model, treatment programme and clinical evaluation. *Archives of General Psychiatry,* **37**, 392–397.

STEIN, E. & BROWN, J. D. (1991) Group therapy in a forensic setting. *Canadian Journal of Psychiatry,* **36**, 718–722.

STEINER, M., ELIZUR, A. & DAVIDSON, S. (1979) Behavioural toxicity: neuroleptic induced paradoxical behavioural toxicity in young borderline schizophrenics. *Confinia Psychiatric,* **2**, 226–233.

STERMAC, L. E. (1986) Anger control treatment for forensic patients. *Journal of Interpersonal Violence,* **1**, 446–457.

STEWART, J. T. (1985) Carbamazepine treatment of a patient with Kluver–Bucy syndrome. *Journal of Clinical Psychiatry,* **46**, 496–497.

STONE, J. L., MCDANIEL, K. D., HUGHES, J. R., *et al* (1986) Episodic dyscontrol disorders and paroxysmal EEG abnormalities: successful treatment with carbamazepine. *Biological Psychiatry,* **21**, 208–212.

STÜRUP, G. K. (1948) Management and treatment of psychopaths in a special institution in Denmark. *Proceedings of the Royal Society of Medicine,* **41**, 765.

— (1953) Sexual offenders and their treatment in Denmark and other Scandinavian countries. *International Review of Criminology Policy,* No. 4, 1.

— (1959) Group therapy with chronic criminals. *Acta psychotherapie (Basel),* **7**, 377–385.

— (1974) Pilot experiment in counteracting violence in a penal institution. *Titus Homo,* **5**, 52–57.

— & REID, W. H. (1981) Herstedvester: an historical overview of institutional treatment. In *The Treatment of Antisocial Syndromes* (ed. W. H. Reid), ch. 4. Van Nostrand Reinhold Company.

TANCREDI, L. R. & VOLKOW, N. (1986) Neural substrates of violent behaviour: implications for law and policy. *International Journal of Law and Psychiatry,* **11**, 13–49.

TANTAM, D. (1988) Personality disorders. In *Recent Advances in Clinical Psychiatry,* Vol. 6 (ed. K. Granville-Grossman). Edinburgh: Churchill Livingstone.

TARTER, R. E. (1988) Are there inherited behavioural traits that predispose to substance abuse? *Journal of Consulting and Clinical Psychology,* **56**, 189–196.

TAUBE, C. A., MORLOCK, K. L., BURNS, B., *et al* (1990) New directions in research on assertive community treatment. *Hospital and Community Pschiatry,* **41**, 642–647.

TAYLOR, J. A. (1953) A personality scale of manifest anxiety. *Journal of Abnormal Social Psychology,* **25**, 31–38.

— (1963) Therapeutic groups outside a prison. *International Journal of Group Psychoanalysis,* **13**, 308–314.

TAYLOR, A. J. W. (1967) An evaluation of group psychotherapy in a girls' borstal. *International Journal of Group Psychotherapy,* **17**, 168–177.

TAYLOR, E. A. (1986) The basis of drug treatment. In *The Overactive Child* (ed. E. A. Taylor). Clinics in Developmental Medicine, No. 97. Oxford: Blackwell.

TAYLOR, F. (1966) Methods of care: Henderson Hospital. In *Psychopathic Disorders* (ed. M. Craft). Oxford: Pergamon Press.

TAYLOR, P., ALEXANDER, M. S., CICCHETTI, D., *et al* (1979) Reliability of a schedule for rating personality disorders. *British Journal of Psychiatry,* **135**, 168–174.

TENNENT, G. & WAY, C. (1984) The English Special Hospital: a 12–17 year follow-up study. *Medicine Science and the Law,* **24**, 81–91.

—, TENNENT, D., PRINS H., *et al* (1990) Psychopathic disorder - a useful clinical concept? *Medicine, Science and the Law,* **30**, 39–44.

TEST, M. (1979) Continuity of care in community treatment. *New Directions in Mental Health Services,* **2**, 15–23.

THOMAS-PETER, B. A. (1989) Cognitive therapy and the treatment of personality disorders. Paper presented to the Birmingham Medical Institute.

— (1993) Sadistic fantasy and its treatment:theoretical formulation and illlustrative case study. In *Advances in Reversal Therapy* (eds Kerr, Murgatroyd & Apter). Netherlands: Swets and Zetlinger.

THORNICROFT, G. (1990) Case managers for the mentally ill. *Social Psychiatry and Psychiatric Epidemiology,* **25**, 141–143.

TIDMARSH, D. (1982) Implications from research studies. In *Dangerousness: Psychiatric Assessment and Management* (eds J. Hamilton & H. Freeman). London: Gaskell.

TONG, J. E. & MACKAY, G. W. (1959) A statistical follow-up of mental defectives of dangerous or violent propensities. *British Journal of Delinquency,* **9**, 276–284.

TREIMAN, D. & DELGADO-ESCUETA, A. (1983) Violence and epilepsy: a critical review. In *Recent Advances in Epilepsy,* Vol. 1 (eds T. Pedley & B. Meldrum). Edinburgh: Churchill Livingstone.

TRUAX, C. B., WARGO, D. G. & SILBER, L. D. (1966) Effects of group psychotherapy with high adequate empathy and nonpossessive warmth upon female institutionalized delinquents. *Journal of Abnormal Psychology,* **71**, 267–274.

Tucker, L., Bauer, S. F., Wagner, S., *et al* (1987) Long-term hospital treatment of borderline patients: a descriptive outcome study. *American Journal of Psychiatry*, **144**, 1443–1448.

Tunks, E. R. & Dermer, S. W. (1977) Carbamazepine in the dyscontrol syndrome associated with limbic system dysfunctions. *Journal of Nervous and Mental Diseases*, **164**, 56–63.

Tupin, J. P., Smith, D. B., Clanon, T. C., *et al* (1973) The long term use of lithium in aggressive prisoners. *Comprehensive Psychiatry*, **14**, 311–317.

Turkat, I. D. & Maisto, S. A. (1985) Personality disorders: application of the experimental method to the formulation and modification of personality disorders. In *Clinical Handbook of Psychological Disorders* (ed. D. H. Barlow). New York: Guilford Press.

Turner, S. & Petersilia, J. (1992) Focusing on high-risk parolees: An experiment to reduce commitments to the Texas Department of Corrections. *Journal of Research in Crime and Delinquency*, **29**, 34–61.

Tuxford, J. (1961) *Treatment as a Circular Process.* Report for the King Edward's Hospital Fund, London.

Tyrer, P. (1988) *Personality Disorders: Diagnosis, Management and Course.* London: Wright.

Tyrer, S. P., Walsh, A., Edwards, D. E., *et al* (1984) Factors associated with a good response to lithium in aggressive mentally handicapped subjects. *Progress in Neuropsychopharmacology and Biological Psychiatry*, **8**, 751–755.

Tyrer, P. & Seivewright, H. (1988) Studies of outcome. In *Personality Disorders: Diagnosis, Management and Course* (ed. P. Tyrer). London: Wright.

—, Casey, P. & Ferguson, B. (1991) Personality disorder in perspective. *British Journal of Psychiatry*, **159**, 463–471.

Vaglum, P., Friis, S., Jírstad, J., *et al* (1982) From panacea to a special treatment method. *International Journal of Therapeutic Communities*, **3**, 24–32.

—, Irion, T., Jons, *et al* (1990) Treatment response of severe and non-severe personality disorders in a Therapeutic Community day unit. *Journal of Personality Disorders*, **2**, 161–172.

Valliant, P. M. & Antonowicz, D. H. (1991) Cognitive behaviour therapy and social skills training improves personality and cognition in incarcerated offenders. *Psychological Reports*, **68**, 27–33.

Van Voorhis, P. (1987) Correctional effectiveness: The high cost of ignoring success. *Federal Probation*, **51**, 56–62.

Virkkunen, M., De Jong, J., Bartko, J., *et al* (1984) Psychological concomitants of history of suicide attempts among violent offenders and impulsive fire setters. *Archives of General Psychiatry*, **46**, 604–606.

Walker, M. & McCabe, S. (1973) *Crime and Insanity in England*, Vol. 2. Edinburgh: Edinburgh University Press.

Walters, G. D. (1990) *The Criminal Lifestyle: Patterns of Serious Criminal Conduct.* Newbury Park, Cal. : Sage Publications.

Weiss, J. M. A., Davis, D., Hedlund, J. L., *et al* (1983) The dysphoric psychopath: a comparison of 524 cases of antisocial personality disorder with matched controls. *Comprehensive Psychiatry*, **24**, 355–369.

Wender, P. H., Reimherr, F. W. & Wood, D. R. (1981) Attention deficit disorder (minimal brain dysfunction) in adults. *Archives of General Psychiatry*, **38**, 449–456.

— , Reinherr, F. W., Wood, D., *et al* (1985) A controlled study of methylphenidate in the treatment of attention deficit disorder, residual type in adults. *American Journal of Psychiatry*, **142**, 547–558.

Wergeland, H. (1980) A follow-up investigation of 39 anti-social children 4–20 years after discharge from hospital. *Acta Paedopsychiatrica*, **46**, 39–55.

Werner, E. E. (1985) Stress and protective factors in children's lives. In *Longitudinal Studies in Child Psychology and Psychiatry* (ed. A. R. Nicol). Chichester: Wiley.

—, Bierman, J. M., French,E. E. (1971) *The Children of Kauai: a Longitudinal Study from the Prenatal Period to Age Ten.* Honolulu: University of Hawaii Press.

— & Smith, R. S. (1977) *Kauai's Children Come of Age.* Honolulu: University of Hawaii Press.

— (1982) *Vulnerable but Invincible: a Longitudinal Study of Resilient Children and Youth.* New York: McGraw Hill.

West, D. J. (1969) *Present Conduct and Future Delinquency.* London: Heinemann Educational Books.

— (1982) *Delinquency. Its Roots, Careers and Prospects.* London: Heinemann Educational Books.

— & Farrington, D. P. (1973) *Who Becomes Delinquent?* London: Heinemann Educational Books.

— (1977) *The Delinquent Way of Life.* London: Heinemann Educational Books.

Wexler, H. K., Falkin, G. P. & Lipton, D. S. (1990) Outcome evaluation of a prison Therapeutic Community for substance abuse treatment. *Criminal Justice and Behaviour,* **17**, 71–92.

Whitehead, J. & Lab, S. (1989) A meta-analysis of juvenile correctional treatment. *Journal of Research in Crime and Delinquency,* **26**, 276–295.

Whiteley, J. S. (1970) The response of psychopaths to a Therapeutic Community. *British Journal of Psychiatry,* **116**, 517–529.

— (1980) A community study: The Henderson Hospital. *International Journal of Therapeutic Communities,* **1**, 38–57.

Wickham, E. & Reed, J. V. (1987) Lithium in the control of aggression and self-mutilating behaviour. *International Clinical Psychopharmacology,* **2**, 181–190.

Widom, C. S. (1977*a*) Interpersonal and personal construct systems in psychopaths. *Journal of Consulting and Clinical Psychology,* **44**, 614–623.

— (1977*b*) An empirical classification of female offenders. *Criminal Justice and Behaviour,* **5**, 35–52.

Williams, D. (1969) Neural factors related to habitual aggression: consideration of the differences between those habitual aggressives and others who have committed crimes of violence. *Brain,* **92**, 503–520.

Williams (1973) Grendon still under dispute. *Prison Services Journal.*

Winkleman, N. W. (1955) Chlorpromazine in the treatment of neuropsychiatric disorders. *Journal of the American Medical Association,* **155**, 18–21.

Wolf, S. M. & Forsythe, A. (1978) Behaviour disturbance, phenobarbital and febrile seizures. *Pediatrics,* **61**, 728–731.

Wolf, M. E., Alavia, A. & Mosnaim, A. D. (1988) Post-traumatic stress disorder in Vietnam veterans. Clinical and EEC findings; possible therapeutic effects of carbamazepine. *Biological Psychiatry,* **23**, 642–644.

Wolfgang, M., Figlio, R. F. & Sellin, T. (1972) *Delinquency in a Birth Cohort.* Chicago: University of Chicago Press.

Wood, R. D., Reimherr, F. W., Wender, P. H., *et al* (1976) Diagnosis and treatment of minimal brain dysfunction in adults. *Archives of General Psychiatry,* **33**, 1453–1460.

Woodside, M., Harrow, A., Basson, J. V., *et al* (1976) Experiment in managing sociopathic behaviour disorders. *British Medical Journal, ii,* 1056–1059.

Woodward, R. (1991) Allowing people to behave well: the role of the Grendon Assessment Unit. *Proceedings of the Prison Service Psychology Conference, October 1991* (ed. S. Boddis). London: Home Office Publications.

Woody, G. E., Luborsky, L., McLellan, T., *et al* (1983) Psychotherapy for opiate addicts: Does it help? *Archives of General Psychiatry,* **40**, 1639–1645.

—, McLellan, A. T., Luborsky, L., *et al* (1985) Sociopathy and psychotherapy outcome. *Archives of General Psychiatry,* **42**, 1081–1086.

Wooff, K. & Goldberg, D. P. (1988) Further observations on the practice of community care in Salford: differences between community psychiatric nurses and mental health social workers. *British Journal of Psychiatry,* **153**, 30–37.

Wooldredge, J. (1988) Differentiating the effects of juvenile court sentences on eliminating recidivism. *Journal of Research in Criminal Delinquency,* **25**, 264–300.

World Health Organization (1989*a*) *Tenth Revision of the International Classification of Diseases, Chapter V (F), Mental and Behavioural Disorders (Including Disorders of Psychological Development).* Geneva: WHO.

— (1989*b*) *ICD–10 Chapter V, Mental and Behavioural Disorders (including Disorders of Psychological Development): Diagnostic Criteria for Research.* Draft for field trials. Geneva: WHO.

Worrall, E. P., Moody, J. P., Naylor, G. J. (1975) Lithium in non-manic–depressives: anti-aggressive effect and red cell lithium values. *British Journal of Psychiatry,* **126**, 464–468.

Yalom, I. (1975) *The Theory and Practise of Group Psychotherapy.* New York: Basic Books.

Zimmerman, M., Coryell, W., Pfehl, B., *et al* (1986) ECT response in depressed patients with and without DSM–III personality disorder. *American Journal of Psychiatry,* **143**, 1030–1032.

Index 1 Subject index

Compiled by Dr John Gibson

Aarvold Committee (1973) 188, 250
adolescents, follow-up 39
aetiological research 269
affective spectrum disorder 66
affective symptoms 65
affective syndromes 65-66
psychopaths with borderline personality disorder 66
alcoholism 41, 54
alprazolam 75 (table), 91 (table), 94 (table), 96, 97
amenability-to-treatment model 271
amitriptyline 75 (table), 84
amphetamine 105, 108-110
challenge test 109-110
anticonvulsants 99-104
antidepressants 76-87, 118 (table)
adverse effects of comorbidity 85
paradoxical response 85-87
tricyclics 77-78, 83-84
antisocial personality disorder (DSM-III-R) 15 (table), 15-18, 64
cognitive therapy 144
anxiety, generalised 66
Ashworth Hospital (UK) 193
attention deficit hyperactivity disorder 40, 105-106
avoidant personality disorder 66
axis I clinical syndromes 30-32, 85

Balderton Hospital (UK) 153-157, 183-185
Barlinnie Special Unit (UK) 166-167
Beck Depression Inventory 251
behavioural dyscontrol 98
behavioural modification 137
behavioural programmes 137-142
behavioural toxicity 69
benzodiazepines 93-99, 118 (table)
for reactive behavioural dyscontrol 98
short-acting 97
birth complications 66
Blackburn's typology derived from MMPI profile 21-22
Block-Ego Identity Scale 251
borderline personality disorder 6, 64, 68
low-dose neuroleptic therapy 68-69
borderline personality organisation 6, 23-24
Briquet's syndrome 27
Broadmoor Hospital (UK) 187, 188, 189 (table), 190
factors related to length of detention 191-192
five-year outcome of men discharged into community 189 (table)
length of detention factors 191-192
men released to non-secure facilities 192

Californian prison 169
Cambridge-Somerville youth study 41-42
Canada
male prison 169-170
psychiatrically disordered offenders 186
carbamazepine 75 (table), 91 (table), 100-101, 102 (table)
for:
borderline personality disorder 100-101
organic brain disorder 101
post-traumatic stress disorder 101
proposed pharmacotherapy 118 (table)
career criminals 60
character spectrum disorder 66
childhood conduct disorder 35-36
chlordiazepoxide 94 (table)
chlorpromazine 69, 71 (table), 83
chronic delinquency, predictive factors 40
clinical trials, randomised 269-272
clomipramine 118 (table)
cognitive behavioural therapy 136, 137, 142-143, 263
for:
adolescents 227 (table)
psychopaths 228 (table)
cognitive therapy 143
cold wet sweet pack 122-123
community supervision 206-219, 265
case management for psychopaths 216-218
evaluation of surveillance of psychopaths 207-212, 213 (tables)
Oxford survey 210-212, 213 (table)
Park Lane Hospital follow-up 208-210
problems 213-216

contemporary diagnosis
approaches 10-32
criminal recidivism 27

decentralisation of
authority 138-139
delinquency development
40-50
atypical 88, 89
Cambridge-Somerville
youth study 41-42
characterological 83-84
subgroups 84
intermittent brief 66
Kauai longitudinal study
45-50
low-grade chronic 83
West & Farrington's
studies *see* West &
Farrington's
longitudinal depression
desipramine 84
deviant children/
adolescents 35-40
grown-up 37-40
diagnostic systems,
recommendations on use
25
diazepam 94 (table)
diphenylhydantoin 101-103
Dr Henri van der Hoeven
Clinic (The Netherlands)
171-172
drug abusers, therapeutic
community treatment 174-
177
DSM-III-R: antisocial
personality disorder 15
(table), 15-18, 64
dysphoria 65, 66
hysteroid *see* hysteroid
dysphoria
dyssocial personality
disorder (ICD-10) 13-15

electro-shock therapy 121-
122, 262
emotionally unstable
character disorder 66
episodic dyscontrol
syndrome 66, 99, 100
Eysenck Personality
Questionnaire 251

fenfluramine 82
prolactin-response 78
fluoxetine 78-82
complications 86-87
flupenthixol 71 (table)
follow-up, length of 252-253
format of review 8-9

General Health
Questionnaire 159, 251
Goal Attainment Scale 159
Grendon Underwood Prison
(UK) 15, 65
changes during treatment
158-160
follow-up studies 160-165
therapeutic career model
163 (table)
therapeutic community
treatment, outcome 231
(table)

haloperidol 69, 71 (table),
72, 73-74, 75 (table)
Harperbury Hospital 155-
156
Henderson Hospital (UK)
147-153
Herstedvester (Denmark)
203-204, 238
Hissar prison (India) 170
Home Office statement 248
homicide rate 50
hospital admission 181-205
careers of legal
psychopaths 185-186
in-patient treatment in
medium-secure units
186-187
in-patient treatment in
non-secure hospitals
182-185
open wards 185
Hostility and Direction of
Hostility Questionnaire
159-160, 251
5-hydroxytryptamine
(serotonin) deficiency 78
hysteroid dysphoria 66, 92
phenelzine for 89

ICD-10: dyssocial
personality disorder 13-15
imipramine 83
in-patient psychotherapy for
psychopaths 226-227
(table)
in-patient treatment in
British special hospitals
187-193
in-patient treatment in
medium-secure units 186-
187
in-patient treatment in non-
secure hospitals 182-185
intensive supervision parole
214-215
interactionist approach to
personality 26
intermittent explosive
disorder 66
IQ test 251
isocarboxazid 88

Justizanstalt Mittersteig
(Austria) 204

Kauai longitudinal study 45-
50

life history measure of
outcome 250-251
lithium 111-16, 118 (table)
aggression in learning-
disabled subjects
114-115
long-term hospitalisation
264-265
lorazepam 94 (table), 96-97
loxapine 71 (table)

maturation 54
maximum-security hospital,
therapeutic communities
173-174
measures of outcome 247-
252
life history 250-251
psychological 251-252
recidivism 247-249
rehospitalisation 250
medium-secure units, in-
patient treatment in
186-187
Mental Health Act (UK,
1959) 185
Mental Health Act (UK,
1983) 5, 192, 207, 215,
267
Mental health review
tribunal (UK) 207
mesoridazine 72-73, 74
(table)
methodological issues 220-
260
cognitive-behavioural
therapy for:
adolescents 227 (table)
psychopaths 228 (table)
definition of psychopathic
disorder 222-239
description of treatment
244-246
non-treatment 245-246
therapist factors 246

what constitutes
treatment? 244-245
in-patient milieu
treatment 234 (table)
in-patient psychotherapy
for psychopaths 226-247
(table)
length of follow-up 252-
253
measurement of outcome
see measurement of
outcome
measurement of
psychopathic disorders
222-239
natural history of
untreated psychopaths
223 (table)
out-patient psychotherapy
for psychopaths 225
(table)
Patuxent, treatment in
237 (table)
physical treatment of
psychopaths 224 (table)
random allocation of
subjects 239-243
comparison samples 241-
243
controlled studies 239-241
statistics *see* statistics
therapeutic community
treatment 229-233
(table)
treatment in Special
Hospitals 235-237
(table)
methylphenidate 105, 106
(table), 107 (table)
mianserin 71 (table)
milieu therapy 22-23, 183-
207
in-patient 234 (table)
non-British maximum-
security units 198-204
therapy packages 181-182
military personnel (US)
141-142
Millon Clinical Multiaxial
Inventory 177
minimal brain damage/
dysfunction 99
chronic conditions
leading to 46
Minnesota Counselling
Inventory 251
Minnesota Multiphasic
Personality Inventory 21-
22, 175-176, 251, 277
psychopathic deviance
scores 50
monoamine oxidase
inhibitors 87-93, 118
(table)
mortality rates 58
Moss Side Hospital (UK)
188
multiple diagnostic
approaches 27-30

narcissistic personality
disorder 22, 24-25
natural history 33-62
untreated psychopaths,
methodology of studies
223 (table)
naturalistic studies 272-276
neuroleptics 68-76, 118
(table)
behavioural toxicity 69
low-dose 68-69
placebo-controlled trials
69-76
uncontrolled trials 70-71
(table)
neurological dysfunction 66
New York mental hospital,
1935–40 182-183
non-treatment 245-246
nortriptyline 84
Novaco Provocation
Inventory 251

open hospital wards 185
out-patient psychotherapy
for psychopaths 225
(table)
oxazepam 94 (table), 96
Oxford survey 210-212, 213
(table)

panic attacks 66
Park Lane Hospital (UK)
192, 208-210
parole 206-207, 214
intensive supervision 214-
215
paternalistic work-training
programme 183-184
Patuxent Institution (US)
199-203, 237 (table), 238
cost-effectiveness analysis
201-202
Personal Experience and
Attitudes Questionnaire
132, 251
Personality Diagnostic
Questionnaire 28
Peterson Delinquency Scale
251
pharmacological treatment
63-120, 261-262
phenelzine 73, 75 (table),
89, 90 (table), 91 (table),
92
phenobarbitone 103
phobias 66, 88
physical treatments 121-125,
224 (table), 262
pimoxide 69, 70 (table)
positive attention behaviour
140
post-traumatic stress
disorder 101
prevention 274-276
probation service 214
procyclidine 83
psychodynamic classification
22-25
psychodynamic therapy 67
psychological outcome
measures 251-252
psychopathic disorder 1-3
aims of current review 7
core features 53
criteria for inclusion in
report 6-7
definition 2220-239
legal category 11-13
legal concept 1-2
measurement 222-239
psychopaths
affective syndrome of
psychopaths with
borderline deficiency
disorder 16
aggressive 51, 99
burn-out 55-57
case management 216-218
immature/inadequate 51
in-patient psychotherapy
226-227 (table)
maturity 55-57
out-patient psychotherapy
225 (table)
untreated, natural history
50-55, 223 (table)
Psychopathy Check-List
(Hare) 5, 18-20, 53, 277
psychopathy, use of term 5
psychostimulants 104-110
psychosurgery 123-125, 262
psychotherapy 126-135
adults in prisons/secure
environments 132-134
dynamic approaches 262-
263

group 129-130
adolescent girls 131-132
in-patient 130-134
out-patient 127-130

Rampton Hospital (UK) 185-186
recidivism 50-52, 58-61
outcome measure 247-249
prediction in criminal population 60-61
recommendations 265-276
aetiological research 269
randomised clinical trials 269-272
treatability 267-268
rehospitalisation as outcome measure 250

schizophrenia
borderline, behaviour neuroleptic toxicity 69
non-pseudoneurotic 89
pseudoneurotic 83, 89
Schizotypal Symptom Inventory 72
Sensation Seeking Scale 175-176, 251
serotonergic reuptake inhibitors 78-82
serotonin (5-hydroxytryptamine) deficiency 78
severity of personality disorder assessment 25-32
influence of personality disorder on course of clinical syndromes 30-32
multiple diagnostic approaches 27-30
trait approaches 25-26
skill training programme 136
sociopath 52
sociopathic behaviour disorders 186-187
sociopathic personality disorder 37-38
sources of material 7-8
Special Hospitals (UK) 187-198
approach of studies 197-198
case register 198
community supervision of released psychopaths 215
in-patient treatment 187-193
integration of male patients into community 190-191
life history factors 197
outcome of discharge 194-195 (table)
patients' disorders 196
recall 193
reconvictions 192-193, 197
subjects 196
treatment in 196, 235-237 (table)
worse outcome for psychopaths 196
see also specific hospitals
spectrum dysphoric pattern 84
Speilberger State Trait Anxiety Scale 251
standardised assessment of psychopathic disorder 277-293
behavioural disorder 278
clinical syndromes 277-278
diagnostic formulation 278-293
interaction of elements 284-285
personality disorder 277
statistics 253-260
confidence intervals of X^2 test 253-255
power of statistical tests 255-258
'survival' or 'time to failure' analysis 258-260
Symptom Check-List 150-151, 251

Taylor Manifest Anxiety Scale 132, 251
Texas Board of Pardons and Paroles 123
therapeutic communities 146-178, 229-233 (tables), 263-264
drug abusers 174-177
hierarchical model 174-178, 233 (table)
maximum-security hospital 173-174
non-British prisons 169-172
thiothixene 71 (table), 74 (table)
thyrotropin-releasing hormone test 82
trait approaches to personality disorders 25-26
tranylcypromine 75 (table), 88, 89, 90 (table), 92, 94 (table)
treatment 244-246
methodologically view 3
pessimistic view 3
previous statements about outcome 3-4
therapist factor 246
what constitutes treatment? 244-245
triazolam 97-98
trifluoperazine 75 (table), 88-89, 90 (table), 91 (table)
'trumping' systems 29
tyramine 88

Ullevål Day Hospital (Norway) 156-157

West & Farrington's longitudinal studies 42-45
getting caught 45
getting married 44-45
going to wrong school 44
moving from inner London 45
Wormwood Scrubs Annexe (UK) 167-168

Index 2 Treatment outcome studies

This index refers to the main empirical outcome studies reviewed in this book.

Aarvold Committee (1973) 188
Acres (1975) 189, 194
Andy (1975) 124
Anton *et al* (1986) 102
Bailey & Maculloch (1992*a,b*) 192, 195, 208
Balasurabramanian & Rammamurthi (1970) 123
Barnes (1977) 72, 74
Basson & Woodside (1981) 186
Berner & Karlick-Bolten (1986) 204
Bick & Hannah (1988) 95, 96
Black (1982) 189, 194
Black *et al* (1988) 85
Boslow & Kohlmeyer (1963) 199, 202
Brinkley *et al* (1972) 70
Buck & Harvey (1986) 102
Cantwell (1972) 105
Carney (1977) 128
Cavior & Schmidt (1978) 139
Charney *et al* (1981) 85
Coccaro *et al* (1989*a*) 78
Coccaro *et al* (1989*b*) 78
Coccaro *et al* (1990*a*) 78
Coccaro *et al* (1990*b*) 79, 81
Cohen & Filipczack (1971) 138
Coid (1991) 67
Coid (1992) 65, 66, 68, 87, 88, 101
Cole *et al* (1984) 71, 77
Collard (1976) 69
Colman & Baker (1969) 141
Cook *et al* (1991) 129
Cooke (1989) 166
Copas & Whiteley (1976) 149
Copas *et al* (1984) 149
Cope & Ward (1993) 216
Cornelius *et al* (1990) 78, 80
Cowdry & Gardner (1988) 72, 73, 75, 91, 92, 93, 94, 96, 97, 98, 100, 101
Craft (1958) 183
Craft (1965) 188, 194
Craft (1968) 183
Craft *et al* (1964) 153
Craft *et al* (1987) 114
Cullen (1992) 165
Dale (1980) 114, 115
Darling & Sandall (1952) 123
Dell (1980) 189
Dell (1982) 189
Dell *et al* (1987) 191
Docherty *et al* (1986) 65, 66
Dolan *et al* (1992*c*) 151
Dolan *et al* (1992d*b*) 153
Dolan *et al* (1993) 193
Essa (1986) 102
Fava *et al* (1993) 79, 81
Fink *et al* (1969) 169
Gabbard & Coyne (1987) 185
Gathercole *et al* (1968) 188, 204
George (1971) 161
Gibbens *et al* (1955) 50
Gibbens *et al* (1959) 51
Goddard & Lokare (1970) 94, 96
Goldberg *et al* (1985) 72, 74
Gray (1974) 158
Green *et al* (1944) 121
Griffith (1985) 97
Gunn *et al* (1978) 158, 161
Gupta *et al* (1979) 102
Guze (1964) 52
Guze *et al* (1969) 52
Harris *et al* (1989) 184
Hart *et al* (1988) 53
Hare *et al* (1988) 51
Heaver (1943) 182, 183
Hedberg *et al* (1971) 88, 90
Hendrix & Heckel (1982) 140
Hill (1944*a*) 99
Hill (1944*b*) 108
Hill & Waterson (1942) 99
Hodges (1971) 200, 202
Jesen & Roosenberg (1971) 171
Jew *et al* (1972) 133
Jones (1988) 168
Jones (1990) 167
Jones *et al* (1977) 141
Kalina (1964) 94, 96
Kernberg (1968) 69
Klein (1967) 83
Klein (1968) 83
Klein & Fink (1962) 85
Kozol *et al* (1972) 134
Lefkowicz (1969) 101
Leon (1982) 71

Liebowitz & Klein (1981) 89, 90
Liebowitz *et al* (1986) 116
Liebowitz *et al* (1988) 89, 91
Lion (1979) 93, 94, 96
Lipper *et al* (1986) 101
Littauer & Kjærgård (1971) 204
Maas (1966) 133
MacCulloch *et al* (1993) 193
Mackay (1948) 124
Maddocks (1970) 53
Mandell (1976) 69
Markovitz *et al* (1991) 79, 81
Mattes *et al* (1984) 107, 108
McAlister *et al* (1985) 102
McCord (1978) 41
McCord & Sanchez (1982) 184
Mehlum *et al* (1991) 157
Miles (1969) 155
Miller (1982) 159
Montgomery & Montgomery (1982) 71
Morrison & Stewart (1971) 105
Moss *et al* (1990) 78
Moyes *et al* (1985) 140
Murch & Dolan (1992) 54
Newton (1971) 160
Newton (1973) 159
Norden (1989) 78, 79, 80
Norris (1984) 190, 194
Norris (1985) 151
O'Donnell (1991) 86
Ogloff *et al* (1990) 169
Parsons *et al* (1989) 89
Persons (1965) 132
Persons (1966) 131
Pfohl *et al* (1984) 85
Poblete *et al* (1970) 123
Quinsey & Maguire (1983) 186
Rampling (1978) 85
Rapoport (1960) 148
Reckless (1970) 127
Redfering (1972) 132
Redfering (1973) 132
Reid *et al* (1981) 102
Reyntjens (1972) 69, 70
Rice *et al* (1992) 173
Rifkin *et al* (1972) 112, 113
Robertson (1989) 192, 195
Robertson & Gunn (1987) 162
Robins (1966) 37, 55
Rosenblatt *et al* (1976) 103
Rosenblaum *et al* (1993) 82
Sadoff *et al* (1971) 129
Sandhu (1970) 170
Serin *et al* (1990) 53
Schmideberg (1959) 69
Schulz *et al* (1988) 109
Serban & Siegel (1984) 71
Sewell & Clarke (1982) 177
Shawcross & Tyrer (1985) 88
Sheard (1971) 111, 122
Sheard *et al* (1976) 112, 113
Shekem *et al* (1989) 107
Shorvon (1947) 108, 109
Skolnick & Zuckerman (1979) 174
Sleap (1979) 159
Soloff (1981) 70, 77
Soloff *et al* (1986*a*) 72, 75, 76, 84
Soloff *et al* (1986*b*) 85
Soloff *et al* (1993) 73, 75, 91, 92
Steadman (1977) 201, 202
Steiner *et al* (1979) 69
Stermac (1986) 142
Stewart (1985) 102
Stone *et al* (1986) 102
Stürup (1974) 203
Taylor (1966) 148
Taylor (1967) 131
Tennent & Way (1984) 191, 195
Tong & Mackay (1959) 187, 188, 194
Truax *et al* (1966) 131
Tunks & Dermer (1977) 102
Tupin *et al* (1973) 111, 112
Tuxford (1961) 148
Tyrer *et al* (1984) 114, 115
Valiant & Antonowicz (1991) 143
van Emmerick (1987) 172
Virkkunen *et al* (1989) 78
Walker & McCabe (1973) 185, 210
Weiss *et al* (1983) 65, 66
Wender *et al* (1981) 106
Wender *et al* (1985) 107, 108
Wergeland (1980) 39
Werner (1971–85) 45
West & Farrington (1969–77) 42, 59
Wexler *et al* (1990) 176
Whiteley (1970) 148
Wickham & Reed (1987) 114
Williams (1969) 99, 100
Winkleman (1955) 69
Wolf *et al* (1988) 101
Wood *et al* (1976) 106
Woodside *et al* (1976) 186
Woody *et al* (1983, 1985) 128
Worrall *et al* (1975) 114, 115